MATERIALS FOR MISSILES AND SPACECRAFT

UNIVERSITY OF CALIFORNIA
ENGINEERING AND SCIENCES EXTENSION SERIES

MATERIALS FOR MISSILES AND SPACECRAFT

JOHN C. McDONALD

JAMES F. WATSON

ALAN V. LEVY

WOLFGANG H. STEURER

E. J. ZEILBERGER

A. HURLICH

GEORGE R. IRWIN

R. P. LIPKIS

L. D. JAFFE

JOHN B. RITTENHOUSE

FRANCIS J. CLAUSS

JOHN E. HOVE

CLARENCE ZENER

D. E. THOMAS

MORRIS A. STEINBERG

Edited by
EARL R. PARKER
Department of Mineral Technology
University of California at Berkeley

McGraw-Hill Book Company, Inc.
NEW YORK   SAN FRANCISCO   TORONTO   LONDON

MATERIALS FOR MISSILES AND SPACECRAFT

The Authors

John C. McDonald, Staff Scientist, Missiles and Space Division, Lockheed Aircraft Corporation, Sunnyvale, California.

James F. Watson, Senior Research Engineer, Materials Research Group, Convair-Astronautics, San Diego, California.

Alan V. Levy, Head, Nozzle Component Materials Department, Research and Development Laboratory, Aerojet-General, Sacramento, California. (Formerly with Hughes Tool Company, Los Angeles, California.)

Wolfgang H. Steurer, Chief of Engineering Materials, Convair, San Diego, California.

E. J. Zeilberger, Supervisor of Materials Engineering, Rocketdyne—A Division of North American Aviation, Canoga Park, California.

A. Hurlich, Research Group Engineer, Materials Research Group, Convair-Astronautics, San Diego, California.

George R. Irwin, Superintendent of Mechanics Division, U.S. Naval Research Laboratory, Washington, D.C.

R. P. Lipkis, Head, Space Vehicle Transfer Section, Space Technology Laboratories, Los Angeles, California.

L. D. Jaffe, Chief, Materials Research Section, Jet Propulsion Laboratory, California Institute of Technology, Pasadena, California.

John B. Rittenhouse, Materials Research Section, Jet Propulsion Laboratory, California Institute of Technology, Pasadena, California.

Francis J. Clauss, Research Scientist, Missiles and Space Division, Lockheed Aircraft Corporation, Palo Alto, California.

John E. Hove, Director, Material Sciences Laboratory, Aerospace Corporation, Los Angeles, California. (Formerly with Atomics International, Canoga Park, California.)

Clarence Zener, Director, Westinghouse Research Laboratories, Pittsburgh, Pennsylvania.

D. E. Thomas, Manager, Materials Department, Astronuclear Laboratory, Westinghouse Electric Corporation, Pittsburgh, Pennsylvania.

Morris A. Steinberg, Manager, Materials and Propulsion Research, Missiles and Space Division, Lockheed Aircraft Corporation, Palo Alto, California.

Preface

The contents of this book were presented as a series of lectures sponsored by the Physical Sciences Extension and the Engineering Extension, University of California, Los Angeles, and the Engineering and Sciences Extension, University of California, Berkeley.

The lecture series was especially organized for design engineers, metallurgists, and ceramists. The subject matter was developed, however, to be of interest to solid-state physicists, chemists, chemical engineers, and instructors of courses in engineering materials. The presentation was at a level suitable for assimilation by those holding B.S. degrees in engineering or science. Approximately 500 people enrolled in the course. In order to provide statewide coverage of the California missiles and spacecraft industries, identical lectures were given in four locations: San Diego, Los Angeles, Corona, and Palo Alto.

Foremost experts in each of the specialized fields were chosen to present the lectures by a committee consisting of Clifford A. Bell, University of California, Los Angeles; John C. Dillon, University of California, Los Angeles; L. D. Jaffe, Jet Propulsion Laboratory, Pasadena; Sam Houston, University of California, Los Angeles; John C. McDonald, Lockheed Aircraft Corporation, Sunnyvale; William Micks, Rand Corporation, Santa Monica; Earl R. Parker, University of California, Berkeley (Chairman); Ernest E. Sechler, California Institute of Technology, Pasadena; Francis R. Shanley, University of California, Los Angeles; George H. Sines, University of California, Los Angeles; C. T. Singleton, University of California, Berkeley; J. L. Waisman, Douglas Aircraft Company, Santa Monica; James F. Watson, Convair-Astronautics, San Diego; O. A. Wheelan, Space Technology Laboratory, Los Angeles; E. J. Zeilberger, Rocketdyne, Canoga Park.

In addition to the subjects discussed herein, three other talks were presented in the series. Charles N. Scully, Senior Technical Specialist, Aero-Space Laboratories, North American Aviation, lectured on "Meteoroid and Ion Impact Effects on Materials;" Joseph M. Denney, Head,

ix

Materials Research, Space Technology Laboratories, discussed "Radiation Effects;" and Harry W. Johnson, Associate Manager, Engineering Mechanics Department, Space Technology Laboratories, talked about "Design Criteria for Pressure Vessels." Unfortunately, manuscripts were not prepared on these three subjects.

This book presents a coordinated analysis of materials problems that confront designers of missiles and spacecraft. It is authoritative because only outstanding experts were selected to participate, and it is comprehensive enough to be of real value to engineers. Materials problems limit progress in this field probably more than in any other manufacturing area at this time. The summary of these problems, as presented in this book, should be of substantial value to all engineers working in the missiles and spacecraft industries.

Earl R. Parker

Contents

MATERIALS FOR MISSILES AND SPACECRAFT

1

General Criteria for the Design and Manufacture of Missiles and Spacecraft

JOHN C. McDONALD

STAFF SCIENTIST, MISSILES AND SPACE DIVISION
LOCKHEED AIRCRAFT CORPORATION
SUNNYVALE, CALIFORNIA

The objective of this book is to aid the reader in an understanding of the problems involved in the use of available materials for the construction of missiles and spacecraft. The technological advances in materials and in engineering design during the past fifteen years have made it possible to realize the dreams of space travel envisioned by early pioneers such as Goddard.

In the chapters to follow, the details of various materials problems will be discussed. In this chapter, a perspective view of the subject as a whole will be presented. Certain special subjects will be covered in some detail, particularly those not considered extensively in later sections, and the general nature of the chapters to follow will be discussed.

Rocket Propulsion

The preferred method of providing power for long-range missiles is to use rocket motors rather than the air-breathing engines such as ramjets or turbojets. For this reason, emphasis in this chapter is placed on the problems encountered in rocket-propelled vehicles. Such propulsion offers many advantages over the older types. In the case of vehicles to be propelled into orbit around the earth, or into the farther reaches of space, use cannot be made of the oxygen in the earth's atmosphere. Consequently, a large industry to produce vehicles propelled by a high-speed jet of hot gases generated by internal burning has developed in recent years. First to be discussed in a general way will be the con-

1

sequences of this method of propulsion on material problems.   Also, an understanding of the fundamental equation of rocket propulsion will be necessary.   This equation indicates the relative roles of propulsive efficiency and structural efficiency in the performance of rocket-propelled vehicles.   From this relationship, an appreciation for the respective roles of propulsion and structure can be developed.   In field-free empty space, the acceleration experienced at any time by a rocket-propelled vehicle is simply the thrust developed by the engine divided by the total mass of the system including the structure, the engine, and the remaining fuel. The velocity obtainable by the complete burning of all the fuel may be found by integrating the instantaneous acceleration over the total burning time of the fuel.   When this is done a simple expression results, relating the ratio of the full weight to the empty weight of the vehicle, M_f/M_e, the force developed when unit mass of propellant is burned in unit time, I_{sp}, and the velocity change ΔV. I_{sp} is called the specific impulse.   This relationship is given below:

$$\Delta V = gI_{sp} \ln \frac{M_f}{M_e}$$

where M_f = mass of system fully loaded
   M_e = mass of system emptied of fuel
   I_{sp} = pound force generated per pound mass burned per second;
      e.g., time in seconds for burning 1 lb of propellant while
      generating 1 lb of thrust
   ΔV = velocity gained, fps

The efficiency of the propulsive system and the effective use of structural materials both play important roles in the achievement of maximum velocity.   The available payload and maximum range for ballistic missiles, or payload and altitude for orbiting vehicles, are strongly dependent upon the chemistry of the fuel and also upon the skill with which available materials are used to achieve minimum weight in the system as a whole.

The importance of effective use of materials was emphasized by the statement of Martin Summerfield and Howard Seifert, which appeared on page 13 of Ref. 1:

Whereas moderate increases in velocity and range can be achieved switching from "ordinary" to "high-energy" propellants, large increases are achievable by reduction of the dead-weight fraction: mathematically velocity at burnout becomes infinite as the empty weight tends to zero.   It is therefore sometimes possible for the structural design engineer to produce performance benefits greater than the propulsion engineer can produce.   The spectacular increase in the range of single-stage chemical rockets in recent years, from the 200-mile range of the V-2 to the 1000-mile-plus range of the IRBM's, has been the result largely of structural improvements rather than of propulsion gains.

The importance of further reduction of structural weight by more skillful application of better materials remains undiminished; great effort is being made in this direction. However, because of recent advances through better structural efficiency there is now less room for improvement in this direction, and a strong effort is being made to improve propulsion by using propellants with the highest possible values of specific impulse. Essentially this means higher combustion temperatures, but higher temperatures require better materials and new designs.

Table 1.1†

Propellant type	Dead-weight factor s	Payload factor l	Mass ratio, $R = 1/(s + l)$	Average I_{sp}, sec	Horizontal velocity, fps	Vertical velocity, fps
Liquid oxygen–alcohol (V-2)........	0.233	0.077	3.23	220	8,300	5,860
Liquid oxygen–kerosene........	0.12	0.08	5.00	300	15,450	11,586
Fluorine-hydrazine	0.12	0.08	5.00	350	18,000	13,500
Nuclear..........	0.24	0.06	3.33	800	31,000	20,970

† Courtesy John Wiley & Sons, Inc., and W. Amster (see Ref. 1).

Structural efficiency in the propulsion units must be maximized by working with the most heat-resistant materials possible. When such materials cannot be utilized effectively, weight penalties will occur. The interaction and the overall effect of the factors in the propulsion equation are well summarized in Table 1.1 and Figs. 1.1 to 1.3, taken from Chap. 3 of Ref. 1.

Table 1.1 shows a few specific examples of velocities attainable with various propellants and mass ratios. Figure 1.1 shows more generally the way in which the velocity gain is affected by reducing structural weight. The ordinate is scaled in three ways, showing the velocity increase ΔV for various values of specific impulse and effective exhaust velocity, as well as for a given effective exhaust velocity (which corresponds to a propellant mixture of reasonably good specific impulse). In this general analysis, the structural weight is divided into two elements: the deadweight structure and the payload fraction. For a modest payload, say 2 per cent of the total weight, and with a deadweight factor of 10 per cent, this particular engine-fuel combination would produce a terminal velocity in the neighborhood of 20,000 fps. The velocity

penalty of an inefficient structure is great.   At a structural efficiency of
80 per cent, 25 per cent of the final velocity would be lost.   As indicated
by the figures in Table 1.1, attainment of orbital velocity in a single-stage
rocket is possible only with engine-propellant combinations which
develop very high specific impulse, or with vehicles which have very high
mass ratios.   The outstanding example to date of a single-stage rocket
reaching orbital velocity was Project Score, in which the Atlas, as a whole,

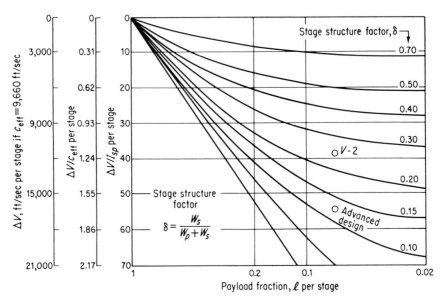

Fig. 1.1   Velocity versus impulse and structure factor.   [*Courtesy John Wiley & Sons,
Inc., and W. Amster (see Ref. 1).*]

was placed in orbit.   Such conditions are generally achieved, however,
by the multistage rockets.

Figure 1.2 shows the velocities attainable versus the gross weight–payload weight ratio for single- and multiple-stage rockets.   Orbital velocities of 25,000 fps or so are attainable with fairly inefficient structures.
At a delta of 0.15, two stages provide a respectable payload-weight fraction.   However, if a velocity suitable for the initiation of interplanetary
travel is to be obtained, say 40,000 fps, the job cannot be done at all in
two stages unless the structural factor decreases to 10 per cent.

In Fig. 1.3, the effect of variation in specific impulse on the capability
of staged rockets is shown.   In this plot, the structural factor has been
held at 0.1, signifying that the mass ratio, if the payload weight be 0, is 9.
With a two-stage vehicle having a payload fraction of 0.5 per cent, a
velocity of 35,000 fps is possible when the specific impulse is 300.   By

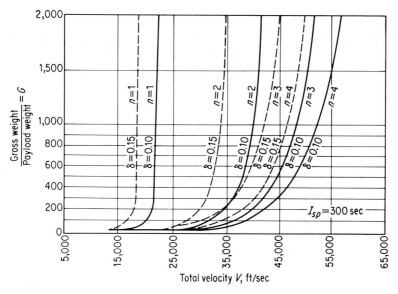

Fig. 1.2 Velocity versus stage and structure factor. [*Courtesy John Wiley & Sons, Inc., and W. Amster (see Ref. 1).*]

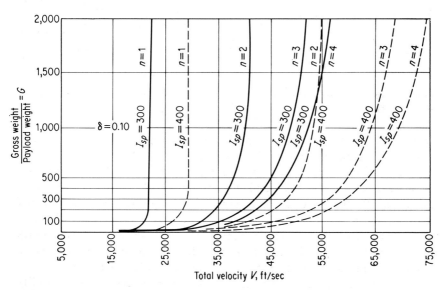

Fig. 1.3 Velocity versus stage and impulse. [*Courtesy John Wiley & Sons, Inc., and W. Amster (see Ref. 1).*]

increasing the specific impulse to 400, the payload fraction is quadrupled for the same two-stage system.

It is evident that there are two general directions in which rocket development can occur to give us maximum payload capability at maximum range. One is to provide materials and designs for propulsion systems that can operate at the maximum possible flame temperatures; i.e., maximum velocity gain is achieved by use of high specific impulse. The other route is the minimization of the weight of all the structural elements, including the engine, the fuel tanks, and all the structure required to house the various subsystems.

This brief introduction leads to a more detailed examination of the requirements of the various parts. By reviewing these requirements, the nature of the material problems with which this relatively new technology is faced can be seen.

Systems Requirements

The stresses to which a missile system is subjected arise from several sources. In addition to the acceleration load produced by the thrust of the engine, bending may be introduced by changes in thrust direction arising from the operation of the guidance system to control the trajectory. In the outer reaches of space, the interactions of the space environment with the materials of construction require special attention. (This subject will be treated in detail in later sections.) If the vehicle is to come back to earth after attaining the high velocities required for satellites and spacecraft, stresses will be introduced by the deceleration of entry into, and passage through, the atmosphere. Compounding the problems of material choices and design is the temperature rise occasioned by rapid motion through the dense atmosphere, whether it be on exit or reentry; temperature problems also arise because of the hot parts of the engine. The portions of the vehicle acting as pressure vessels are designed primarily to withstand tension stresses, while other portions will be stressed critically only in compression. It is appropriate now to consider in more detail the particular problems associated with each element of a system and the changes in these problems with each phase of the mission.

In the propulsion unit (the engine), the problems will differ depending on the nature of the fuel. Solid propellants generally burn for shorter times and produce higher accelerations than do liquid propellants. In either case, the fuel will exert pressure. In the first case the combustion of the fuel provides the pressure, and in the second case pressure must be applied to feed the fuel to the engine. In the case of liquid propellants, combustion takes place at a high pressure in a combustion chamber. The hot gas is then ejected through a suitably designed nozzle and expansion chamber to optimize the thrust. Before being burned, the liquid fuels may be circulated through the walls of the combustion chamber and nozzle in order to cool these parts. When this is done, materials having less heat resistance may be used.

The advantage of the generally higher specific impulse of the liquid-fueled engine is partially offset by the complexity of the mechanism required to get the fuel to the combustion chamber. For engines having relatively low thrust it has been profitable to force the fuel from a reservoir to the chamber by gas pressure alone. Tank weight is minimized by the use of materials of the highest possible strength, but relatively heavy gauges are still required to withstand the pressure. Engines having larger thrust can be fed more effectively with high-speed pumps; the pressure in this case is just enough to prevent cavitation at the entrance to the pump. Depending on the size of the engine, pumping may permit the use of lower-strength materials when manufacturing limitations preclude the use of very light gauges; or, in the very large engines, higher-strength materials may be advantageously used. The system, as a whole, will require valving, seals, and gaskets which must be compatible with the particular chemicals used. Certain chemical fuels are very corrosive to many materials. Serious problems of incompatibility must be anticipated and avoided in the selection of materials. Nitric acid and other nitrogenous compounds are notable examples of corrosive fuels. When one of the fuels is a liquified gas, such as oxygen, which must be kept at an extremely low temperature, the properties and characteristics of the structural materials to be used at these low temperatures must be known.

The fuel tanks constitute an example of the general class of pressure vessel in which minimization of the weight is so important if high structural efficiencies are to be attained. In the selection of pressure-vessel materials and the choice of an appropriate design stress, the use of tensile-test data alone is not sufficient. For all materials, as their strength is increased by a variety of alloying, working, and heat-treating procedures, a strength level is finally reached where brittle behavior begins to occur under the complex system of stresses present in a structure. A simple tension bar, particularly if it is a round bar, does not give evidence of this undesirable behavior. How to determine the maximum usable strength level of any material is a big and controversial question. Much more attention will be devoted to this subject in a later chapter.

Propulsion units of the future may derive their thrust from other mechanisms than the reaction of chemical fuels and oxidizers. For example, liquid hydrogen may be heated to high temperatures in a nuclear reactor, producing the very high specific impulse listed in Table 1.1. An advance of this kind would lead to many specialized problems of concern in the design of nuclear reactors of minimum weight and maximum operating temperature. The pressure-vessel problem would still exist because the liquid hydrogen would have to be confined under pressure; also, in the reactor itself, high pressures are generated when the gas is heated to the exit temperature. Other propulsion schemes with much higher specific impulse have been devised, but with these the thrust is low. In general, such schemes involve the electrical acceleration of particles through the application of power to plasmas or to ions.

Guidance of missiles or space vehicles is accomplished by means of complicated mechanisms which measure acceleration forces and convert the information into signals that operate guidance control systems. Such devices can change, vary, or terminate the thrust vector so as to achieve the planned course through the air or into space. The problems in the design and choice of materials for this system will not be discussed except for a comment on the problems encountered where a vane-type device is used to change the direction of the thrust vector. The nozzle of a liquid-fueled engine may be swiveled to provide change in thrust direction. However, for solid-propellant engines it is difficult, although not impossible, to change the direction by swiveling the nozzle. The other method for directing a solid-propellant vehicle is to insert vanes into the rocket exhaust that will deflect the stream in an appropriate manner. The destructive effects of the high-temperature and high-velocity gas stream have posed real problems in the development and choice of vane materials.

Electric power has to be supplied for varying lengths of time to operate the guidance, control, and communication devices. To date, reliance has generally been placed on chemical-type batteries for these power requirements. For missions of any length, in orbit or in space, the weight of batteries would become prohibitive and so other power sources must be provided. This will introduce new and difficult problems. The nuclear reactor, for example, has its own set of materials problems and so does the gas-operated turbine with which the reactor is to be coupled. In addition to all the usual problems that are encountered on the ground, the new problem arises of constructing a radiator that can reject heat into space at the minimum temperature of the heat cycle. The lower this temperature can be, the more efficient will be the operation. However, the lower the minimum temperature the larger the radiating area must become. This problem is still under study; the solution will probably not be optimized for some time. Another method of converting the energy of the nuclear reactor to electric power involves the heating of a junction of thermoelectric materials to a high temperature. Certain intermetallic compounds are now being developed which may function with maximum efficiency at the maximum operating temperature,

A device currently in use converts solar radiation directly into electricity; this device is commonly known as the solar cell. It is a sensitive photovoltaic material and has, of course, its own characteristic set of problems. It might be thought that providing suitable electric circuitry, antennas, and waveguides should pose no particular problems in the choice of materials. However, by the time these devices have been miniaturized, or designed with minimum-weight materials, problems of quality control arise as do problems of satisfactory coatings.

Following this brief introduction to system requirements is a discussion of the effects of the operational phase on material choice and design.

Design Criteria

Powered Flight. In the first place of operation of a rocket-powered vehicle, loading will occur in compression because of the acceleration, and bending and shear also will result because of turbulent air or guided maneuvers. Certain types of missiles may have auxiliary surface lift, or aid in control, but in the simplest case (which is exemplified by the larger designs) such loads are applied to a long tube-like structure. The solid-propellant missile, with its high thrust-weight ratio, has high accelerations and correspondingly high acceleration loads. The liquid-propellant missile generally operates at lower accelerations than does the solid-propellant vehicle. However, in both cases, high velocities are attained while the atmosphere is still dense enough to provide a considerable input of heat at the surface of the vehicle. When a liquid is in contact with the outer skin of a vehicle, a negligible rise in temperature may occur. The motor case of a solid rocket, however, may experience some rise in temperature. In all missiles, some portions will experience a rise in temperature due to flights at high velocities within the atmosphere.

As a consequence, minimizing the weight of the design in the interest of maximizing the payload or the range is a complicated and iterated procedure. The expected critical temperature in a design of a given weight must be estimated and the result used to predict material performance or requirements. Different materials of construction not only start out at room temperature with different properties but differ in the way in which these properties vary as the temperature rises. For a given aerodynamic condition, the temperature rise in the skin of a ballistic vehicle will depend upon the ability of the material to absorb heat, i.e., upon its heat capacity. The heat capacity is directly proportional to the product of density and specific heat. Specific heat is inversely proportional to atomic weight for metals, while density is only approximately proportional to atomic weight. Because of these factors, it is not a simple matter to state a priori what combinations of design and materials will minimize dead-load weight for a given mission. In the pressurized portions of the structure where the tension loads created by the pressure govern the design of the structure, and where large temperature changes do not occur, minimum weight can be expected with the material whose ratio of tensile strength (or rather its *usable* strength) to density is the highest.

An unpressurized structure will be critical in compression because of its tendency to buckle. In such structures, attention must be paid not only to the actual temperatures obtained but also to the uniformity of the temperature rise. In structures designed to utilize materials having a maximum ratio of strength to density, the design often involves a thin skin with internal stiffener. In this case there may arise considerable temperature variations within the skin and between the skin and the interior structure. Such temperature differences may cause buckling and thus decrease the load-carrying capacity of the structure. The occurrence of buckling would defeat the original intent of weight minimization through use of materials of maximum strength-density ratio. Pure monocoque construction, that is, cylinders stiffened at the most by a few rings, may be expected to have a fairly uniform skin temperature. In this case, the criterion for failure would be the ratio of the square root of the modulus of elasticity to density, because elastic buckling would be the critical factor in design. At room temperature, this relationship tends to favor material of minimum density. At elevated temperatures, plastic buckling may enter the picture and the problem becomes much more complex.

A type of construction combining the best features of both kinds of design is known as "sandwich" construction. In this method, two walls of thin-gauge material separated by stiffening webs at extremely small intervals are employed. There has been a tremendous effort in recent years to develop sandwich-type materials because of the weight savings potentially obtainable with this kind of construction. Optimum design may dictate the use of gauges so thin that manufacturing limitations prevent optimization. As applied to missiles and spacecraft, there is some lack of flexibility in development, compared with monocoque construction, because of the inability to make cutouts or to add brackets, etc., to the structure.

Operation in Space. Short-range missiles never leave the earth's atmosphere. Long-range missiles proceed in a Keplerian orbit to their target and are well above the atmosphere at the highest point above the earth. Their time out of the atmosphere is but a few minutes, however, and problems of operation well outside the atmosphere really do not arise except for satellites and spacecraft. Enough has already been learned about the conditions in outer space so that it is certain that new material problems will arise. Such problems will be the subject of detailed consideration in several of the chapters to follow. As an introduction to this subject, it is worthwhile to consider at this point those peculiarities of space environment that should be taken into account when spacecraft are being designed. Above about 100 miles, the particle density and the attendant air pressure become so low that evaporation or sublimation can proceed unhindered, in accordance with the vapor pressure of each material at the temperature it attains. Experimental determination of surface changes, or weight losses due to evaporation, is now underway in several laboratories. Predictions of the expected phenomena have also been made, based on physical theory, plus measured and extrapolated values of vapor pressure. Much remains to be done to provide reliable engineering data for the design of spacecraft that will not suffer from these phenomena during long periods of operation. A few of the metals, it now appears, could easily attain temperatures where evaporation could be of great significance. More important, perhaps, is the question of organic materials, particularly structural plastics, which may have relatively high vapor pressures. It would appear, however, that those polymers which we now know to possess maximum temperature stability, and which are fabricated without the use of high-vapor-pressure plasticizers, may be quite useful even for long periods of time.

Even though the basic materials are resistant to evaporation, films of adsorbed gases may evaporate and thus produce a clean metal surface of a kind obtainable on earth only by means of a high-temperature bakeout in a high vacuum. Experiments with such materials indicate that they can weld quite strongly on contact. The length of time that might be required for such conditions to develop in a space vehicle is unknown at the present, but the high probability of its occurrence makes it desirable to provide permanent films of a nonwelding nature wherever metals come into contact. Very important are antifriction surfaces which will be required for the operation of many of the motors, gear trains, and mechanisms that cannot be effectively sealed from the vacuum of outer space. Nonwelding materials must be provided for these locations, or the presence of lubricating films must be ensured, either through design or through proper choice of materials. Where components can be hermetically sealed, the period of useful life can be measured by laboratory tests. For components that must operate in vacuum, design data are sadly lacking. It is not even known whether high enough test vacua can be obtained in the laboratory to provide a reliable evaluation test condition.

The discussion thus far has been based upon the assumption that space is empty; actually it is not. Some particles are actually present, and among the most prevalent is the group called meteoroids, which are small solid particles. When sufficiently large, such particles may penetrate a vehicle, destroying it or rendering it inoperative. Extremely small particles or "dust" can produce erosion of surfaces and thus change the optical characteristics. The probability of occurrence of these events has been the subject of much study and speculation.

The sun emits a continuous stream of ionized hydrogen (i.e., protons) with occasional strong bursts of much higher intensity. In the near neighborhood of the earth, clouds of electrons and protons exist in belts surrounding the geomagnetic equator. Toward the polar regions, additional electrons are associated with the visible northern lights as observed in the north central United States. All these energetic particles can produce damage to sensitive material. Secondary radiation in the form of X rays is produced by the impact of electrons on solid material, and these rays may penetrate further into the interior of a vehicle. Engineering for and protection against such radiation will be discussed in succeeding chapters.

Close to the earth the concentration of atoms, ions, and molecules in the atmosphere may be high enough to cause erosion of the surface of the vehicle. Also, chemical changes of the surface may occur and this would alter the optical characteristics.

Why are optical characteristics of so much concern? Because these characteristics affect the equilibrium temperature arising from the absorption of electromagnetic radiation. The greater portion of this radiation is concentrated in the wavelength region of visible light. It warms any object on which it falls, in accordance with the absorption characteristics of the surface of that object for visible radiation. The vehicle, at the same time, is losing energy at the long wavelengths characteristic of its relatively low temperature. The rate of cooling, then, is dependent on the emissivity for infrared radiation. The engineering aspects of temperature control via control of the absorptivity and the emissivity of the surface is the subject of a later chapter. It is sufficient to point out here that any change in the surface characteristics will change the average temperature in the interior of the vehicle. Active devices to compensate for this, if required, will, of course, only subtract from the amount of useful payload otherwise available. Before closing the discussion on radiation, it is worthy of note that short-wavelength radiation from the sun, i.e., ultraviolet rays and soft X rays, can have a deleterious effect on exposed organic materials.

A very large question is how can experiments be conducted on earth which will qualify our vehicles and components for long operating lifetimes in the rigorous environment of space? Can the necessary high vacuum be obtained? Will the ultraviolet radiation to which parts may be exposed in this vacuum correspond in energy distribution from sunlight? Can adequate coverage of the energy and particle densities exhibited by protons and electrons be obtained? How can meteorites be simulated with appropriate distribution of particle sizes and velocities? These questions will be discussed at greater length in subsequent chapters.

For unmanned instrumented satellites and spacecraft, such as have been considered in the earlier discussions, there are no special structural requirements other than to survive the exit phase and to operate satisfactorily in the space environment. When life is to be sustained in a spacecraft, the structures obviously must be pressurized to provide the necessary life-giving atmosphere. Again, the new requirement imposes new problems. How can light weight and structural integrity be achieved? An attractive possibility now undergoing study is the inflatable structure. This has already been demonstrated as feasible for large balloons that serve as passive communications satellites. The concept is now being extended to flexible materials that can be folded into a small space until an orbit is attained and then expanded by internal pressure.

Reentry. The last phase of operations to be mentioned in this brief summary is the return to earth through the atmosphere. Quite a bit is known about the design criteria for this operation, and certainly for the case of ballistic missiles the reentry problem has been solved. Passage back to earth through the atmosphere at high speed produces a layer of hot gas at the leading edge of the vehicle. This rise in temperature is determined by the speed, the duration of passage, and the thermal properties of the material.

The initial velocity on entrance into the atmosphere will vary depending on the mission. Shorter-range missiles might be traveling as slow as 12,000 to 14,000 fps, while longer-range missiles may travel at speeds exceeding 18,000 fps. Orbiting satellites may have velocities around 25,000 fps, while vehicles returning from the moon, or beyond, will be going a great deal faster, for example, around 36,000 fps. The total heat generated will be a function of the initial energy, which is proportional to the square of the velocity. The rate of energy dissipation will depend on the time allowed for entry. A steep and rapid entry will demand the ability to withstand high rates of heat for short periods. The deceleration under such conditions will be high. For the ultimate case of manned reentry, maintenance of deceleration at a tolerable level will demand a relatively slow reentry. The temperatures generated will still be extremely high by the standards of present-day materials, considering the length of time over which this temperature must be borne while the vehicle is moving down through the atmosphere as it circles the earth to a speed where parachutes can take over. There is currently a competition between reentry vehicles that use a certain amount of lift to control reentry deceleration and heat and other vehicles that slow down solely because of the drag and angle of reentry. Design and material may be different for these two different constructions.

Materials for proper construction of parachutes would be a perfectly legitimate topic for discussion in this book. The drag-type entry vehicle just mentioned cannot land safely in any other way. The lift-type vehicle, of which the Dynosoar is the prototype, should be able to land in controlled fashion without the aid of a parachute. For the nonlifting case, auxiliary structures may be used to cushion the impact. For landing on the moon, for example, the vehicle or entry capsule might be surrounded with a pressurized balloon. Compression of the balloon, with deflation at the instant of maximum compression, would then take up the shock of landing. In another concept, the shock would be taken up through a crushable structure, possibly of honeycomb metal.

The purpose of this chapter up to this point has been to provide a background for the technological problems of the missile and spacecraft industry. The requirements of the rocket propulsion engine and of the structural elements of the rocket-propelled vehicle have been reviewed. The factors in operation that provide criteria for the selection of materials for the construction of the vehicle and its engine have been summarized. The kinds of materials that can be considered for minimizing the weight of these structures will be discussed next, along with a summary of problems common to the development and use of all materials.

Types of Materials

The major components of missiles and spacecraft are made of metals. Nevertheless, various nonmetals, both inorganic and organic, perform vital functions in the operation of a vehicle. The succeeding sections of this chapter will be devoted to a brief review of the kinds of materials used for rocket-propelled vehicles and the ways in which such materials are used.

The missile industry is fabricating fuel tanks of enormous capacity from stainless steel and aluminum alloys. Magnesium alloys probably rank third in importance. Although not used for tanks, such alloys serve well as framing, brackets, and interstage structures. The relatively new lightweight metal, titanium, has entered the commercial stage; it is already a preferred material for the construction of high-pressure-gas bottles.

What other metals are there whose usage to date is small compared with the previously mentioned four metals? As was pointed out earlier, extremely high temperatures are encountered both in the power plant and at the leading edges during high-speed flight in the atmosphere.

During the past ten years, extensive development work has made possible the use, in such locations, of metals of high melting points, such as Mo, Cb, Ta, and W. Beryllium is a low-density metal with attractive properties, but with a number of weaknesses to be enumerated later, which leaves the question open at this time as to the extent of its future use in the missile industry.

So extreme have the temperature problems become that the possibilities are being investigated of using nonmetals having higher melting points than those of the refractory metals. A form of carbon, graphite, has been known for many years to remain in the solid state up to temperatures in the neighborhood of 6000°F. Very recently a new form of graphite, known as the pyrolytic variety, has attracted great interest. This material exhibits an extreme anisotropy in thermal properties. A number of metal compounds, such as oxides, borides, nitrides, and carbides, have very high melting points. However, the use of such compounds is limited because of their brittleness. Even the thermal stresses generated during heating and cooling may cause cracking in these compounds.

The brittle behavior of compounds has led to the development of composite materials in which the brittle material is reinforced by the inclusion of a multitude of tiny fibers of one of the high-melting-point ductile metals. Such products are similar to the familiar composite material *fiber glass*, which is made up of organic resins reinforced with glass fibers. Fiber glass can be made in special forms and in several ways. The reinforcing glass can be laid down in a continuous fiber, and in a calculated fashion, with a minimum of resin to bond the strands together. This variation of the process is known as filament winding; it has been extended to include the use of continuous strands of metal, particularly steel, that have been cold-drawn to strength levels in excess of half a million pounds per square inch.

In addition to being employed as binding resins, organic materials find considerable use as sealants, insulators, or potting compounds. Materials having good electrical insulation properties as well as strength and rigidity are useful for fastening electrical components in place. This fastening method has found considerable use because of its durability under vibration and because of its light weight. Vibration failures are frequent and serious, as was clearly demonstrated by recent malfunction of a Juno, ascribed to a vibration failure in the guidance circuit immediately after lift-off.

Materials in Particular Designs

The detailed analysis of a particular configuration to determine the combination of design and material which will minimize weight can be extremely lengthy. It will be interesting, for selected cases, to see how the accepted solutions affect the choice of materials. As described earlier, compression and bending loads in tubelike structures are often most conveniently handled by using a simple tube structure stiffened at periodic intervals by rings of suitable shape. This construction offers maximum simplicity in construction, flexibility in modification, and uniformity of temperature distribution. In its simplest form, the analysis shows that the structure will buckle between the rings at a load which is proportional to the modulus of elasticity and to the square of the thickness. Since the mass of the structure is directly proportional to the density and to the first power of the thickness, it follows that the weight for a given load will be directly proportional to the density of the material and inversely proportional to the square root of the modulus, as shown below for the buckling of cylinders:

$$m \propto \frac{d}{\sqrt{E}}$$

As shown in Table 1.2 for a selected list of materials of varying density and moduli, beryllium would be the best material for making tubes. In practice, however, beryllium is not used because of its brittleness and so magnesium is employed.

Table 1.2   Parameters Affecting Buckling Strength of Hollow Cylinders

Material	d	E	$d/\sqrt{E}$	Per cent increase
Be	0.068	44	102	−60
Mg	0.065	6.5	255	0
Al	0.10	10.5	308	+21
Ti	0.16	16	400	+57
Fe	0.29	29	540	+111
Mo	0.37	46	546	+114

The subject of beryllium will receive more extended treatment in a subsequent chapter, but a brief discussion of this material is worth presenting at this point. Its specific heat is higher than that of any other metal, and its melting point is high enough so that it can absorb the heat generated on reentry of certain vehicles without melting or changing shape. Thus beryllium can be useful as a nose-cone material even though its brittleness precludes its use in thin-walled tubes. The material in tubes, as a matter of actual practice, is so thin that it is hard to conceive of manufacturing methods that would permit beryllium to be fabricated in the necessary sheet form. Unfortunately, all beryllium made to date is quite brittle when compared with even the poorest of the previously used structural materials. Although sheet or forgings can be made with attractive mechanical properties in two directions, the ductility in the third direction is usually extremely low. Because of the stress raisers inevitably present in all engineering structures, the load-carrying capacity of the beryllium is a good deal lower than that implied by tensile-strength measurements. Nevertheless, the usable strength is often high enough to justify the use of this metal in certain parts of a structure. However, the cost of such constructions is generally very high and this tends to restrict its use to only the most vital applications.

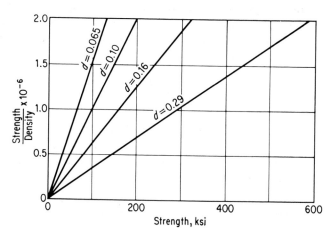

Fig. 1.4 Strength versus strength-density ratio.

The pressure vessel is a structural configuration of great importance. An apt saying is that a missile is nothing but a flying pressure vessel. This subject is so important and so complex that it will be the topic of Chaps. 6 and 7, but a few comments seem appropriate here.

The criteria governing pressure-vessel design are different from those previously discussed for compression structures. Insofar as the allowable pressure is concerned, the ultimate strength of the vessel is related to the ultimate usable strength of the material. To a first approximation, the weight of the vessel is a function only of the ratio of the strength to the density of the material. The higher this ratio, the lower the weight of the vessel, as is shown by plots in Fig. 1.4. Although steels have generally been the preferred material of construction in the past, titanium is now making some inroads; also, aluminum producers are working hard to demonstrate the utility of their alloys. Magnesium is not competitive for this application, even for those fluids with which it is chemically compatible. The problem of brittleness in beryllium will have to be solved before it can be considered for pressure-vessel applications. The problems with composite materials are numerous and complex, but it is conceivable that at some future date such materials may turn out to have the highest strength-density ratio.

As should be evident by now, design criteria must include consideration of the operating temperature and the time at temperature. When the temperature is extremely high, the design criteria may not necessarily be different, but the materials to be used will certainly not be the same as those used at low temperatures. The so-called "refractory" metals and compounds are being studied because their melting points far exceed the melting points of the common engineering materials. There are numerous problems connected with the use of refractory materials; these will be considered in detail in Chap. 3. The next section will be concerned with a discussion of general problems that must be recognized in the selection and evaluation of materials.

Necessary Information about Materials

Without certain basic information on the properties of materials, it is impossible for a designer to determine whether a given material should be selected for a given component. Property values have to be used in the initial design stages to determine the relative weights of various components. The need for good data about properties is well recognized. The oldest test in the materials field is the tensile test. Properly carried out, such a test will provide values for the modulus of elasticity, the yield strength, the ultimate strength, and the ductility as indicated by the elongation and reduction of area. The elongation and reduction data are not usable in any design formula, but engineers realize that for the materials with which they are constantly working, when this number is too low the structures might fail before reaching the critical design stress. This has led to the specification of minimum values for elongation—a device to help ensure against failure at stress levels lower than those indicated by the tensile test. However, experience has shown that elongation, as measured in the tensile test, is not a reliable guarantee of ductility in structures. There is undoubtedly a level of ductility, as measured in the tensile test, below which premature brittle failure is almost certain to occur in service. To some extent, then, the elongation serves a useful purpose in discriminating among materials of equal strength.

The magnesium industry recognized many years ago that high-strength alloys may behave in a brittle manner, even though such alloys may have 10 per cent or more elongation. Bitter experience in the field demonstrated the brittleness of these alloys, and so laboratory tests were devised to reveal the materials with brittle-fracture tendencies. New alloys were eventually developed with comparable strength and elongation, but freed from the brittle behavior previously encountered.   In recent years, the push for ultrahigh strength in other metals such as iron, titanium, and aluminum has produced similar unfortunate results.   In a recent case, one of the leading steel companies was asked to provide a steel that could be heat-treated to a yield strength of 240 ksi with an elongation of 6 per cent.   After considerable work, the producer came up with a steel that met these specifications.   Unfortunately, when it was made into pressure vessels, it did not show the high strength observed in the tensile bar. The elongation specification had been inadequate to ensure proper performance in the pressure vessel.   Neither the customer who specified the properties nor the producer who developed the alloy had recognized the danger of brittle fracture and hence they had not checked the material for this characteristic.

Brittle behavior is no longer unusual.   A large volume of literature has accumulated since the early papers on the brittle fracture of magnesium, and many kinds of tests have been devised to disclose potentially dangerous materials.   Details of such tests will be described in later chapters, but a brief introduction to the subject will be given here.

Toughness may be measured in various ways.   The most common method is the Charpy test, in which a sharply notched bar is broken by a heavy pendulum, and the energy absorbed during fracture is measured. To have a high value in this test, the material must be capable of redistributing stress by plastic flow at points of stress concentration. This is the characteristic needed if a material in a complex structure is to be able to deform, rather than to break.   Appropriate values for toughness are different for different metals.   Sheet can be evaluated in bending tests, with or without side notches; notch sensitivity in tension is also used with considerable success.   Various parameters related to crack propagation, or tearing, have been measured and correlated, with some success, with the strength of a structure, but there is no general agreement on any one method for evaluating the notch sensitivity of a material.   Table 1.3 shows how toughness can vary for materials having nearly identical tensile properties.   The low-toughness alloy shown in this table had to be replaced by a high-toughness alloy because of impact failures in service.

There are two other mechanical properties that are commonly used in design: the shear strength and the bearing strength.   The test for determining these properties is specialized but not difficult.   However, as was shown earlier, the conditions of use in missiles and spacecraft may well involve elevated temperatures and lengthy periods of time.

Another characteristic of many materials of construction, both metallic and nonmetallic, is the nonuniformity in properties measured in different directions.   Sheet material often has substantially different properties in

Table 1.3   Static Notched-bend Test Data

Alloy	Energy to rupture, in.-lb	Properties			
		Tensile strength	Elonga-tion, %	Tensile yield strength	Com-pression yield strength
FS-1	15.3	37.7	15.2	24.8	14.7
J-1	15.6	42.8	16.8	24.5	14.9
O-1HTA	3.1	52.8	10.8	35.1	34.4
Mg–5 Zn–0.75 Zr	15.0	49.0	9.5	40.0	35.0

the rolling and cross directions; some materials have different strengths in compression and tension; the properties of massive forgings can be measured in three directions—longitudinal, long transverse, and short transverse—and often they are different. Proper design requires information about such anisotropic properties.

Because of the complex environment discussed earlier, it is necessary to know the values for a number of physical properties, including the specific heat, the thermal conductivity, and the coefficient of expansion. In order

Table 1.4   Modulus of Elasticity and Coefficient of Expansion Data for Several Metals

Metal	E, psi $\times 10^{-6}$	α per °F $\times 10^6$ (70° F)	$E\alpha$
Be	44	6.4	281
Mg	6.5	14.5	94
Al	10.5	12.1	127
Ti	16	5.0	80
Fe	29	9.2	266
Mo	46	5.4	248

to determine the change in dimensions with temperature, or, more probably, to calculate the stresses developed in the constrained parts of the structure when it is heated, such properties must be known. Thermal stresses are proportional to the product of elastic modulus and coefficient of expansion. This quantity is shown in Table 1.4 for a number of common materials. However, the magnitude of the stress developed is only part of the story; the important question is whether or not the stresses can cause damage. Only careful analysis can provide an answer to this question. One of the phenomena which might not be taken account of in ordinary analyses is that of thermal fatigue. This also will be discussed later.

Too often a new material has been evaluated and recommended for use solely on the basis of an attractive combination of the properties important in design. Actually, unless the material can be fabricated at a tolerable cost into the desired configuration, the attractive design properties will be of no use whatsoever. The problem of cost will not be treated extensively herein. In regard to evaluation, a demonstration in the laboratory that a material in a certain form has desirable properties is a long way from demonstrating that large portions of a missile or spacecraft can be constructed from the same material. This is particularly true of the complex structures that make up many of today's boosters and satellites.

The original producer of a material must be able to compound it with a reasonable degree of chemical uniformity, in batches of sufficient size to permit fabrication of the sheets, forgings, castings, extrusions, or filaments that are needed. The material must have the characteristics necessary to allow large volumes to be formed into sheets, extrusions, castings, or other useful shapes. There are many slips between laboratory demonstration and full-scale plant production. Before any high hopes are held out for a new material, its producibility on a plant scale must be demonstrated.

This is by no means all. Even though material is delivered that looks like the usual raw material from the producer, it may be defective and crack during forming operation, or it may develop a rough surface on machining, or welds may be porous or cracked. Each new material must be checked to be sure that it possesses the requisite qualities of fabricability.

There are still other material characteristics that should be evaluated before the final commitment about design and material is made. Special consideration should be given to the possibility of fatigue failure, that is, rupture after a number of repeated applications of load. It cannot be taken for granted that a structure satisfactory from the standpoint of static test will automatically survive severe vibrations in service. The prediction of structural life under fatigue conditions is difficult and, in fact, often impossible, but the possibility of such failures must be kept in mind.

Material selection must also be based on compatibility considerations. All aspects of the service environment must be taken into account. This will include not only ordinary and extraordinary weathering but also the chemical action of fuels or other fluids with which the material may come in contact. If the bare material is not compatible, means for protection must be found. These means, in turn, must be demonstrated as being producible under the prevailing conditions of manufacture. Further-more, any coatings desired to protect the material against the environ-ment must also have the optical properties needed to ensure control of the temperature within the structure. Truly, with all the factors that must be satisfied, it is a wonder that any successful missiles have been built. Yet, the record of this new industry speaks for itself. Long-range missiles can, with a very small dispersion, be brought to target; and satellites can, with small error, be placed in orbits of desired altitude and eccentricity. The final factor to be discussed, and one that contributes significantly to success, is the control of quality of the material.

Quality Control

All the factors discussed previously in this chapter have been directed toward producing systems that will operate as intended 100 per cent of the time. Bitter experience has shown that things do not work out in this way without the exercise of a great number of precautions. In fact, practically a whole new technology called *reliability engineering* has evolved. Its purpose is to predict the percentage of failures that may be expected in the operation of a particular system. One of the factors that was underrated in the early days of rocket-powered vehicles was the vibration from the engines. Components in various portions of the structure resonated, either from the sound waves or by transmission of vibrations directly through the structure. As a consequence, it is now an established practice to prove by actual vibratory or firing tests that a component will survive the expected vibration environment. It is also standard practice in the development of new components to specify all the factors in the service environment under which its capability of survival must be demonstrated. This general subject has become another branch of technology called *environmental engineering.* Part of the eventual reliability of the system and its components resides in the adequacy of the design, but another large part is due to the adequacy of the materials used, and the uniformity with which they can be produced.

It is easy enough to show by a great deal of testing, much of it destruc-tive in character, that a machine will survive in the specified environment for the requisite period of time. As long as we can be assured that the machines are identical, satisfactory performance can be relied upon. A great deal of energy has gone into the devising of acceptance methods of a nondestructive character to ensure uniformity of quality. This endeavor is fostered by the Society for Nondestructive Testing and has the support of most engineers. Long discussions could be devoted to this subject—to the best techniques and to the limitations of radiography, ultrasonics, and magnetic and eddy-current inspection methods—but obviously this would not be appropriate here.

Within the limits of sensitivity of the detection methods it is possible to state that a particular part, or the material from which it is made, is homogeneous, i.e., free from any flaw. Once the method provides any indication of a flaw, comparisons must be made with standards that correlate the indication of the test method with the mechanical properties or service behavior of the part. Otherwise, either unsatisfactory parts might be put into service or satisfactory parts might be rejected. As everyone who has worked in this field knows, it is much easier to talk about standards than to establish them. In any event, there are undoubtedly many factors affecting performance that are not susceptible to check by presently available nondestructive methods. The complete adequacy of a product can only be ensured by rigid control of the manufacturing process; the importance of such control cannot be over-emphasized. Too often it is assumed that nondestructive testing alone can ensure reliability.

Rigid control of the manufacturing process presumes that all the pertinent variables in that process have been defined and operating limits have been established. Sometimes the effects of certain critical variables are not discovered in the development stage of processing and only emerge later through service failures or, more hopefully, during acceptance testing. Until such variables are recognized, defined, and controlled, performance behavior in the end product cannot be ensured. After the discovery of such variables, inspection procedures can be instituted in the manufacturing plant that will ensure the production of materials within allowable operating limits. A statistical study of the performance of units made under controlled conditions will indicate the probable lifetime.

Failure to recognize certain obscure failures has led to disastrous service failures. This is particularly true when the causes cannot be detected by nondestructive test methods.

For example, a new product was made by mixing certain ingredients in powder form and subsequently processing the mixture into a material with an attractive combination of properties. The technical man who invented this new product did not actually make it, but an hourly employee had done all the actual work under his direction. When the hourly rated employee was drafted into the Army, his replacement was unable to duplicate the results of his predecessor. Very considerable study failed to reveal the change in procedure that had occurred. After two years, the original employee returned. He was asked to duplicate his original work. He went to the storeroom, found the jar from which he had originally taken one of the essential chemicals, mixed his ingredients, and turned out exactly the same product that he had made two years earlier. The new employee had been using a different jar of the same ingredients off the same shelf, sold to exactly the same specifications; yet there were significant differences between the two batches of raw material. It took a great deal of subsequent work to isolate the significant variables in the manufacture of that particular powder.

For some materials, forming operations can significantly affect the properties obtained, and it is very often impossible to detect the differences by nondestructive methods. When magnesium is worked, the preferred orientation of the grains changes, and this can have a marked effect on the properties. For this reason it is usually necessary to determine the properties in different directions in drawn or spun parts, or in forgings, and then depend on process control to produce these same properties in subsequent production. Heating at various stages in metalworking and processing may, on occasion, produce coarse grains with a corresponding reduction in properties. Such occurrences are not likely to be detected except by stringent destructive testing of a number of prototypes. Again, once the product has been defined, the manufacturing process must remain the same.

It is usually wise to have test coupons accompany articles that undergo heat treatment. The coupons do not necessarily exhibit the same properties as the material in the part being heat-treated, but this practice at least reveals whether or not the heat treatment is adequate.

In summary, rocket-propelled missiles and spacecraft must be built as light as possible and must have a propulsion system of maximum efficiency. This can be accomplished only through the most sophisticated use of all the materials available at the present time. While waiting for the improved materials that will come as time goes on, we must exercise maximum care to ensure uniformity in those now available. The succeeding years will be exciting, indeed, as vehicles that can operate for long periods of time in the exploration of the moon and neighboring planets are developed.

REFERENCE

1. Seifert, H. S.: "Space Technology," John Wiley & Sons, Inc., New York, 1959.

2

Materials at Cryogenic Temperatures

JAMES F. WATSON

SENIOR RESEARCH ENGINEER
MATERIALS RESEARCH GROUP
CONVAIR-ASTRONAUTICS
SAN DIEGO, CALIFORNIA

The use of cryogenic propellants in current and proposed missiles and space vehicles has stimulated interest in the low-temperature properties of high-strength materials. The first generation of intermediate- and long-range ballistic missiles such as Atlas, Titan, Thor, and Jupiter used liquid oxygen (boiling point $-297°F$) and RP-1 (a petroleum derivative) as propellants to generate a specific impulse (I_{sp}) of about 280 sec. The next generation of upper-stage space vehicles, such as the Centaur and various Saturn upper stages, has been designed around liquid oxygen–liquid hydrogen (boiling point $-423°F$) propulsion systems that generate a specific impulse of about 400 sec. The forthcoming generation of nuclear-powered upper-stage space vehicles will use liquid hydrogen as a working fluid and will generate specific impulses of about 800 sec. Thus the future of cryogenic propellants appears to be firmly established in the national space exploration program, and the associated cryogenic materials problems are demanding increasingly widespread attention.

Since these upper-stage space vehicles experience a variety of loading conditions at cryogenic temperatures during their flight profiles, their structural integrity demands that their mechanical properties be accurately measured at temperatures ranging down to $-423°F$. In addition, the physical properties of nonstructural members, such as thermal insulations, must be known in order to calculate such characteristics as propellant boil-off rates.

Cryogenic Testing Equipment

With these requirements in mind, Convair-Astronautics developed the cryogenic testing facilities needed to determine the various mechanical

25

and physical properties necessary for reliable design.   To obtain the best advice about equipment, safety devices and procedures, and test techniques, visits were made to the leading cryogenic testing laboratories in the country, including the Cryogenics Laboratory of the National Bureau of Standards (NBS) at Boulder, Colorado; Ohio State University; Westinghouse Research Laboratory; Battelle Memorial Institute; and Massachusetts Institute of Technology.   In connection with other work under contract to the Air Force, personnel of the Cryogenics Laboratory of NBS served as consultants to Convair-Astronautics during the time that the latter's facilities were being developed.

As the result, two separate facilities were established for liquid-hydrogen-temperature testing of materials.   One was an indoor facility for the tensile, impact, and hardness testing of relatively small specimens, and the other was an outdoor facility for tensile and fatigue testing of large base-metal and welded coupons which simulate actual weld joints in full-scale missile tanks.

The indoor test facility consists of a room approximately 20 by 20 ft in size, with a gastight ceiling sheathed with welded steel sheet.   The ceiling tapers upward toward the center of the room, leading to three outlets topped by explosion-proofed motors and fans capable of completely exhausting the air from the room at a rate of four changes per minute. All ceiling lights and electrical connections higher than 3 ft above the floor were also explosion-proofed.   A detailed description of the tensile cryostat and accessories is given by Watson and Christian [1].

Since the test console of the tensile machine used for determining mechanical properties contained a large number of electrical connections that could not be explosion-proofed, a sheet-steel room was constructed around it, and air was piped into this room at a slight positive pressure to safeguard against the entry of hydrogen.   Most of the hydrogen gas emanating from the test chamber was sucked directly out through a flexible steel hose attached to the top cover of the test chamber and leading up through the ceiling vent to one of the suction fans.   As a safety precaution, the amount of liquid hydrogen allowed in the room at one time was limited to 50 liters.   Liquid hydrogen was trucked to the plant from the Stearns Rogers Company, Bakersfield, California, and was stored outdoors in large dewar trailers.

The indoor test facility was also employed for liquid-nitrogen tests. For testing at still higher temperatures, a steel chamber was available in which alcohol and dry ice could be used to establish temperatures between $-100°F$ and room temperature.   In addition, a large insulated test chamber was available which could be fitted between the platens of the tensile machine and which could be maintained at any desired test temperature between $-320°F$ and room temperature by means of circulating liquid and gaseous nitrogen through the chamber.

The test facility for the tensile and fatigue testing of large base-metal and welded coupons was located outdoors. In fatigue testing, the rate of loading was 6 cpm. With specimens fracturing in the range of 1,000 to 5,000 stress cycles, tests could be completed within 3 to 15 hr. The number of cycles was low because the testing was performed at high levels of stress, i.e., in the range of 80 to 95 per cent of yield strength. Such high stresses are realistic because the allowable design stresses are established as high as safety permits in order to minimize the weight of missile structures. To date, several hundred fatigue tests of large welded joints have been performed at $-320°F$, and several dozens of tests have been performed at $-423°F$.

Experimental Programs

A wide variety of high-strength sheet materials, including aluminum-, titanium-, nickel- ,and cobalt-base alloys, cold-rolled austenitic stainless steels, and several heat-treated stainless steels, have been tested at temperatures ranging down to $-423°F$ to determine their suitability for application in missile and space-vehicle systems. These alloys were selected for study because they exhibited one or more of the following characteristics: high strength-density ratio; good toughness (i.e., resistance to brittle fracture); adequate weldability; retention of properties at both cryogenic and moderately high temperatures (in the range of 700 to 1200°F); corrosion resistance; and good formability. In order to obtain optimum strength levels, the alloys selected for study were either cold-worked (cold-rolled) or heat-treated (age-hardened or quenched and tempered) to the highest strength level commensurate with adequate toughness. In addition, since weldability is of prime importance in the fabrication of these vehicles, alloys were tested in both the base-metal and the heliarc butt-welded configurations.

The alloys were normally tested in tension at 78, -100, -320, and $-423°F$, in both smooth and notched configurations, to provide values of yield strength, tensile strength, elongation, and notched-unnotched tensile ratios (stress concentration factor $K_t = 6.3$). Tensile strength only was measured for the heliarc butt-welded specimens.

The notched tensile tests were included to provide information on toughness, a property that indicates the resistance to catastrophic brittle fracture. Toughness is of vital importance to the designer because missile structures are subjected to shock-type loads which occur during hydraulic hammering, vibrations due to rocket-engine firing, and the action of quick-closing valves. They contain built-in stress concentrations of varying degrees of intensity due to welding defects, tool marks, assembly eccentricities, and random defects in the metal. These conditions all favor brittle failure, a condition that becomes even more severe at low temperatures.

The severest type of toughness test combines high strain rates, sharp notches, and low temperature. Notched-unnotched tensile-strength ratios were used at Convair-Astronautics as an index of toughness. Almost all the data reported herein were obtained on relatively thin sheet material. The notched tensile samples permitted the use of sharp notches and low testing temperatures but did not permit high strain rates to be employed. The strain rate at the root of the notch was, however, greater than that imposed on the material in tests of smooth tensile specimens because of the strain-concentrating effect of the notch.

The stress concentration factor of 6.3 was selected for use because previous axial fatigue tests of complex welded joints on 301 extra full hard stainless steel had exhibited a good correlation with notched-unnotched tensile ratios obtained with this value of K_t, over a range of temperatures from $+78$ to $-423°F$. Table 2.1 presents test data on cold-worked stainless steels showing the correlation that has been obtained between the notched-unnotched tensile ratios and the fatigue resistance of complex welded joints. A large body of data generated as part of the Atlas and Centaur programs shows that less acute notches (e.g., K_t of 2.5 to 3.0) are less discriminatory in distinguishing between tough and brittle materials; in fact, in some cases, tests with this low notch acuity on materials known to be brittle have yielded notched-unnotched tensile ratios of about unity. The less sharp notches tend to indicate that many materials are tough, whereas they actually may be brittle when tested under actual service conditions. At the other extreme, however, stress concentration factors of 15 to 18 have been employed on a variety of materials by some investigators; and these tests, in general, tend to make all materials, including tough ones, appear to be brittle. Thus, a K_t of 6.3 lying midway between these two extremes has been found to correlate well with service behavior, which is the ultimate goal of any laboratory test procedure.

A point of interest is that low notched-unnotched tensile ratios are frequently found at $-423°F$, where elongation values in unnotched tensile tests are relatively high and may even be tending to increase as the temperature is reduced. This simply demonstrates that elongation in the smooth tensile test is *not* a measure of toughness or notch sensitivity. Until recently, many investigators have used the terms ductility and toughness interchangeably, whereas they actually measure two distinctly different properties of the material. Elongation, which is a measure of ductility, describes the ability of a material to deform plastically under conditions of slowly applied uniaxial tension in the absence of notches or other stress concentrations. Toughness, which may be measured by the Charpy V-notch tests, by the notched-unnotched tensile ratios, or by

Table 2.1   Correlation of Base Metal Notched-Unnotched Tensile Ratios with Fatigue Properties of Complex Welded Joints[a] of Cold-worked Stainless-steel Sheet 0.020 in. Thick

Material	Test temperature	Notched-unnotched tensile ratio ($K_t = 6.3$)		Cycles to failure in axial fatigue tests[b]			
				0–140,000 psi		0–120,000 psi	
		Long.	Trans.	Av.	$\pm 3\sigma'^c$	Av.	$\pm 3\sigma'^c$
Type 301 CRES (60% cold-rolled)...........	+78	1.05	0.97	934[d]	776		
					1,123		
	−320	0.99	0.87	2,671[d]	2,066		
					3,444		
	−423	0.92	0.68	633[d]	196	1,964	765
					2,004		4,650
Type 310 CRES (75% cold-rolled)...........	+78	1.10	0.97				
	−320	1.11	1.07	1,855[e]			
	−423	1.11	1.03	2,000[f]			
Type 301 NCRES (60% cold-rolled)...........	+78	1.06	0.94	632[g]	497		
					800		
	−320	0.95	0.87	327[g]	17		
					3,503		

[a] Welded joints $3\frac{1}{2}$ in. wide, 20 in. gauge length, 38 in. overall length.   Midsection contains heliarc butt-weld joint, roll-planished and reinforced with 4-in.-wide doubler resistance spot weld with four rows of spots on each side of the butt weld. All sections 0.020 in. thick.

[b] Fatigue test of weld joint consists in axially loading and unloading between 0 and 140,000 psi in tension at a rate of 6 cpm.

[c] A statistical analysis which means that in an infinite series of identical tests, the cycles to failure would fall within the given limits 99.9 per cent of the time.

[d] Average of three tests.

[e] Average of two tests.

[f] Test stopped after 2,000 cycles after which one small crack was evident in heat-affected zone of one of resistance spot welds in outer row of spots.   Based on prior experience in fatigue tests where final failure occurs at 50 per cent or more of the number of cycles in which crack initiates, it can be estimated that fatigue life is in the order of 3,000 cycles.

[g] Average of five tests.

various tear tests, is a measure of resistance to fracture propagation under conditions of stress concentrations, such as those caused by notches, rivet holes, inclusions, sharp reentrant corners, or similar structural discontinuities.   Combinations of impact loads, stress concentrations, and low temperature provide the severest types of toughness test; all these conditions are present in a Charpy V-notch test conducted at low temperature.

As a result of these considerations, it is seen that a material may have a large amount of ductility as measured by elongation, yet have very poor toughness, as measured by notched-unnotched tensile ratios, Charpy V-notch tests, or crack-propagation tests. For example, many of the carbon steels exhibit elongations of as much as 15 per cent in tensile tests at −320°F; yet they are glass-brittle in notched-bar impact tests at this temperature. Conversely, some high-strength stainless steels may have elongations as low as a few per cent and yet have excellent toughness, as measured by any of the previously mentioned tests.

Thus, when considering a material for use in a highly stressed missile structure at low temperature, the designer must rely on toughness data rather than ductility data for an intelligent selection of materials. This is especially true in the case of missile applications, because all conditions favoring brittle failure are present, i.e., high strain rates (vibration of rocket engines, hydraulic hammer, and action of quick-closing valves), stress concentrations (spot welds, sharp reentrant corners, and tooling scratches), high operating stresses because of weight considerations, and low temperatures associated with cryogenic fuels.

Cold-worked 300-series Stainless Steels

In the cold-rolled condition, this alloy class exhibits an outstanding combination of properties which suit it for structural application in missiles and space vehicles utilizing cryogenic propellants. These properties include good strength-density ratio, excellent toughness over the range of −423 to +800°F, good weldability, good corrosion resistance, and excellent formability.

Type 301 cold-rolled about 60 per cent is the skin material used in the Atlas and Centaur vehicles. As such, it has been subjected to an extremely wide variety of mechanical and physical property tests including mechanical property tests over the temperature range of −423 to 1000°F; weldability tests involving heliarc butt, seam, and spot welds and resistance spot welds; stress corrosion tests; thermal conductivity tests; and many others. At present this alloy is being produced to a Convair specification which requires fractional standard AISI tolerances for thickness, camber, flatness, and surface appearance. These closer tolerances, resulting from cold-rolling by the Sendzimir process, ensure a more uniform product, which in turn improves the design accuracy in such vitally important areas as stress distribution and weight.

The 301 extra full hard exhibits a tensile strength which increases from about 220 ksi at +78°F to about 330 ksi at −423°F, while the yield strength increases from about 200 to 285 ksi over the same temperature range. This immediately raises the possibility of using the low-temperature properties as the basic of design allowables when the structure is subjected to maximum loading only at low temperature. Typical data for this material are given in Table 2.2.

Where higher fatigue life for a given stress level is desired, a more stable steel (i.e., one in which the austenite-to-martensite reaction does not occur) would be specified. Such a steel is AISI Type 310 CRES, which has been tested in the 40, 60, and 75 per cent cold-rolled conditions. In

Table 2.2 Mechanical Properties of Type 301 Cres†
Extra Full Hard 0.032 in. Thick

Test temp., °F	Direction	F_{ty}, ksi	F_{tu}, ksi	Elong., %	Notched‡ tensile strength, ksi ($K_t = 6.3$)	Notched-unnotched‡ tensile ratio ($K_t = 6.3$)	Heliarc‡ butt weld tensile strength, ksi	Joint efficiency, %
RT§	Long.	205	224	5	241	1.08	148	66
−110	Long.	210	243	21	253	1.04	207	85
−320	Long.	249	316	20	301	0.95	287	91
−423	Long.	290	322	15	303	0.94	215	67

† Sheet material, produced by Washington Steel Company, heat No. 56760, coil No. 40151.
‡ Roll-planished, no doubler reinforcement.
§ Room temperature.

the 75 per cent cold-rolled condition, the strength of this alloy at 78°F is lower than that of full hard Type 301. However, the strength of 310 at lower temperatures exceeds the room-temperature strength of Type 301. Typical data for this alloy are given in Table 2.3.

Further studies of austenite stability, as influenced by chemistry, were made on Type 301 N steel, cold-rolled about 60 per cent. This alloy has tensile and yield strengths approximately equal to those of Type 301 in the extra full hard condition. However, the lower notched-unnotched tensile ratios at low temperatures show that this steel is unsuitable for use in cryogenic application. At low temperatures, 301 N is unstable in the cold-worked state and it transforms in part to the more brittle martensitic phase. Table 2.4 shows typical data for this alloy.

The investigations of the 300-series stainless steels have been accompanied by thorough metallographic, X-ray diffraction, and magnetic examinations so that the effect of structure on properties could be determined. All these studies showed that Type 301 extra full hard (currently in use on Atlas and Centaur vehicles), Type 304 ECL 50 per cent cold-

Table 2.5   Mechanical Properties of 75% Cold-rolled Type 310 Stainless Steel, 0.020 in. Thick†

Test temp., °F	Direction	F_{ty}, ksi	F_{tu}, ksi	Elong., %	Notched tensile strength, ksi ($K_t = 6.3$)	Notched-unnotched tensile ratio	Heliarc‡ butt tensile strength, ksi	Joint efficiency, %
+78	Long.	157	181	2	194	1.07	87.9	49
+78	Trans.	163	199	4	193	0.97	89.0	45
−100	Long.	190	204	3	220	1.08	112	55
−100	Trans.	192	225	8	236	1.05	113	50
−320	Long.	223	251	10	278	1.11	165	66
−320	Trans.	225	273	11	292	1.07	167	61
−423	Long.	261	290	...	329	1.12	203	70
−423	Trans.	280	317	10	328	1.03	199	63

† Data are the average of three tests in the longitudinal direction and two tests in the transverse direction.

‡ X-rayed, roll-planished, no doubler reinforcement.

Table 2.4   Mechanical Properties of Extra Full Hard Type 301 N Cres†

Test temp., °F	Direction	F_{ty}, ksi	F_{tu}, ksi	Elong., %	Notched tensile strength ksi ($K_t = 6.3$)	Notched-unnotched tensile ratio
RT‡	Long.	200	223	12	240	1.08
	Trans.	177	228	11	222	0.97
−320	Long.	244	340	18	287	0.84
	Trans.	226	296	8	232	0.80
−423	Long.	296	334	12	264	0.79
	Trans.	290	312	6	152	0.49

† Sheet material, 0.027 in. thick, produced by Allegheny-Ludlum Steel Company, heat No. 31131, coil No. 27306. Data represent average of three tests for each condition.

‡ Room temperature.

rolled or more, or Type 310 cold-rolled 75 per cent would make excellent structural skin materials for space vehicles.

Aluminum Alloys

Aluminum alloys have been favorite cryogenic structural materials because of their good low-temperature toughness, low density, moderately high strength, and good weldability. Such generalities do not apply to all aluminum alloys, of course. Each type of alloy must be investigated separately for application in aerospace vehicles.

The 5000-series aluminum alloys, which contain varying amounts of magnesium in solid solution, are noted for their weldability and low-temperature toughness—properties attributable to the fact that they are simple solid-solution alloys. A high-magnesium aluminum-base alloy was used for the liquid-oxygen tanks on the German V-2 rocket. An alloy of this type, 5456-H321, is still in use today on the first stage of the Saturn. This material contains about 5 per cent magnesium in solid solution and is cold-rolled a small amount to increase the strength. Similar alloys used on earlier missiles, such as the Jupiter and Jupiter C, were 5052 and 5086. They contain about 3 and 4 per cent magnesium, respectively, with the higher-magnesium alloy being stronger but more

Table 2.5   Mechanical Properties of 5052-H38 Aluminum Alloy 0.040-in. Sheet†

Test temp., °F	Direction	F_{ty}, ksi	F_{tu}, ksi	Elong., %	Notched tensile strength, ksi ($K_t = 6.3$)	Notched-unnotched tensile ratio	Heliarc‡ butt weld tensile strength, ksi	Joint efficiency, %
+78	Long.	40.0	45.1	7	48.3	1.07	30.2	67
+78	Trans.	41.5	45.9	9	51.1	1.11		
−100	Long.	41.0	47.0	11	50.5	1.07	31.8	68
−100	Trans.	42.0	47.0	11	54.2	1.13		
−320	Long.	48.0	62.6	25	63.6	1.01	46.8	75
−320	Trans.	47.9	59.0	26	64.1	1.09		
−423	Long.	54.7	89.7	32	80.6	0.90	64.9	72
−423	Trans.	56.5	81.2	37	78.2	0.96		

† AlCOA, heat No. 635-521.
‡ X-rayed, roll-planished, no doubler reinforcement.

notch-brittle at low temperatures. Higher magnesium content also makes stress corrosion problems more severe. By cold-rolling the softer alloys such as 5052 and 5086, strength levels equivalent to those of 5456-H343 can be obtained with much better low-temperature toughness. This avenue of alloy development has been actively pursued in a number of laboratories with promising results. Properties of 5052-H38, 5086-H34, and 5456-H343 are given in Tables 2.5 to 2.7.

The 2000-series aluminum alloys are the well-known age-hardening alloys containing copper as their major alloying constituent. These alloys, notably 2014-T6 and 2024-T4, have much higher tensile and yield strengths than do the 5000 series, and for this reason they are much more attractive for airborne tankage. However, since pressurized cryogenic fuel tanks require welded joints for pressure integrity, the weldability of the alloys used becomes of major concern. Fusion welding of 2014-T6,

Table 2.6   Mechanical Properties of 5086-H34 Aluminum Alloy 0.040-in. Sheet

Test temp., °F	Direction	F_{ty}, ksi	F_{tu}, ksi	Elong., %	Notched tensile strength, ksi ($K_t = 6.3$)	Notched-unnotched tensile ratio	Heliarc† butt weld tensile strength, ksi	Joint efficiency, %
+78	Long.	35.7	47.8	9	48.7	1.02	39.0	82
+78	Trans.	32.9	46.9	15	46.8	1.00		
−100	Long.	36.6	48.9	15	50.3	1.03	39.5	81
−100	Trans.	32.4	47.7	15	47.4	1.00		
−320	Long.	40.8	65.4	24	61.9	0.95	56.4	86
−320	Trans.	37.7	61.9	28	55.0	0.89		
−423	Long.	47.0	95.3	30	71.4	0.75	75.3	79
−423	Trans.	44.2	85.7	30	58.4	0.68		

† X-rayed, roll-planished, no doubler reinforcement.

Table 2.7   Mechanical Properties of 5456-H343 Aluminum Alloy 0.050-in. Sheet

Test temp., °F	Direction	F_{ty}, ksi	F_{tu}, ksi	Elong., %	Notched tensile strength, ksi ($K_t = 6.3$)	Notched-unnotched tensile ratio	Heliarc† butt weld tensile strength, ksi	Joint efficiency, %
+78	Long.	47.2	58.6	6.5	54.2	0.92	47.6	81
+78	Trans.	45.4	60.4	8.7	52.8	0.87	47.4	78
−100	Long.	47.8	59.8	8.3	50.5	0.84	49.2	82
−100	Trans.	45.5	61.2	9.2	48.7	0.80	51.9	85
−320	Long.	53.0	72.7	8.2	49.5	0.68	68.2	94
−320	Trans.	51.3	70.9	7.0	48.2	0.68	69.9	99
−423	Long.	60.4	83.5	6.0	55.1	0.66	77.3	93
−423	Trans.	58.7	80.3	4.5	49.7	0.62	79.5	99

† X-rayed, roll-planished, no doubler reinforcement.

Table 2.8   Mechanical Properties of 2024-T4 Aluminum Alloy 0.032-in. Sheet

Test temp., °F	Direction	F_{ty}, ksi	F_{tu}, ksi	Elong., %	Notched tensile strength, ksi ($K_t = 6.3$)	Notched-unnotched tensile ratio
+78	Long.	42.8	67.7	19	59.0	0.87
+78	Trans.	41.5	67.1	29	57.5	0.86
−100	Long.	43.7	69.8	22	60.7	0.87
−100	Trans.	42.7	68.0	24	58.9	0.87
−320	Long.	54.1	84.9	27	71.9	0.85
−320	Trans.	53.6	81.8	19	68.2	0.83
−423	Long.	73.3	107	16	88.3	0.83
−423	Trans.	67.5	97.1	10	85.4	0.88

for example, has always been regarded as marginal at best; welded joints exhibit poor ductility as measured by bend ductility tests. However, by designing around the weld-joint problem with thickened weld joints

Table 2.9 Mechanical Properties of 2014-T6 Aluminum Alloy 0.063-in. Sheet

Test temp., °F	Direction	F_{ty}, ksi	F_{tu}, ksi	Elong. %	Notched tensile strength, ksi ($K_t = 6.3$)	Notched-unnotched tensile ratio	Weld tensile† strength, ksi	Joint efficiency, %
+78	Long.	65.7	73.1	11	74.5	1.02	53.1	73
+78	Trans.	62.8	71.5	11	70.0	0.98		
−100	Long.	69.3	76.4	12	79.2	1.04	56.7	74
−100	Trans.	63.3	74.1	11	71.0	0.96		
−320	Long.	74.4	87.1	14	85.5	0.98	61.9	71
−320	Trans.	70.3	78.7	14	78.7	1.00		
−423	Long.	86.2	104	17	97.8	0.94	75.6	73
−423	Trans.	82.3	102	15	84.5	0.83		

† Filler-metal 2319 weld, tested with bead in place.

Table 2.10 Mechanical Properties of 2219-T81 Aluminum Alloy 0.063-in. Sheet

Test temp., °F	Direction	F_{ty}, ksi	F_{tu}, ksi	Elong., %	Notched tensile strength, ksi ($K_t = 6 3$)	Notched-unnotched tensile ratio	Weld tensile† strength, ksi	Joint efficiency, %
+78	Long.	52.0	67.5	10	64.4	0.95	48.1	71
+78	Trans.	51.0	67.2	10	66.0	0.98		
−100	Long.	56.7	73.3	9	68.6	0.94	49.7	68
−100	Trans.	54.7	72.3	10	67.0	0.93		
−320	Long.	62.2	85.2	11	77.4	0.91	64.3	75
−320	Trans.	61.4	84.6	12	76.1	0.90		
−423	Long.	70.6	102	15	93.4	0.92	72.4	71
−423	Trans.	67.5	102	15	91.3	0.90		

† Manually welded with 2319 aluminum filler metal, no post heat treatment, tested with bead in place (all fractures occurred in heat affected zone).

(usually done by chem-milling), satisfactory structures have been produced. This type of design is typified by the Thor and Titan missiles, which utilize 2014-T6 as a primary structural material. The base-metal properties of 2024-T4, 2014-T6, and 2219-T81 sheet are all acceptably good at −423°F; they are shown in Tables 2.8 to 2.10.

The 7000-series aluminum alloys contain zinc, copper, and magnesium. In the heat-treated condition they are the strongest aluminum alloys commercially available. Unfortunately, these alloys have a low resistance to brittle failure at cryogenic temperatures. For this reason, none of the 7000-series alloys are recommended for liquid-hydrogen service, and of the series only 7079-T6 is acceptable for use at liquid-oxygen temperature ($-297°F$). The weldability problem also places severe

Table 2.11 Mechanical Properties of 7075-T6 Aluminum Alloy 0.025-in. Sheet

Test temp., °F	Direction	F_{ty}, ksi	F_{tu}, ksi	Elong., %	Notched tensile strength, ksi ($K_t = 6.3$)	Notched-unnotched tensile ratio
+78	Long.	70.4	79.5	9	81.4	1.02
+78	Trans.	69.4	77.6	10	77.6	1.00
−100	Long.	76.2	85.1	10	84.6	0.99
−100	Trans.	74.1	83.2	9	80.6	0.97
−320	Long.	86.5	97.2	10	75.7	0.78
−320	Trans.	81.8	94.9	12	73.9	0.78
−423	Long.	100	116	8	84.3	0.73
−423	Trans.	96.6	112	12	78.7	0.70

Table 2.12 Mechanical Properties of 7079-T6 Aluminum Alloy 0.080-in. Sheet

Test temp., °F	Direction	F_{ty}, ksi	F_{tu}, ksi	Elong., %	Notched tensile strength, ksi ($K_t = 6.3$)	Notched-unnotched tensile ratio
+78	Long.	68.9	77.1	11	83.2	1.08
+78	Trans.	66.7	76.0	11	81.2	1.07
−100	Long.	73.2	81.5	12	84.7	1.04
−100	Trans.	69.7	81.0	12	84.0	1.04
−320	Long.	82.1	94.3	16	91.2	0.97
−320	Trans.	78.7	93.8	12	82.1	0.88
−423	Long.	91.1	112	8	78.6	0.70
−423	Trans.	90.5	113	6	77.8	0.69

limitations on the range of applicability of this alloy class at low temperatures. Typical data for 7075-T6, 7079-T6, and 7178-T6 are given in Tables 2.11 to 2.13.

The 5000- and 2000-series aluminum alloys will undoubtedly remain as primary structural materials in the forthcoming series of upper-stage space vehicles because, in addition to the advantages enumerated, aluminum, by virtue of its low density, can be used in relatively thick sections. This is of major importance in contributing stiffness to compression-loaded structures. In most cases, tank stiffness increases with the square of the wall thickness. Thus for various alloys of the

Table 2.13   Mechanical Properties of 7178-T6 Aluminum Alloy 0.036-in. Sheet

Test temp., °F	Direction	F_{ty}, ksi	F_{tu}, ksi	Elong., %	Notched tensile strength, ksi ($K_t = 6.3$)	Notched-unnotched tensile ratio
+78	Long.	82.7	89.9	12	91.8	1.02
+78	Trans.	80.0	90.4	11	84.0	0.93
−100	Long.	87.8	95.2	11	76.8	0.81
−100	Trans.	83.5	95.7	10	74.3	0.78
−320	Long.	98.8	106	4	57.6	0.54
−320	Trans.	93.4	106	3	51.9	0.49
−423	Long.	111	123	2	62.7	0.51
−423	Trans.	112	124	3	56.7	0.46

same strength-density ratio, only magnesium and beryllium would exceed the stiffness of an aluminum structure, and neither of these metals is an acceptable choice for low-temperature structural application.

Titanium Alloys

The titanium-base alloys are of major interest for missile and space-vehicle application because of their outstanding strength-density ratios, accompanied by good weldability and excellent corrosion resistance. Convair-Astronautics uses titanium alloys in missile applications. This work is best typified by the successful development and use of the 6Al-4V titanium alloy in the helium pressurization bottles which form part of the pneumatic system of the Atlas missile. These bottles contain helium gas under high pressure and are cooled in liquid nitrogen (at −320°F) until just prior to takeoff in order to increase their gas-storage capacity. Immediately after takeoff, these bottles are subjected to extremely severe vibrational loading because of their proximity to the rocket engines. This application requires the high order of resistance to brittle fracture that this alloy possesses. For the helium-bottle application, the 6Al-4V titanium alloy is solution-quenched and aged to a tensile strength in the range of 155,000 to 165,000 psi.

Additional work has been in progress for over a year in the evaluation of numerous titanium sheet alloys at temperatures ranging down to −423°F, including A110AT, 6Al-4V, R120 VCA, 6Al-4Zr-1V, 7Al-12Zr, and RS 140. Data for the A110AT program are given in Table 2.14. This alloy exhibits an excellent notched-unnotched strength ratio at the lower temperatures. This alloy was investigated because of its all-alpha (hexagonal close-packed) structure, as well as its excellent strength-density characteristics and its good weldability. No generalities can be stated concerning the behavior of hexagonal close-packed (hcp) alloys at cryogenic temperatures. Although magnesium and zinc (both hcp) tend to be brittle at low temperatures, the 6Al-4V titanium alloy (containing a heat-treated alpha and beta structure) has given excellent service at

Table 2.14   Mechanical Properties of Titanium 5Al-2.5Sn Alloy 0.040-in. Sheet

Test temp., °F	Direction	F_{ty}, ksi	F_{tu}, ksi	Elong., %	Notched tensile strength, ksi ($K_t = 6.3$)	Notched-tensile ratio	Heliarc butt weld tensile strength, ksi	Joint efficiency, %
+78	Long.	113	118	19	158	1.34	121	100
+78	Trans.	115	120	14	159	1.33		
−100	Long.	135	142	18	175	1.23	142	100
−100	Trans.	137	144	11				
−320	Long.	184	196	15	226	1.15	192	98
−320	Trans.	185	199	11	220	1.11		
−423	Long.	230	247	15	239	0.97	233	94
−423	Trans.	230	244	11	208	0.85		

−320°F, in the form of helium pressure bottles for pneumatic system pressurization, as mentioned above (see Table 2.15).

Alloy A110AT is characterized by large increases in both tensile strength and yield strength and by very small decreases in elongation,

Table 2.15   Mechanical Properties of Titanium 6Al-4V Alloy 0.063-in. Sheet†

Test temp., °F	Direction	F_{ty}, ksi	F_{tu}, ksi	Elong., %	Notched tensile strength, ksi ($K_t = 6.3$)	Notched-tensile ratio	Heliarc butt weld tensile strength, ksi	Joint efficiency, %
+78	Long.	129	141	11	157	1.11	142	100
+78	Trans.	136	146	13	169	1.16		
−100	Long.	158	166	11	167	1.01	168	100
−100	Trans.	161	169	11	185	1.09		
−320	Long.	211	219	10	191	0.87	221	100
−320	Trans.	215	219	10	187	0.85		
−423	Long.	245	253	2	183	0.72	275	100
−423	Trans.	248	255	2	187	0.73		

† TMCA, heat M-8907, mill-annealed.

with decreasing temperature. The large increase in yield strength is of prime importance in missile design because many designs are based on yield strength rather than tensile strength. The large increases in yield strength at low temperature can be used to advantage in structures that are highly stressed only at low temperatures.

However, in most cases where the yield strength increases rapidly with decreasing temperature, the toughness of the alloy undergoes a transition from ductile to brittle behavior at relatively high temperatures (depending on chemical composition, heat treatment, strain rate, and type of test). However, this particular titanium alloy displays an excellent notched-unnotched tensile ratio down to $-423°F$, and it appears to be a promising alloy for cryogenic application in all respects.

The welded joint of A110AT is as strong as the parent metal because this alloy is used in the annealed condition. In tensile tests of heliarc butt-welded joints, fracture occurred in the base metal rather than in the weld metal because the weld has been roll-planished to increase its strength.

The other titanium alloys studied were newer alloys obtained through a close working relation between Convair-Astronautics and the titanium producers. The 6Al-4Zr-1V and 7Al-12Zr alloys were selected because of their predominantly alpha structure. However, these alloys become notch-sensitive at cryogenic temperatures, probably because of the small amount of beta present in their structure and possibly because of high interstitial impurities such as oxygen, hydrogen, nitrogen, and carbon. The same effect was noted in alloys RS 140 and R12 VCA, which also had a large amount of beta phase present in the microstructure.

The two alloys that showed the most promise for cryogenic applications were the A110AT alloy in the form of sheet at temperatures down to $-423°F$ and the 6Al-4V alloy in the form of sheet and high-strength heat-treated forgings down to $-320°F$.

Conclusion

In summarizing these data, as they pertain to application in missiles and spacecraft, the ratios F_{tu}/density and F_{ty}/density versus temperature are presented in Table 2.16 for those alloys shown to have promise for cryogenic application. The outstanding feature in this table is the good performance of the A110AT titanium alloy. It has a marked advantage over its closest competitor, Type 301 stainless steel, at $-423°F$, and is especially promising on the F_{ty} comparison, which is usually the more important criterion. Thus, the A110AT titanium alloy is seen to show marked promise for use at cryogenic temperatures, with resultant weight savings ranging up to 25 per cent. In addition to this major weight reduction, the high welded-joint efficiency (100 per cent at $78°F$, 94 per cent at $-423°F$) of this alloy means that little or no doubler reinforcement would be required to achieve optimum joint efficiency. This effect not only eliminates doubler weight but removes the doubler spot-welds which act as stress concentrations that tend to be sources of crack initiation in axial fatigue tests. It should be noted that the high-temperature

Table 2.16 Strength-density Ratios and Notched-Unnotched Tensile Ratios for High-strength Sheet Alloys at Cryogenic Temperatures

Alloy	Test temp., °F	F_{ty}, psi density, lb/in.³ $\times 10^6$	F_{tu}, psi/ density, lb/in.³ $\times 10^6$	Notched-unnotched tensile ratio ($K_t = 6.3$)	Gauge, in.	Density, lb/in.³
301 CRES	+78	0.64	0.76	1.08	0.032	0.29
(60% cold-	−100	0.73	0.83	1.04		
rolled)	−320	0.86	1.10	0.99		
	−423	1.00	1.10	0.92		
301 N CRES	+78	0.63	0.71	1.06	0.017	0.29
(60% cold-	−320	0.80	0.91	0.95		
rolled)	−423	0.96	1.03	0.79		
304 ELC CRES	+78	0.55	0.61	1.09	0.012	0.29
(50% cold-	−100	0.64	0.68	1.09		
rolled)	−320	0.65	0.87	1.04		
	−423	0.80	1.05	1.09		
310 CRES	+78	0.55	0.62	1.10	0.020	0.29
(75% cold-	−100					
rolled)	−320	0.74	0.84	1.11		
	−423	0.88	0.97	1.11		
5052-H38	+78	0.41	0.47	1.07	0.040	0.097
aluminum	−100	0.42	0.48	1.07		
	−320	0.50	0.65	1.01		
	−423	0.57	0.92	0.90		
2014-T6	+78	0.66	0.73	1.02	0.063	0.10
aluminum	−100	0.69	0.76	1.04		
	−320	0.74	0.85	0.98		
	−423	0.86	0.98	0.94		
2024-T3	+78	0.48	0.68	0.89	0.025	0.10
aluminum	−320	0.61	0.87	0.88		
	−423	0.73	1.10	0.81		
6061-T6	+78	0.44	0.48	1.05	0.020	0.098
aluminum	−320	0.52	0.63	1.00		
	−423	0.56	0.82	0.93		
7178-T6	+78	0.83	0.90	1.02	0.036	0.10
aluminum	−100	0.88	0.75	0.81		
	−320	0.99	1.06	0.54		
	−423	1.11	1.23	0.51		

Table 2.16 Strength-density Ratios and Notched-Unnotched Tensile Ratios for High-strength Sheet Alloys at Cryogenic Temperatures (*Continued*)

Alloy	Test temp., °F	F_{ty}, psi/density, lb/in.³ × 10⁶	F_{tu}, psi/density, lb/in.³ × 10⁶	Notched-unnotched tensile ratio ($K_t = 6.3$)	Gauge, in.	Density, lb/in.³
A110AT titanium	+78	0.70	0.74	1.34	0.040	0.161
	−100	0.84	0.88	1.22		
	−320	1.14	1.22	1.15		
	−423	1.43	1.52	0.97		
6A1-4V titanium (annealed)	+78	0.76	0.88	1.06	0.063	0.16
	−100	0.81	1.07	0.93		
	−320	1.13	1.36	0.89		
	−423	1.38	1.55	0.71		
K-Monel (age-hardened)	+78	0.32	0.51	0.93	0.020	0.306
	−100	0.35	0.54	0.93		
	−320	0.39	0.60	0.95		
	−423	0.45	0.66	0.99		

properties of A110AT begin to decrease rapidly at about 600°F, while 301 stainless steel retains its properties up to 1000°F before deterioration occurs. Thus, in applications where such effects as aerodynamic heating may occur, the A110AT must not be heated above 600°F, while 301 stainless steel can withstand temperatures of 1000°F.

The poor performance of the 5000-series aluminum alloys, as shown by Table 2.16, shows why these alloys cannot compete in the *pressure-stabilized* missile design concept. They compare favorably only on the compression type of structure where elastic stability (proportional to thickness squared), rather than F_{ty}, controls the design.

Further generalizations regarding the influence of crystal structure can be made only insofar as they pertain to exceptions to the general rule that face-centered cubic lattices remain tough down to absolute zero. Body-centered cubic lattices undergo a ductile-to-brittle transition that may vary from 800°F for molybdenum to −150°F for specially quenched and tempered steels; and a hexagonal close-packed lattice conforms to no rule, but rather depends on each element under consideration.

The face-centered cubic lattice may be altered in ways that will cause it to exhibit brittle behavior, but these cases are all exceptions to the general rule. For instance, in this study, K-Monel was shown to exhibit excellent toughness at all temperatures down to −423°F, yet it contains a precipitate of $Ni_x(Ti, Al)_y$ distributed throughout its matrix. Aluminum-base alloy 7075-T6, by contrast, becomes very brittle at $-320°F$, although it too possesses a face-centered cubic matrix containing a finely distributed precipitate. Thus, even for the special case of precipitates in face-centered lattices, no generalizations can be made, but consideration must be given to the size, shape, and distribution of the precipitate; the degree of its coherency with the parent lattice; and the relative magnitudes of

Table 2.17   Strength-density Ratios and Notched-Unnotched Tensile Ratios for Selected Alloys at Various Temperatures

Test temp., °F	Material	F_{ty}/density, in. $\times 10^6$	F_{tu}/density, in. $\times 10^6$	Notched-unnotched tensile ratio ($K_t = 6.3$)
+78	7178-T6 aluminum A110AT	0.83	0.90	1.02
	titanium 301 CRES, 60%	0.70	0.74	1.34
	cold-rolled 5052-H38 alumi-	0.64	0.76	1.08
	num K-Monel	0.41	0.47	1.07
		0.32	0.51	0.93
−320	A110AT titanium 301 CRES,	1.14	1.22	1.15
	60% cold-rolled 5052-H38	0.86	1.10	0.95
	aluminum K-Monel	0.50	0.65	1.01
		0.32	0.51	0.95
−423	A110AT titanium 7178-T6	1.43	1.52	0.97
	aluminum 301 CRES, 60%	1.11	1.23	0.51
	cold-rolled 5052-H38 alumi-	1.00	1.10	0.94
	num K-Monel	0.57	0.92	0.90
		0.45	0.66	0.99

the coefficient of thermal expansion between the precipitate and the matrix.

The body-centered martensite phase formed in alloys such as AM 355 and certain 300-series stainless steels has been found to behave in a brittle manner, although tempering treatments and carbon content exert large influences on the degree of embrittlement.

The variation of the yield strength–density and tensile strength–density ratios with temperature for the various alloys studied in this program are outlined in Table 2.16.   Data for cold-rolled tempers of AISI Types 301 (60 per cent cold-rolled), 304 ELC (50 per cent cold-rolled), and 310 (75 per cent cold-rolled) stainless steel and 2024-T3, 6061-T6, and 7178-T6 aluminum are included for comparison purposes.   The selected alloys are listed in Table 2.17 in order of decreasing strength-density ratios at each temperature studied. Notched-unnotched tensile ratios are included to indicate the reason why some alloys such as 7178-T6 aluminum, which have high strength-density ratios at low temperature, cannot be used in structural application because of their notch sensitivity.

REFERENCES

1. Watson, J. F., and J. L. Christian: Cryostat and Accessories for Tension Testing at −423°F, *Mater. Res. Std.*, vol. 1, p. 87, February, 1961.
2. DeHaas, W. J., and R. A. Hadfield: Effect of the Temperature of Liquid Hydrogen (−252.8°C) on the Tensile Properties of Forty-one Specimens of Metals Comprising (a) Pure Iron 99.85% (b) Four Carbon Steels (c) Thirty Alloy Steels (d) Copper Nickel (e) Four Non-ferrous Alloys, *Phil. Trans. Roy. Soc. London, Ser. A*, vol. 232, p. 297, 1933.
3. Wessel, E. T.: Some Exploratory Observations of the Tensile Properties of Metals at Very Low Temperatures, *Trans. ASM*, vol. 49, p. 149, 1957.
4. Haasen, P.: Plastic Deformation of Nickel Single Crystals at Low Temperatures, *Phil. Mag.*, vol. 38, p. 384, 1958.
5. Special ASTM Committee on Fracture Testing of High-strength Sheet Materials, *ASTM Bull.*, January and February, 1960.
6. Low, J. R.: The Relation of Microstructure to Brittle Fracture, "Relation of Properties to Microstructure," p. 163, American Society for Metals, Cleveland, Ohio, 1954.
7. Parker, E. R.: Modern Concepts of Flow and Fracture, *Trans. ASM*, vol. 50, p. 52, 1958.
8. Barrett, C. S.: Metallurgy at Low Temperatures, *Trans. ASM*, vol. 50, p. 53, 1958.
9. Hanson, M. P., G. W. Stickley, and H. T. Richards: Sharp Notch Behavior of Some High-strength Sheet Aluminum Alloys and Welded Joints at 75°, −320°, and −423°F, paper presented at ASTM Annual Meeting, Atlantic City, June, 1960.
10. Sachs, G., and R. Ford Pray, II: "Air Weapons Materials Application Handbook: Metals and Alloys," 1st ed., ARDC TR 59–66 under USAF Contract No. AF18(600)-1794, Syracuse University Research Institute, 1959.
11. Barrett, C. S.: "Structure of Metals," 2d ed., p. 576, McGraw-Hill Book Company, Inc., New York, 1952.
12. Seventh Sagamore Ordnance Materials Research Conference, Raquette Lake, N.Y., 1960.

3

Extreme High Temperature Materials

ALAN V. LEVY

HEAD, NOZZLE COMPONENT MATERIALS DEPARTMENT
RESEARCH AND DEVELOPMENT LABORATORY
AEROJET-GENERAL, SACRAMENTO, CALIFORNIA

The application of materials at extreme elevated temperature is generally taken to mean an application where the operating temperature of the material exceeds 2000°F. Many applications exist where the materials are exposed to considerably higher temperatures than 2000°F but, because of the design of the system, the actual operating temperature of the material is less than that of the working media.

The present applications for the refractory-type materials that can be used at temperatures in excess of 2000°F are quite well defined, are relatively few in number, but are critical to the success of several important weapon systems. Refractory materials are generally classified as those metals and ceramic materials that melt or otherwise change from solid form at temperatures above 3000°F. Some of the more readily available refractory materials are listed in Table 3.1 along with their melting or decomposition temperatures. The use of refractory materials will grow in future years as the technology established for one weapon system advances the state of the art sufficiently to make new systems feasible. However, refractory materials will probably not be used in large quantities in the future. Rather, they will be used in critical areas that will be the key to the feasibility of the system.

An analysis of the utilization of refractory materials in aerospace systems can best be presented by dividing the subject into two major areas: composite-material systems and refractory metals. The composite-material systems combine several materials into an integrated system to produce material combinations which can successfully perform in extreme temperature environments, usually above 3000°F. The refractory metals, on the other hand, are homogeneous metallic materials that extend the use of the metallic state beyond 2000°F. Each type of

44

Table 3.1 Some Materials Stable above 3000°F [16]

Name	Formula	Melting (or decomposition) temperature, °F
Metals:		
Chromium	Cr	3430
Columbium	Cb	4380
Iridium	Ir	4449
Molybdenum	Mo	4730
Platinum	Pt	3224
Rhenium	Re	5740
Rhodium	Rh	3571
Tantalum	Ta	5425
Thorium	Th	3300
Tungsten	W	6170
Vanadium	V	3150
Graphite	C	6700
Oxides:		
Thoria	ThO_2	5970
Magnesia	MgO	5070
Hafnia	HfO_2	5020
Zirconia	ZrO_2	4850
Beryllia	BeO	4620
Yttria	Y_2O_2	4380
Urania	UO_2	4140
Chromia	Cr_2O_3	4115
Alumina	Al_2O_3	3722
Silica	SiO_2	3110
Complex oxides:		
Thorium zirconate	$ThZrO_3$	5070
Beryllium zirconate	$Be_3Zr_2O_7$	4590
Zirconium silicate	$ZrSiO_3$	4390
Calcium zirconate	$CaZrO_3$	4240
Carbides:		
Hafnium carbide–tantalum carbide		7250
Hafnium carbide	HfC	7025
Tantalum carbide	TaC	7015
Zirconium carbide	ZrC	6890
Columbium carbide	CbC	6330
Titanium carbide	TiC	5680
Tungsten carbide	W_2C	5170
Vanadium carbide	VC	5090
Boron carbide	B_4C	4440
Silicon carbide	SiC	4350
Uranium carbide	UC_2	4260
Borides:		
Hafnium boride	HfB_2	5540
Zirconium boride	ZrB_2	5430

Table 3.1　Some Materials Stable above 3000°F [16] (*Continued*)

Name	Formula	Melting (or decomposition) temperature, °F
Tungsten boride....................	WB	5290
Titanium boride....................	TiB_2	4710
Beryllides:		
Molybdenum beryllide...............	$MoBe_2$	3344
Zirconium beryllide.................	$ZrBe_9$	3180
Silicides:		
Tantalum silicide...................	Ta_9Si_2	4550
Zirconium silicide..................	Zr_3Si_2	4050
Molybdenum disilicide...............	$MoSi_2$	3686
Columbium disilicide................	$CbSi_2$	3542
Nitrides:		
Hafnium nitride....................	HfN	5990
Boron nitride......................	BN	5430
Tantalum nitride...................	TaN	5400
Zirconium nitride..................	ZrN	5390
Titanium nitride...................	TiN	5340
Vanadium nitride...................	VN	4280
Silicon nitride.....................	Si_3N_4	3452
Aluminides:		
Chromium aluminide................	CrAl	3920
Molybdenum aluminide..............	Mo_3Al	3900
Nickel aluminide...................	NiAl	3000

refractory material has its own pattern of use with some engineering considerations in common and others that are unique.

Composite Materials

Requirements and Principles. The development of airframes with components that will be heated to temperatures of the order of 3000°F and higher; of propulsion devices where materials must exist in high-mass-flow gas streams that heat components to 6000°F and above; and of advanced direct-conversion power devices where electric energy is converted to propulsive force by components that must operate at temperatures in the 4000 to 5000°F range requires that a new concept in materials be created. In such severe environments, the ability of any known single material is exceeded, and combinations of materials must be developed to withstand successfully the rigors of the service. The combination of materials must be carefully engineered, taking into account many factors that have not been important in the utilization of materials in contact with one another at lower temperatures.

In addition to materials engineering inputs, information from other technologies is required to produce the most reliable and efficient material systems for specific applications. Such variables as the heat-transfer analysis of the component, gas dynamic forces present, and even the gross trade-off between vehicle reentry control requirements and resulting environmental variations must all be considered in the development of the materials system.

Component Systems Analysis. As in any engineering problem, a series of trade-offs must be analyzed in laying out a program to produce a composite-material system for extreme-temperature operation. An extensive aerothermodynamic analysis must be conducted to determine the envelope of the environment that affects the composite-material component. This analysis differs in detail depending on whether the component is a reentry body, a rocket nozzle, or the electrode of an ion engine. However, the general approach is the same. The analysis of a typical rocket-nozzle application is presented to represent the approach that must be used in designing a composite ceramic-metal system.

In the heat-transfer analysis of a composite-material system for a solid-rocket-motor nozzle, many factors must be integrated into the analysis and the variation of the system with time determined for various combinations and thicknesses of materials. In order to optimize the system from a performance and weight standpoint, an automatic computer program has been developed that can separately analyze every portion of the nozzle system in small increments and subsequently integrate the separate analyses into a total documentation of the complete nozzle. This is accomplished by breaking the nozzle up into individual blocks or nodes, each of which can be analyzed by using the finite-difference technique of dividing the geometry of the problem into a three-dimensional network of nodes. Figure 3.1 shows a typical composite-material nozzle. The dotted lines represent the division of the nozzle into nodes for thermal analysis. In the example, 36 nodes are used. The computer program is so designed that up to 200 nodes can be analyzed. Figure 3.2 shows a typical node and some of the thermodynamic factors affecting it.

Material properties and states are considered to be uniform within a given node and correspond to the temperature at the centers of the nodes, which are the junctions of analogous thermal networks. The coordinate dimensions of each node, with the physical properties of the node materials as functions of temperature (up to 20 different materials can be handled in a single analysis) and the boundary conditions as functions of times or temperature, make up the input data for the computer program. The output consists of node temperatures for desired time intervals, measured from the beginning of operation of the component. The analysis, therefore, completely determines both the transient and the steady-state

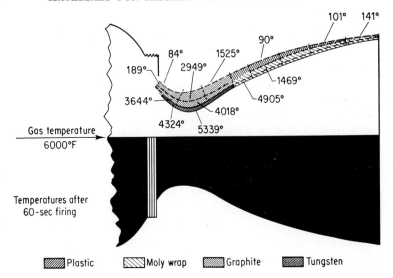

Gas temperature
6000°F

Temperatures after
60-sec firing

Plastic   Moly wrap   Graphite   Tungsten

Fig. 3.1 Typical rocket nozzle divided into nodes for thermal analysis.

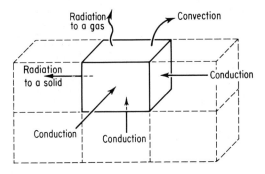

Fig. 3.2 Thermal analysis of typical node in rocket nozzle, including (1) radiation, convection, and conduction; (2) transient and steady state; (3) three-dimensional heat flow; (4) both solid and fluid system; (5) time-temperature profiles for 200 locations; (6) material properties variable with temperature; (7) boundary conditions variable with time.

operational environment temperatures throughout the service life of the component.   Figure 3.3 shows typical temperature-time curves for the nozzle shown in Fig. 3.1.

The computer program is designed to solve simultaneously the following fundamental heat-flow equations:

For conduction in a substance at rest

$$\frac{K}{\rho C_p}\left(\frac{\partial^2 T}{\partial x^2} + \frac{\partial^2 T}{\partial y^2} + \frac{\partial^2 T}{\partial z^2}\right) + \frac{Q_0}{\rho C_p} = \frac{\partial T}{\partial t}$$

For conduction in a moving substance

$$\frac{dT}{dt} = \frac{\partial T}{\partial t} + u \frac{\partial T}{\partial x}$$

For convection

$$q = hA(T_g - T)$$

For solid radiation

$$q = F\sigma\epsilon_1\epsilon_2 A(T_2{}^4 - T_1{}^4)$$

For gaseous radiation

$$q = \sigma A \frac{\epsilon + 1}{2}(\epsilon T_2{}^4 - \alpha T_1{}^4)$$

These equations are solved by using finite differences. A network of nodes is set up, and the computer calculates the thermal resistances for each of the six connections to adjacent nodes. A heat balance is made for

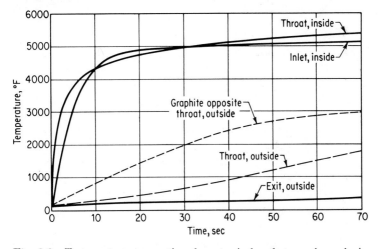

Fig. 3.3　Temperature versus time for a typical rocket-nozzle analysis.

each of the n number of nodes in terms of the unknown temperatures of the adjacent nodes. The nodal heat balance equation used by the computer can be expressed as

$$\frac{C_p\rho V}{\Delta t}(T_0 - T_0') = \sum_{n=1}^{6}\left(\frac{A_n}{\Delta x_n/K_0 + \Delta x_n/K_n + 1/h_n + 1/h_c}\right)(T_n - T_0)$$

$$+ C_p W(T_{nx} - T_0) + V_0 Q_0 + \sum_{h=1}^{3}\sum_{i=1}^{3}\sigma A_h F h_r \epsilon_1\epsilon_2(T_h - T_0')$$

$$+ \sigma A_n \frac{\epsilon + 1}{2}(\epsilon_q T_q{}^4 - \alpha_q T_0{}^4)$$

where K = thermal conductivity, Btu/(ft)(hr)(°F)

    ρ = density, lb/ft³

    C_p = heat capacity, Btu/(lb)(°F)

    T = temperature, °R

  x, y, z = distance in x, y, z directions, ft

    Q_0 = internal heat generation, Btu/(hr)(ft³)

    t = time, hr

    u = velocity, fps

    q = heat flux, Btu/hr

    A = area, ft²

    σ = Stefan-Boltzmann constant, Btu/(hr)(ft²)(°R⁴)

    ϵ = emissivity (dimensionless)

    α = absorptivity (dimensionless)

    V = volume, ft³

    h = heat-transfer coefficient, Btu/(ft²)(hr)(°F)

    W = weight flow, lb/hr

    F = radiation geometry factor (dimensionless)

This heat-transfer program, performed on advanced computers such as the IBM 704 and 7090, calculates the surface areas and volumes of the nodes, interpolates physical properties of materials and boundary conditions of operation from tables given to the computer, assembles a heat balance in implicit form for each node in accordance with the equation presented above, and applies the accelerated Gauss-Seidel method to the system of n equations relating the n unknown node temperatures. This process is repeated for each specified time step in the transient portion of the nozzle operation until temperatures at node centers have been computed for all the time steps within the iteration limit specified. Since the program is based on the implicit form of heat-transfer equations, the solution is stable for any length of time step. It is therefore possible to determine the steady-state operational temperature of each node in addition to the transient temperatures by breaking up the entire operational life into a series of time steps. Because of the extreme speed of the computer program in going through one time step for the system of equations (of the order of $\frac{1}{2}$ sec of machine time), it is economically feasible to take sufficiently small time steps (up to 300 time steps for a 70-sec motor operation) to reduce the truncation errors which are inherently present in finite-difference solutions to under 2 per cent.

Some of the composite-material-system physical property and performance parameters that must be included in the computer program are:

1. Variable film coefficients at fluid boundaries, as functions of time

2. Thermal radiation from adjacent sources; up to three sources per

node face, and up to three faces per node; the temperature of the adjacent sources may be specified as a function of time

3. Thermal radiation between nodes when the node system "sees" itself

4. Thermal radiation from combustion gas, with the temperature of the gas specified as a function of time and the emissivity and absorptivity of the gas specified as functions of temperature

5. Variable specific heat, thermal conductivity, and emissivity of the node material, all as functions of temperature

6. Internal heat generation or absorption in the solid nodes as a result of chemical or physical transformation of temperature or as a function of time

7. Internal generation in the fluid boundary

8. Surface heat flux as a function of time

9. Film cooling, by adjusting the adiabatic wall temperature (if applicable)

10. Transpiration cooling (if applicable)

11. Variable temperature of bounding fluid (adiabatic wall temperature) or bounding surface, as function of time

12. Irregular nodes (nonrectangular parallelepipeds) by including the face areas and the volume in the program input data

By using the sophisticated thermodynamic analysis program described above, the temperatures for any point in the nozzle at any time in the operational life can be accurately determined. The principal factors limiting the accuracy of the analysis are (1) a sufficient knowledge of the heat-transfer characteristics of the combustion gases at the nozzle interface and (2) the physical properties of the individual materials that make up the nozzle composite.

Figure 3.1 shows the type of temperature distribution that occurs in a solid-rocket nozzle. Once this information has been determined, the analysis of how these temperature patterns that vary with geometry and time affect materials performance can be made. Without such information, it is extremely difficult to design efficient composite-materials systems.

Structural and Material Analysis. The principal variables that are investigated in the second step of composite-materials development for solid-rocket nozzles are:

1. Thermal gradients present within single materials and over multi-material segments of the nozzle

2. Thermal stress levels that are within single materials resulting from thermal gradients and that are the result of thermal expansion and modulus of elasticity differences between materials

3. Physical and chemical reactions that could occur as a result of the service temperature within single materials, between adjacent materials, and between the combustion gases and exposed nozzle materials; the results of these reactions with respect to degradation of the materials and/or the creation of additional thermally induced stresses are determined

4. Optimization of thicknesses of composite-material layers to produce a temperature-distribution pattern that minimizes thermal gradients, limits the operating temperature of each layer to a safe level for the chosen material, and produces an outside shell temperature that is compatible with the surrounding environment

5. Determination of structural loads from operational pressures, gas shearing forces and bending loads, acceleration loads, and nozzle vectoring loads

If the operational temperatures of the nozzle components are known in detail, the effects of the above-listed variables can be more readily and accurately established and the best composite-materials system for the type of application determined. Without the availability of the above analysis of thermal as well as chemical and mechanical environmental parameters, it is extremely difficult to develop a composite material for such severe service. There are too many critical interactions that occur at extreme temperatures to use a cut-and-try method of materials development that is based on only a single parameter or a few, rather than on the multitude of factors that actually apply. The use of these factors in representative composite developments is discussed in subsequent sections.

Reentry-component Analysis. The analysis of a specific system must take into account the limitations of the materials available. It may be considerably more efficient from the standpoint of the whole device to temper the environment of the limiting hot component by modifying the performance envelope of the device. The weight or complexity of a hot component for an excessive environment may exceed its worth to the system. This is particularly true for leading-edge and nose-cap configurations for manned reentry vehicles [1, 2].

The altitude-velocity corridor width through which a vehicle reenters the atmosphere has a critical effect on aerodynamic heating temperatures. Analysis of various aspects of this problem show how significant temperature differences are possible, depending on the reentry path chosen [3, 4]. A sufficiently narrow band of altitude can be selected for deceleration to markedly lower the operating temperatures of the severely aerodynamically heated portions of the vehicle. Since the temperature variation involved in such a consideration falls within the 2000 to 5000°F range where a material composite is required, it becomes extremely important to select an optimum vehicle trajectory. The compromising feature of this major design variable involves the complexity, reliability, and weight of the vehicle trajectory control equipment required to keep the vehicle within the narrow reentry corridor where flight can occur with a prohibitive increase in temperature. Ideally, from a controls standpoint, it would be desirable to operate nose caps and leading edges at temperatures above the melting temperature of any known substance to widen the reentry corridor and to simplify the controls problem.

The critical dependence of materials performance of such a major consideration as vehicle trajectory control is another example of how important the user's information is to materials development. The materials producer could easily spend several years developing a material for a given elevated-temperature environment and find when he was finished that the weight or reliability of his product was completely unacceptable to the vehicle developer. In the meantime, the vehicle developer could anxiously await the material, based on its preliminary promise to resist temperature and oxidation, and not refine his control system to the degree that would be possible if he knew all the critical properties of the material. In the development of composite-material systems where such factors as weight, internally induced stresses, volume of constituents, and other factors can vary to large degrees, it is important to have day-to-day guidance from the vehicle development personnel.

Materials System Principles. Homogeneous materials with melting temperatures above 3000°F all have critical shortcomings that prevent them from being used by themselves in structural and nonstructural applications. Table 3.2 lists representative materials that possess high melting temperatures and their key properties for potential service in the 3000 to 6000°F range. It can be seen that every material listed has one or more shortcomings that prevent it from being used at extreme temperatures.

The principal material limitation for +3000°F service is the melting temperature. The vast majority of materials suitable for applications in structures as load-carrying members, or even as unloaded members, have melting temperatures below 3000°F. The materials that melt above 3000°F are limited primarily by ductility, thermal shock, and poor oxidation resistance and secondarily by strength.

It can be seen by reference to Table 3.2 that a combination of acceptable properties could conceivably be realized with certain materials, provided the materials would lend their attractive properties to the composite and have their unattractive properties overcome. This goal has long been sought in materials technology and, until fairly recently, has been elusive to the materials engineer. Various factors have prevented a

Table 3.2 Materials for Use at 3000 to 6000°F

Material	Melting point, °F	Theoret. density	Room temp. strength, psi × 10⁻³			Oxidation resist.	Thermal expansion, in./(in.)(°F) × 10⁺⁶	Thermal conductivity, Btu/(°F/in.)(hr)(ft²)	Modulus of elasticity, psi × 10⁻⁶	Thermal shock resist.	Erosion resist.
			Tensile	Comp.	Flex.						
Refractory metals:											
Columbium, Cb	4532	8.57	60	.....	.....	Fair	3.9	.....	15	Good	Good
Molybdenum, Mo	4757	10.2	100	.....	.....	Poor	2.7	967	46	Good	Good
Tantalum, Ta	5432	16.6	60	.....	.....	Poor	3.7	377	27	Good	Good
Tungsten, W	6098	19.3	200	.....	.....	Poor	2.4	1,397	59	Good	Good
Oxides:											
Thoria, ThO₂	6400	9.69	14	.....	14	Good	5.8	24	36	Very poor	Good
Magnesia, MgO	5070	3.58	12	112	17	Good	8.9	43	40	Poor	Fair
Hafnia, HfO₂	5020	9.68	.....	.....	.....	Good	3.5	.....	.....	.....	.....
Zirconia, ZrO₂	4880	5.56	21	280	21	Good	4.8	10	25	Poor	Good
Beryllia, BeO	4650	3.00	20	200	28	Good	5.3	108	41	Good	Fair
Alumina, Al₂O₃	3540	3.97	38	425	100	Good	4.3	30	51	Good	Good
Carbides:											
Hafnium carbide, HfC	7032	12.2	.....	.....	.....	.....	3.6	153	91.4	.....	Good
Tantalum carbide, TaC	7022	14.5	.....	.....	22	.....	3.6	142	49.0	.....	Good
Zirconium carbide, ZrC	5740	6.7	.....	.....	.....	.....	3.8	98	.....	.....	Good
Columbium carbide, CbC	6334	7.82	.....	.....	68	.....	4.1	118	45	Fair	Good
Titanium carbide, TiC	5712	4.25	15	250	53	Good	2.4	290	68.5	Good	Good
Silicon carbide, SiC	4712	3.17	.....	.....	.....	Good	.....	.....	.....	Good	Good
Graphite	Sublimes at 6600°F	2.26	1.4	6	2.1	Fair	.....	900	2.3	Good	Fair

completely successful refractory combination material from being developed for all but the simplest of applications. The combinations of metals and ceramics that have been attempted in the past have produced composites that retained the worst properties of the constituents rather than the best. This has been primarily due to a lack of fundamental knowledge of how materials in intimate contact react as a result of the integration of their individual sets of properties. This lack of knowledge resulted in combinations of materials in the wrong shape and size and sometimes with incompatible physical properties that would not complement each other's performance.

The extensive development of pressed and sintered cermets for the most part employed the right combination of materials, i.e., a ductile member and a refractory member. However, in practically all instances, the combination was made by mixing fine powders of the constituent together. In the shape of individual particles surrounded by unlike neighbors, the materials could not exert their individual behavior. The ductile member was too small to sustain mechanical or thermal loads, and the brittle refractory member was prevented from proper bonding by the presence of the ductile member.

Recent developments in the field of refractory composite materials have overcome the shortcomings of past work and have, indeed, produced systems where the individual members complement each other's behavior. This has been done by utilizing the materials in sizes and shapes where they could exert their own behavior and still bolster their shortcomings. In all successful extreme-temperature composites, each member is at least macroscopic in size and can be visually discerned in the compact. In order to accomplish this, careful attention was paid to the physical and mechanical properties of each member. In particular, such properties as thermal coefficient of expansion, tensile and compression strength at various temperatures, modulus of elasticity, surface chemical and physical compatibility, and oxidation resistance had to be taken into strict account.

Matching of properties and sizes, to produce prestressed bodies, to have the oxidation-resistant member completely covering the oxidation-susceptible member, to have the resulting structure segmented to produce optimum-sized ceramic mosaics that resisted thermal shock, and for many other considerations, was required to successfully combine metals and ceramics. Once the massive-size approach to composites was taken and the microscopic-powder-combination approach of cermets discarded, a new field of engineered materials could be entered into. The remaining portion of this chapter describes in some detail representative approaches that have been taken in producing ceramic-metal composites for service in the 3000 to 6000°F temperature range.

Composite-materials Systems. The composite-materials systems described in this section are the results of efforts conducted by the writer and his coworkers. Other agencies are also pursuing approaches that show great promise, many of which utilize the principles discussed in earlier sections. Reference to the bibliography will guide the reader to excellent presentations of other approaches to the development of metal-ceramic composites.

The utilization of graphite as a rocket-nozzle material has been widespread in the development and production of solid-propellant rocket motors for several years. As the operating environment and firing duration of solid-rocket nozzles has been extended in the present-day large motors, the shortcomings of graphite (considered as a ceramic for this discussion) have surpassed its advantages. Table 3.3 lists the

Table 3.3   Advantages and Disadvantages of Graphite as a Nozzle Material [16]

Advantages	Disadvantages
High decomposition temperature (6500°F)	Poor erosion resistance
Good thermal conductivity	Low tensile strength
High strength above 5000°F	Nonuniformity
Good compressive strength	
Good heat sink	
Low cost	
Ease of fabrication	
Availability in large sizes	
Low density	

advantages and disadvantages of graphite as a rocket-nozzle material. By combining graphite with other materials that overcome its inherent shortcomings, it is now possible to extend the use of graphite nozzles up to 6000°F for firing durations in excess of 1 min.

The use of tungsten metal in rocket nozzles has shown that, for flame temperatures up to at least 5500°F, a zero per cent erosion condition is possible. The high density of tungsten, however, results in a substantial weight penalty if it is used in massive form as a nozzle-insert material. A material composite that could take advantage of the high erosion resistance of the tungsten and the light weight of graphite would produce a nozzle-insert system ideal for large long-duration solid-rocket-motor applications.

An additional shortcoming of graphite would also have to be overcome in systems operating at the high end of the scale near 6000°F. The high thermal conductivity of graphite causes the outside surface of the insert to reach temperatures beyond the stable operation temperature of backup materials. In some designs, the degradation of the backup material could leave voids and place the graphite in tension due to the high internal-combustion-gas operating pressures. This would result in failure of the graphite because of its low tensile strength. To prevent this occurrence, the third component of the laminate composite-material system would be an intimately bonded stable material such as a refractory-metal sleeve or stable ceramic material that would keep the graphite in compression, where it is many times stronger than it is in tension.

Such a system is shown pictorially in Fig. 3.1. It consists of a thin tungsten-sheet-metal liner that is formed to the desired contour and intimately bonded to the graphite. A sleeve wrapped in a strip of molybdenum alloy is wound around the graphite to keep it in compression. Beyond the sleeve is a plastic insulation layer to protect the hoop-tension-carrying steel shell. Each component of the system is intimately bonded to its supporting material to create a true composite lamination. The thickness of each member of the composite at each position in the nozzle is determined by use of the thermal analysis discussed in the section on Requirements and Principles. To fulfill the rest of the requirements for a successful composite, each material overcomes the shortcomings of the others and is present in a large enough homogeneous mass to maintain its attractive properties.

A successfully fired system of this type has been developed at the Hughes Tool Company, Aircraft Division. It utilizes tungsten in wrought form to provide the erosion barrier, ATJ graphite of density 1.70 to 1.75 g/cm^3, unalloyed molybdenum wire wrapping to keep the graphite in compression, and a plastic-and-steel outer shell. The composite has been able to meet the following requirements:

1. It is corrosion- and erosion-resistant, both chemically and mechanically, to an aluminized polyurethane-base solid propellant.

2. It has dimensional and directional stability at the throat during operation.

3. It is resistant to propellant flame temperatures up to at least 5500°F for at least 60 sec.

4. It is resistant to thermal shock upon ignition of the rocket motor.

5. It has overall light weight and has maximum reliability.

6. It uses available materials and is amenable to production.

By modifying the techniques developed to hot-spin sheet molybdenum surfaces of revolution, it was found possible to manufacture thin-walled tungsten nozzles (see Fig. 3.4). After the flat pattern was prepared by machining, the tungsten disk was hot-spun over an appropriate number of breakdown mandrels before the finished contour was formed. It was determined that the amount of metal that could be moved during the forming operation was similar to that permissible with molybdenum; however, the forming temperatures were higher than those used for molybdenum in a similar operation.

Two-piece blocks of National Carbon Company grade ATJ graphite were contour-machined to fit the outside dimensions of the spun nozzle liner. Machining was accomplished through the use of a tracer and template attachment. A reservoir was machined into the graphite blocks at the exit end of the nozzle. This reservoir served as a crucible

Fig. 3.4 Spun tungsten-sheet-metal nozzle.

for the filler materials during the brazing operation. Following the forming of the liner and the fabrication of the graphite blocks, the composite nozzle was ready for assembly and brazing. The two graphite blocks were fitted around the nozzle liner and placed vertically in a modified induction-heating-type furnace with the graphite reservoir in the upward position. The brazing filler material was formed into a ring which was placed over the exit end of the liner, concentric to the graphite reservoir. This assembly was then heated until the brazing ring melted and flowed down into the cavity, bonding the graphite halves to the tungsten liner.   To determine the optimum temperature at which braze metal would flow throughout the cavity, as well as the proper heating rate, an induction furnace was calibrated by conducting flow-test measurements in simulated nozzle assemblies.   From these experiments, optimum time and temperature were determined for this particular set of conditions.   After the desired temperature had been reached and held for the required time, the furnace was turned off and the nozzle allowed to

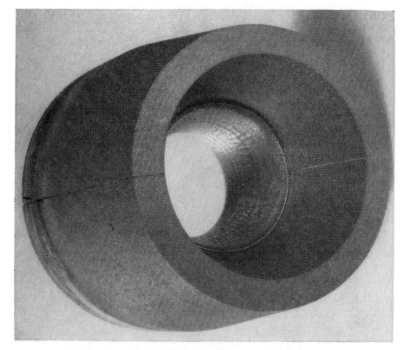

Fig. 3.5   Tungsten-sheet-lined graphite nozzle insert.

cool to room temperature under special atmospheric conditions.   Because of the high sensitivities of the tungsten flame barrier to atmospheric gases at elevated temperatures, and to avoid the use of brazing fluxes, inert-gas cladding techniques were utilized for brazing firings.   During these initial brazing experiments, an argon atmosphere was used; however, later experimentation included an atmosphere free of argon and under a vacuum.   A view of the completed nozzle is shown in Fig. 3.5.   Metallographic examinations of the brazed nozzles revealed that slight alloying occurred between the filler-metal interface and tungsten, as did a conversion of brazing alloy to a thin layer of complex carbide at the graphite interface.   Complete penetration of the insert resulted, as a cross section of the bonded area (Fig. 3.6) shows.

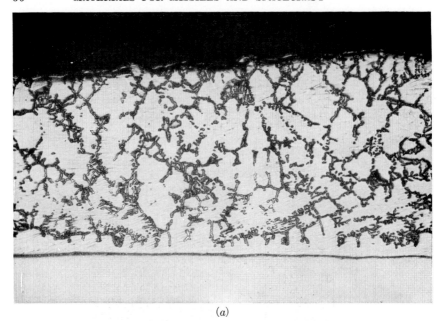

(a)

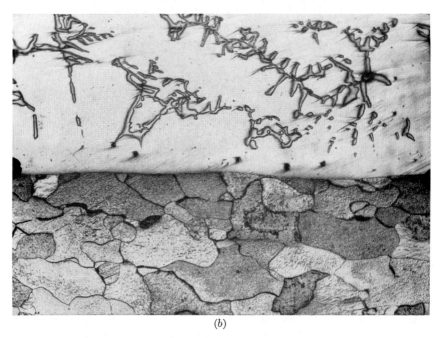

(b)

Fig. 3.6 Cross section of tungsten-graphite bond. (a) Cross section of graphite-tungsten brazed joint (unetched); (b) interface of tungsten brazing compound (Murochamis etch).

After the nozzles had been bonded, a molybdenum wire wrapping was applied at a level of pre-tension designed to place the graphite in compression for the duration of the nozzle firing.   Figure 3.7 shows a typical molybdenum-wire-wrapped assembly.   A ceramic-fiber-reinforced phenolic-plastic case was integrally molded around the composite and cured.   The resultant composite system was then placed in its steel outer shell to complete the assembly.

Fig. 3.7   Example of molybdenum-wire-wrapped assembly.

Ceramics Reinforced with Refractory-metal Fibers.   There are several materials that have melting temperatures above 5000°F.   Table 3.2 lists some of the most promising of these materials.   It can be seen, however, that the thermal-shock sensitivity of the ceramic materials is excessive for use in a rocket-nozzle application where heating rates in excess of 1000°F/sec are experienced.   An analysis of the physical characteristics of these materials shows that, while the thermal conductivity of the carbides is relatively high, they are unable to sustain appreciable thermal gradients because of extreme crack sensitivity.   The high-melting oxides such as hafnia and thoria suffer from the same mechanical-property shortcomings as do the carbides and, in addition, they have low thermal conductivities. A combination of thermal-shock-sensitive ceramics with a ductile refractory metal has always held promise of producing a usable composite.

Since development work has been initiated utilizing metal fibers rather than particles as the means of improving the thermal-shock resistance, many advances have been made in the state of the art. A discussion of some of the mechanisms of thermal shock that are applicable to ceramic composite bodies will lead to a better understanding of why the change from metal particles to metal fibers has been the key to successful metal-ceramic composites.

The expression for the thermal-shock behavior of a material is

$$\text{Thermal shock index} = \frac{TK}{\alpha E}$$

where T = tensile strength, psi

K = thermal conductivity, Btu/(hr)(in.²)(°F/in.)

α = coefficient of thermal expansion, in./(in.)(°F)

E = modulus of elasticity, psi

The high modulus of elasticity and coefficient of expansion of pressed and sintered ceramic bodies and their low tensile strength and thermal conductivity combine to produce a low thermal-shock index or resistance (see Table 3.2). The addition of metal in powder form as in classical cermets does not greatly affect any of the above mentioned properties of the ceramic because, in particle form, there are no continuous paths for the flow of heat or transmission of stress, and the matrix can completely surround each particle without any tendency to precrack. The use of fibers instead of particles of the same metal to the same weight percentage produced markedly changed thermal-shock resistance.

A fiber compact made from a felt of sintered fibers has several advantages. The fibers can transmit stresses over long distances and thereby absorb the strains induced by thermal gradients. Particles, on the other hand, cannot do this. The continuity of the ductile fiber network also tends to hold the composite together in the event that micro or macro cracks occur in the ceramic matrix during fabrication or service.

An additional load-carrying ability is imparted because of the thermal expansion differential between the metal and the ceramic. During the rapid heating that occurs in a rocket nozzle, the ceramic with its higher expansion coefficient tries to expand at a greater rate than the metal-fiber reinforcement. In the heating temperature where thermal-shock failures occur in solid ceramic nozzles, the metal is strong enough to restrain the expanding ceramic and actually place it in compression. With the precompression load applied, the tension-stress-inducing thermal gradients have to overcome the precompression stress before they can becomes operative.

The increase in thermal conductivity that could normally be expected when a metal is added to a ceramic is also a function of shape. In order to provide an effective increase in the thermal conductivity of the composite, continuous paths of high-conductivity metal must be provided through which to transfer the heat. Metal fibers provide the necessary continuous paths. Metal-particle additions do not because each particle is surrounded by the ceramic matrix, effectively isolating the metal particles and preventing heat-transmission paths.

The high modulus of elasticity of ceramics in general (see Table 3.2) is another factor that promotes thermal-shock sensitivity. To improve the thermal-shock resistance of a ceramic composite, its modulus of elasticity must be reduced. Fiber reinforcement provides a mechanism that reduces the modulus by an acceptable degree.

The differential thermal expansion between metal and ceramic promotes microcracking of the matrix during the sintering operation by placing the ceramic in the vicinity of each fiber in tension on cooling. Other mechanisms also contribute to cracking of the matrix. Some of these are as follows: voids in the ceramic phase from the fabrication processes, entrapped reaction gas bubbles that promote pressure microcracks, and stress-concentration cracks caused by the noncontinuous-phase metal reinforcement. The presence of the metal-fiber lattice, rather than ineffective individual particles, provides two saving functions to a precracked matrix: (1) it presents ductile energy-absorbing barriers to propagating cracks and thus retards crack growth, and (2) it provides a ductile continuous network that intimately holds the cracked ceramic mosaic together. The end result is a marked lowering of the effective modulus of elasticity of the ceramic (because it no longer is a continuous substance) and a consequent increase in thermal-shock resistance. Table 3.4 shows how the compressive strength and modulus of elasticity of thoria are affected by the presence of molybdenum fibers.

Large thermal expansions promote thermal-shock failure in homogeneous ceramic bodies by inducing tension stresses in the compact during transient heating or cooling cycles where different parts of the ceramic are at different temperatures. The larger the thermal coefficient of expansion, the higher the stresses that can be induced by a thermal gradient. The severe thermal gradients in rocket nozzles on ignition can cause "explosive" fracture stresses to occur in ceramic bodies. The presence of a fiber-network reinforcement reduces the level of thermal-gradient stresses.

The thermal expansion differential between metal and ceramic (the ceramic is higher) causes tension fracture stresses to occur in the ceramic

Table 3.4 Properties of Molybdenum-fiber-reinforced Thoria at
Room Temperature [16]

Composition†	Percentage of theoretical density	Compressive strength, psi	Modulus of elasticity, psi $\times 10^{-6}$
ThO$_2$..........................	99	190,000–220,000	36.9
ThO$_2$-5 weight % molybdenum fibers......................	99	51,300	26.9
ThO$_2$-10 weight % molybdenum fibers.......................	98	49,700	21.5
ThO$_2$-20 weight % molybdenum fibers.......................	99	62,100	15.7
Molybdenum.......................	...	....	42.7

† Fibers 0.002 in. in diameter and 0.125 in. in nominal length.

on cooling from the sintering temperature in the immediate vicinity of each fiber. The cracks that form are limited in length by the latticework of metal fibers and therefore produce a controlled precracked mosaic that is held together by the metal-fiber network. The tension stresses that are induced by transient thermal gradients can now act either through the ductile metal or over only a relatively short distance of ceramic. In either case, the stresses thereby created are not detrimental. The information required to design a fiber-reinforced ceramic structure includes the following areas of technology:

1. Heat-transfer analysis to define temperature levels at all locations in the nozzle. The heat-transfer analysis discussed in the section on Component Systems Analysis is an extremely important element to the successful development of a metal fiber–ceramic composite.

2. Physical and mechanical properties of each constituent in the composite and the way they vary with temperature.

3. Chemical and thermal stability of each constituent at anticipated service temperatures.

4. Reaction rates and diffusion rates between adjacent dissimilar materials.

5. Fabrication techniques that will produce composite with each material in an optimum condition to resist the thermal environment.

6. The bonding characteristics of the constituents.

Baskin, Arenberg, and Hardwerk [8] in their work on reinforcing thoria with molybdenum fibers, have shown that a marked improvement in the thermal cycling and shock behavior of thoria can be obtained by incorporating 20 per cent by weight of molybdenum fibers of nominal dimensions 0.002 in. diameter by 0.125 in. long. The mechanism of improving the thermal cycling behavior is primarily a mechanical one rather than a modification of physical properties. The presence of a ductile metal in fiber form rather than in particle form provides both crack-inducing and crack-confining mechanisms that combine to prevent catastrophic failure of the type referred to earlier in this section. When molybdenum *particles* at 20 per cent by weight were added to thoria, little or no improvement in thermal-shock sensitivity occurred, proving that increased thermal conductivity alone does not affect thermal-shock resistance.

The work described in Ref. 8 documented the mechanisms of crack initiation and control in metal fiber–ceramic composites. One of the important concepts that should be recognized in the development of successful metal-ceramic composites is that micro and macro cracks in the matrix ceramic, if properly controlled by a strong metal reinforcement network, are actually advantageous. These advantages can be summarized as follows:

1. The high residual stress levels induced in a ceramic during pressing and sintering are relieved.

2. The high stresses generated by thermal gradients acting over long distances are prevented.

3. The crack sensitivity of the body is reduced by the presence of a multitude of already built-in cracks.

4. The ability of the composite to move elastically or plastically under the influence of applied stresses is made possible by the segmenting of the ceramic blocks.

5. The modulus of elasticity is reduced.

Figure 3.8 shows a molybdenum-fiber magnesium-oxide compact fabricated by hot-pressing and sintering a 70 per cent by weight molybdenum-fiber (of 0.005 in. nominal diameter) felting impregnated with a magnesia slurry. The resulting compound was greater than 97 per cent of theoretical density. It was exposed to flame temperatures of 4500°F and quenched in water for five cycles with no apparent damage to the compact. While the metal content of this compact was higher than the minimum necessary to achieve thermal-shock resistance, the remarkable improvement in thermal-shock resistance of magnesia that was achieved indicates the great promise of this approach to composite materials.

A promising technique for fabricating a tungsten-fiber-reinforced ceramic rocket-nozzle-insert configuration has been developed by the Armour Research Foundation. The technique involves the fabricating of the nozzle shape from tungsten metal fibers 0.005 in. in diameter by a felting technique [9] and the subsequent impregnating of the shaped fiber skeleton with a ceramic phase.

The shaped-tungsten-fiber throat insert is placed in a porous mold, into which an aqueous base slip of the ceramic material is vacuum-

Fig. 3.8   Magnesium oxide molybdenum-fiber compact.

filtered through the fiber skeleton. After the impregnated piece is dried, the composite is consolidated by hot-pressing and sintering in a carbon mold at 4,000 psi. Figure 3.9 shows a typical fiber network.

Experimental structures have been made of tungsten-fiber-reinforced SiC, TaC, B₄C, TiC, TiC plus Ti, HfC, and ZrC by Hodson and Fisher [10]. The first three have been eliminated as base materials for tungsten-reinforced nozzles because of extensive reactions that occur with the metal phase. It was found that SiC reacts with tungsten, producing brittle networks of tungsten silicides. Similar reactions have occurred between tungsten and tantalum and boron carbides. However, this was not the case with the HfC-W, ZrC-W, and TiC-W hot-pressed composites. Reactions with systems were apparently different from those encountered between tungsten and the other carbides. In these three systems, there seem to be good metallurgical bonds between the metal fibers and the ceramic phases, with no detrimental interactions occurring if the processing conditions are properly controlled. However, the fibers do react with the matrix to some extent. For example, 2-mil tungsten fibers were reacted completely in specimens hot-pressed at 2500°C, but others

Fig. 3.9 Tungsten fiber network.

treated at 2250°C were only partially penetrated. The factors that appear to restrict the reinforcing of ceramics with refractory metals are:

1. Reactions between metal and ceramic phases
2. Contamination of either phase by foreign elements
3. Lack of sintering of the ceramic because of the presence of the metal during sintering

The results of test rocket-nozzle firings of hot-pressed tungsten-reinforced titanium carbide showed no apparent signs of erosion, and the nozzles exhibited excellent resistance to thermal shock.

Ceramics Reinforced with Refractory-metal Sheet or Wire. The third type of metal-ceramic composite material that will be discussed involves an extension of the concept developed in the preceding section for metal-fiber-reinforced ceramics. The reinforcement principles discussed above also apply for the types of materials to be described in this section. The principal differences between fiber-reinforced ceramics and sheet- or wire-reinforced ceramics are the dimensions and configurations of the reinforcement and the types of ceramic mixes that can be used. In felted fiber-reinforced ceramics, the mean distance between adjacent fibers requires that the ceramic be impregnated by means of a liquid slurry. This type of impregnation requires a pressing and sintering operation to produce usable quality shapes. The use of metal sheet or wire reinforcement configurations opens up the spacing between adjacent reinforcement elements, thereby permitting a large variety of ceramic consistencies and application methods to be used.

The work performed by the author and his coworkers in the field of reinforced ceramics pioneered in the field of troweled-on sheet- or wire-reinforced ceramics and has tended to concentrate in this field. The work to date has produced extremely promising composite systems for use as insulating coatings or structural elements in large sizes for cyclic service up to approximately 4500°F [11].

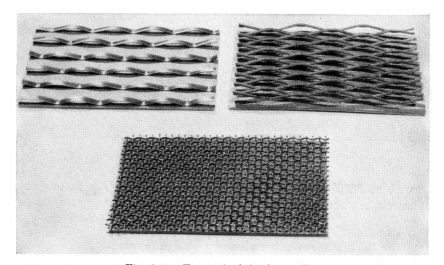

Fig. 3.10   Types of reinforcing media.

The reinforcement of ceramic bodies by additions of metal in sheet or wire form requires that certain factors be considered in order to prevent fracture of the ceramic due to metal inclusion planes of weakness. These can be summarized as follows:

1. The expansion coefficients of reinforcement and the ceramic matrix must be compatible; they do not necessarily have to be the same.

2. The reinforcement-metal spacing should be such that the void space will produce an unreinforced ceramic column of sufficient strength to withstand thermal and mechanical loads and yet not large enough to build up a thermal gradient sufficient to produce fracture. Void spacings varying from $\frac{1}{8}$ to $\frac{1}{4}$ in. have proved to be satisfactory.

3. The reinforcement-metal configuration and location in the matrix should not produce in-line planes of weakness in the matrix along which cracks can propagate. Figure 3.10 shows some of the types of metal reinforcement that have been successfully used.

4. The thickness of the metal reinforcement should be limited to that which will remain flexible with respect to the ceramic under applied thermal and mechanical loads. Thicknesses and widths ranging from 0.125-in.-wide by 0.010-in.-thick strip to 0.020-in.-diameter wire woven mesh represent the successful limits in reinforcements used to date.

5. The ceramic should have a level of porosity that will enable it to act as a mosaic under thermal or mechanical induced deflections. Porosities ranging from 20 to 40 per cent have proved successful. Figure 3.11 shows the type of ceramic structure used in the composities.

Fig. 3.11   Texture of reinforced ceramic matrix.

In addition to ensuring that the metal reinforcement will not contribute to the uncontrolled fracture of the ceramic matrix, several other factors must be considered in developing a reinforced ceramic for a specific application. For example, if it is desired to use the composite as an insulating coating for a metal-wall combustion chamber, a means of securing the reinforcement to the wall must be developed. The refractory metal selected for the reinforcement must be protected against oxidation to use the component in an oxidizing atmosphere. The coating-surface emissivity must be modified to best serve the particular application. Total normal emissivities varying from 0.2 to 0.85 can be developed in alumina- and zirconia-based ceramics. If it is desired to apply the coating as thermal insulation on comparatively large bodies, a simple, economical method of application must be devised and a composition must be selected that can be cured or set at relatively low temperatures. These and many other considerations must be satisfied before a composite-material design can be successfully developed into a usable material.

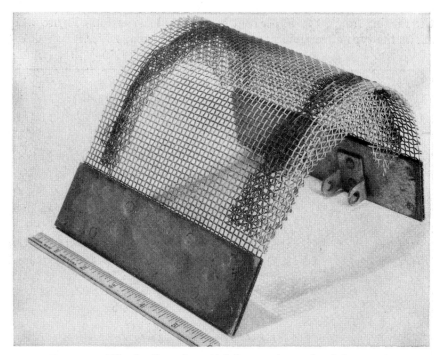

Fig. 3.12   Wing-leading-edge molybdenum wire mesh reinforcement.

The presence of relatively large masses of metal inside a ceramic matrix, with physical properties that do not match those of the ceramic, can cause reliability problems in severe thermal gradients, or over long distances (several feet), unless the distribution of heat throughout the system is known in advance and taken into account in the design. The heat-transfer program presented in the section on Component Systems Analysis can produce valuable information to guide the materials engineer in the selection of the reinforcement and ceramic matrix materials, their thicknesses, the relative distribution of materials in the composite, and other factors in the overall development of the system.

The concept of producing a reinforced ceramic coating capable of insulating a combustion chamber and reducing its operation temperature by at least 500°F was achieved by the development of an aluminum phosphate–bonded alumina reinforced with a stainless-steel corrugated strip.   The composite material that resulted has been used successfully in ramjet combustion chambers up to several feet in diameter by 8 ft long.   Its use has also been extended to structural applications, such as the wing-leading-edge configuration shown in Figs. 3.12 and 3.13, by substituting molybdenum wire mesh precoated with a pack cementation

Fig. 3.13 Wing leading edge after application of aluminum phosphate–bonded alumina matrix.

coating for the corrugated-metal strip.   The resultant components have successfully withstood several 20-min cycles of exposure up to 3500°F.

To extend this concept to higher operating temperatures, zirconia was selected as the most likely material to produce composites that would successfully withstand exposures to 4400°F for extended periods of time. Time-stabilized zirconia, Type H (cubic crystalline form), was selected for the application.   As in the alumina-base composite, a phosphate bond was used by providing phosphate radicals from acids and salts. The primary bonding was obtained by using monofluorophosphoric acid according to the following equation:

$$ZrO_2 + 2H_2PO_3F \rightarrow Zr(PO_3F)_2 + 2H_2O$$

In order to retard the bonding action and increase the shelf life of the troweling medium, ammonium dihydrogen phosphate was added to the composition and reacted in the following manner:

$$3ZrO_2 + 4NH_4H_2PO_4 \rightarrow Zr_3(PO_4)_4 + 4NH_3 + 6H_2O$$

An additional constituent, chromia, was added to improve the workability of the mixture and to increase the emissivity. It was reacted in the following manner:

$$Cr_2O_3 + 3H_2PO_3F \rightarrow Cr_2(PO_3F)_3 + 3H_2O$$

The composition of the final matrix material was:

Constituent	Parts by Weight
ZrO_2 (coarse particles)	80
ZrO_2 (fine particles)	5
Cr_2O_3	15
$NH_4H_2PO_4$	9
H_2PO_3F	5
H_2O	15

The particle-size distribution of the final composition was 22.6 per cent particles through 60 mesh on 80 mesh and 77.4 per cent particles through 80 mesh on 150 mesh. The resulting bulk density was 204 lb/ft^3 and the apparent porosity was 22 per cent.

The hard crack-free matrix developed through the above reactions had excellent erosion resistance when blasted at room temperature with a constant flow of 20-grit silicon carbide. It possessed the same erosion resistance as dense graphite, four times the resistance of dense 99 per cent alumina brick, and over four times the erosion resistance of zirconia brick.

The ceramic matrix was incorporated into a reinforced ceramic coating system consisting of a base-metal substrate of 0.5% Ti molybdenum alloy sheet to which was resistance-welded a corrugated-strip reinforcement of 0.010-in.-thick by 0.125-in.-wide molybdenum alloy. The resistance welding was facilitated by applying plasma-flame-sprayed chromium to both surfaces. The chromium also served to protect the molybdenum against oxidation. The welded assembly was covered with a Type 418 vitrified coating to enhance further the oxidation resistance of the molybdenum. The matrix was then trowel-impregnated into the surface. The composite was low-temperature-cured at 300°F.

The resulting system exhibited a thermal drop of approximately 2300°F across a thickness of 0.250 in. when exposed to a plasma flame on the ceramic side. The ceramic surface temperature was measured at 4200°F while the back surface was only 1900°F at steady-state conditions.

The total normal emissivity over the temperature range from 2000 to 4000°F was, nominally, 0.8 for a rough surface and 0.68 for a ground surface.

The resistance to thermal shock was determined by a series of heating and cooling cycles and by heating and water-quenching.   In the first test, the ceramic surface was plasma-torch-heated to 4200°F for $2\frac{1}{2}$ min, then cooled with an air blast at a rate of 650°F/sec to 1000°F, and then at a

Fig. 3.14 Thermal-shock-test sample of molybdenum-reinforced zirconia ceramic after test (ceramic removed after test).

somewhat slower rate to room temperature.   The composite successfully withstood seven such cycles.   Figure 3.14 shows the sample after testing and with the ceramic chipped away to show that the reinforcement was not oxidized.   The second test consisted in heating the ceramic face to 4400°F, holding the temperature constant for 2 min, and dropping the sample into water.   No damage was observed after two such cycles.

The elevated-temperature moduli of rupture of the matrix material in an unreinforced condition are given in Table 3.5.

The great promise of this type of metal-ceramic composite has not been thoroughly explored to date.   It is expected that systems similar to that described will find considerable use as thermal-barrier and structural materials in those applications where temperatures above 4000°F are encountered.

Table 3.5

Temperature °F	Load rate, lb/min	Modulus of rupture, psi
1000	19.8	1,940
1500	19.5	1,878
2000	19.9	1,565
2400	13.8	543

Refractory Metals

Material Consideration. The use of refractory metals in structural components of airborne vehicles introduces a new philosophy of material utilization; the refractory metals do not possess universally acceptable properties for all aspects of a design. There are important shortcomings in the use of refractory metals that must be compensated for in design and fabrication. The severity of the problems varies from base metal to base metal and from alloy to alloy. Generally, it can be stated that some sacrifices must be made to attain attractive strength-weight ratios at operating temperatures above about 2200°F. Some of the more recently developed alloys of columbium hold considerable promise of reducing this weight penalty.

The principal problem in the behavior of the higher-strength refractory metals is their room-temperature brittleness. Most of the alloys have ductile-brittle transition temperatures at or above room temperature. This means that they behave in a brittle manner at ambient temperatures and below. Above a few hundred degrees Fahrenheit, the refractory metals are extremely tough and excellent performers, from both a fabrication and a service standpoint. However, at room temperature where the material must be handled and where it is most economical to conduct fabrication operations, the material can display very detrimental brittle behavior. While this statement does not apply to all the refractory metals, it does apply to most of the attractive alloys. In general, all molybdenum and tungsten alloys and some of the stronger columbium alloys are brittle to some degree at room temperature. The lower-strength columbium and tantalum alloys are ductile at room temperature and even well below room temperature.

Another major weakness of refractory metals is their lack of oxidation resistance at elevated temperatures. This behavior makes their integrity at service temperatures dependent upon some type of protective coating. The rates of oxidation at temperatures above 2000°F are so high that almost catastrophic failures can occur if the coatings are penetrated. While considerable work has been done to provide satisfactory protective coatings, the basic reliability of refractory metal structures protected from oxidation must still be determined.

The third major consideration in utilizing refractory metals that is not required for lower-temperature materials to the same degree is their cost. Rough values for limited quantities of sheet product for commercially available alloys are:

Alloy	Cost per pound
Columbium alloy	$80–100
Molybdenum alloy	30–40
Tantalum alloy	80–100
Unalloyed tungsten	30–40

The principal fact that offsets these costs is that for service temperatures above 2000°F there are no other usable metals.

The strengths of the principal refractory metals are summarized in Table 3.6. Since all the available alloys of the refractory metals are solid solutions, the principal strengthening mechanism available is cold work. For this reason, the reported 1-hr recrystallization temperatures are listed where known. Another important effect of the recrystallization temperature has to do with the mechanism of embrittlement of these metals. From the present state of knowledge, these metals are embrittled by a network of compounds of oxygen, nitrogen, carbon, and certain other elements that form envelopes around each grain. Cold-working breaks up these films and therefore improves the overall ductility. However, when the metal is recrystallized, continuous networks reform in the grain boundaries and these can decrease the ductility. It is therefore desirable not to exceed the recrystallization temperature in service, even for one-shot applications, but especially when multicycle operation is required.

It can be seen from Table 3.6 that, for the most part, alloys of molybdenum have the greatest strength up to temperatures of about 3000°F. Above this temperature, tungsten is the strongest material. In the 2000 to 2500°F range, columbium alloys have attractive strength properties that combined with superior room-temperature ductility and oxidation behavior, make their use in reentry structures quite interesting. Tantalum and its alloys available to date do not appear to be very applicable to reentry structures because of their low strength-weight ratio. Tantalum, however, has the best combination of room-temperature ductility and fabricability.

Figure 3.15 is a curve of tensile strength versus temperature for a typical high-strength nickel-base alloy and some of the most attractive refractory metals. It should be pointed out that the data presented reflect a state of the art near the beginning of the history of the refractory metals. Large variations in strength occur between the various data

Table 3.6

Alloy	Recrystallization temp. (1 hr), °F	RT			1600°F			2000°F			2200°F			2400°F		
		UTS	YS	EL	UTS	YS	EL	UTS	YS	EL	UTS	YS	EL	UTS	YS	EL
Molybdenum alloys:																
Comm. pure	1800–2200	...	...	...	...	...	...	...	...	...	...	...	...	30	...	...
0.5% Ti	2200–2450	110	95	22	65	60	12	58	52	11	45	42	15			
0.5% Zr	2600	108	88	18	77	67	8	64	55	6	46	41	10			
T. Z. M. (0.5% Ti–0.05% Zr)	2600	134	122	14	85	71	8	74	...	...	61	...	...	47	...	...
T. Z. C. (1.25% Ti–0.15% Zr)	2800	115	105	30	...	...	...	58	52	13	50	45	17	40	35	25
25% W–0.1% Zr–0.05% C	3200	141	137	0	...	...	...	...	...	...	...	...	...	74		
1.45% Nb–0.25% C	2400	156	120	1	...	...	...	...	...	...	...	...	...	64	...	36
3.2% Ti–0.5% C	2500	135	127	23	...	...	...	...	...	...	...	...	...	36	26	57
1.27% Ti–0.29% Zr–0.3% C	2800	121	98	1	...	...	...	...	...	...	...	...	...	61	41	26
Columbium alloys:																
Comm. pure																
GE F48	2600	122	110	16	...	...	...	65	43	19	40	37	41	31	14	29
GE F50	2500	122	80	24	...	...	...	50	34	28	35	27	35	21	17	45
Fansteel F80	2200	60	46	17	...	...	...	14	...	10						
Fansteel F82	2200	82	70	11	65	52	7	45	40	8	10	7	80	...	...	...
Fansteel F83	....	...	...	...	...	...	...	...	...	...	38	34	16	...	...	...
Du Pont D31	2200	100	92	22	...	...	...	34	33	12	25	22	14	17	...	8
Du Pont D41	....	125	...	10	...	...	...	50	...	25	45	...	...	30		
Du Pont D42	....	...	...	...	...	...	...	85	...	...	55					
Westinghouse NC31	....	103	100	17	...	...	...	43	34	5						
Westinghouse NC32	....	77	54	26	...	...	...	49	46	25						
Union Carbide Cb65	2200	96	86	20	37	...	32	16	...	71	9.5	...	88			
Tantalum alloys:																
90% Ta–10% W	.....	162	160	9	100	95	12	...	...	...	...	...	...	...	...	...
Tungsten:																
Unalloyed	....	...	...	...	...	...	...	...	...	...	...	...	...	...	...	...
1% thoria	....	...	...	...	...	...	...	...	...	...	...	...	...	...	...	...

RT = room temperature or 70°F; UTS = ultimate tensile strength, in thousands of pounds per square inch; YS = yield

available because of variations in the degree of cold work of different heats of the same material, different heat treatments for stress relieving and annealing, different impurity-element contents, and different accuracies of testing. Therefore, any given set of data, such as that presented herein, can vary markedly from any other set and should, therefore, be used only as a relative indication of the behavior of the material. Considerable additional testing will have to be done on material that is being steadily refined and made more uniform before representative design data will be available.

Figure 3.16 presents some 100-hr creep and rupture data for molybdenum alloys presently available. It is interesting to note the difference in the strength levels of the alloys between short-time tensile properties

Strength of Refractory Alloys

2500°F			2600°F			3000°F			3500°F			4000°F			4500°F			5000°F		
UTS	YS	EL	UTS	YS	EL	UTS	YS	EL	UTS	YS	EL	UTS	YS	EL	UTS	YS	EL	UTS	YS	EL
...	...	...	17	11	10	10	7	20												
40	...	...	30	...	...	13														
27	25	47																		
12	11	53																		
26	23	28																		
22	20	22	...	...	...	12	...	33	7	...	37	4	...	35	2	...	30	0.6	...	20
50	...	...	42	...	...	21	...	...	12	...	...	7	...	...	4					
50	...	...	47	...	...	37	...	...	29	...	...	16	...	...	11					

strength, in thousands of pounds per square inch; EL = elongation, in per cent.

and 100-hr creep properties. Most applications for the refractory metals center around the $\frac{1}{2}$- to 10-hr service of life. The importance of determining the creep properties, even for these fairly short lives, cannot be overstressed. The importance of creep strength for short-time service at elevated temperatures is discussed in more detail in Ref. 2. As in the case of the tensile properties, much more testing must be done to obtain creep design data for these alloys.

Table 3.7 presents an overall comparison of the four principal refractory metals using alloys that are commercially available in quantities and sheet sizes that can be considered for structural component design. While improved alloys exist over and above those listed in Table 3.7, especially in terms of strength, their availability is still limited, with respect

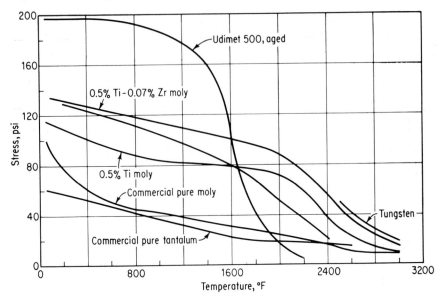

Fig. 3.15 Ultimate tensile strength versus temperature for various refractory metals and Udimet 500.

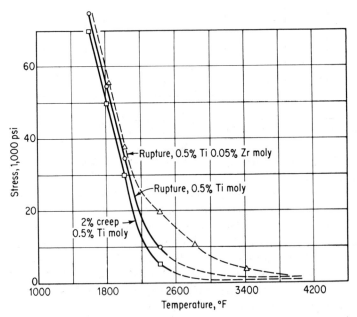

Fig. 3.16 Creep and rupture strength of molybdenum alloys—100-hr exposure. Dashed line indicates estimate.

Table 3.7   Comparison of Refractory-metal Properties

Property	0.5% Ti molybdenum	0.4% Zr–40% Ta columbium	Comm. pure tantalum	Comm. pure tungsten
Melting temperature, °F.......	4750	4500†	5425	6150
Density, lb/in.³..............	0.368	0.368	0.600	0.697
Ultimate tensile strength, psi:				
Room temp................	115,000	109,000	60,000	80,000
2000°F...................	74,000	29,000	19,000	34,000
2400°F...................	40,000	11,000	16,000	25,000
3000°F...................	10,300	....	12,500	20,000
Per cent elongation at room temp.....................	10	45†	40	0
Bend transition temp., °F......	100	Below −40	Below −40	
Modulus of elasticity.........	46×10^6	20×10^6†	27×10^6	59×10^6
Formability................	Fair	Good	Good	Poor
Thermal expansion at 2000°F, in./(in.)(°F)...............	3.4×10^6	3.8×10^{-6}	3.6×10^{-6}	2.8×10^{-6}
Thermal conductivity at 20°C, cal/(cm²)(cm/°C)(sec).......	0.35	0.13†	0.13	0.40
Weldability................	Fair	Good	Good	Poor
Coatings...................	Good	Good	Poor	Poor

† Extrapolated values.

to either delivery or sheet size.   An analysis of this table will quickly show the trade-offs that must be made in selecting a refractory metal.

Quality Consideration.   The quality of the presently available refractory metals is an important consideration in their selection for a structural component, for either a *heat shield* or a *hot structure* part.   The present state of the art of the ore refinement, melting, mill production of shapes, and physical metallurgy of the refractory metals reflects an early stage in the development of these metals.   The most important consideration that reflects on quality concerns the reliability of components fabricated from the refractory metals.   Although the developments in refractory metals are rapidly moving toward consistent products, parts fabricated from today's products must still be considered as highly developmental in nature, and their use in structures considered to be primarily feasibility tests of the use of metallic components at extreme temperatures.   Assurance can be made, however, that when refractory-metal components are needed to carry a man into the atmosphere from space, a reliable mill product will be available.

The performance of the refractory metals at their service temperatures can be relied upon even in today's alloys.   It is the performance of the alloys at ambient temperatures that varies over wide ranges and is still unreliable. The following properties reflect the behavior that cannot be predicted:

1. Bend and impact ductile-brittle transition temperature
2. Ambient tensile strength and elongation
3. Energy adsorption at less than impact velocities
4. Laminations and planes of weakness
5. Forty-five-degree angle preferred cracking
6. Elevated-temperature fabricability
7. Recrystallization temperature
8. Hardness
9. Crack propagation
10. Trace-element chemistry and its effects
11. Weldability

The properties listed affected room-temperature handling, fabricability, and the load-carrying ability of the part at the beginning and end of a flight. Since these considerations are critical to the overall performance, they cannot be belittled even though they occur during a phase of the operational cycle of the component that is not the determining factor in the selection of refractory metals for the component. This is another example of the "new" thinking that must be used in applying refractory metals to designs. It must be pointed out that these properties apply to the stronger, more attractive refractory-metal alloys and not to all of the alloys.

The Department of Defense refractory-metal sheet-rolling program presently underway should in the period of the next year or two eliminate the problem of reproducible quality from the utilization of refractory-metal alloys. Until that time, extensive testing of individual sheets of material will be required to ensure that only acceptable-level material is used in actual structures.

Fabrication. The fabrication of the refractory metals has advanced considerably in the past two or three years [3, 4]. Much work must still be done, especially on the newer, higher-strength alloys of columbium and molybdenum and on unalloyed tungsten. A review of the fabrication status of each of the four refractory metals indicates the present state of the art in actually making parts from these materials. The fabrication of hardware from refractory metals requires considerably more engineering input than is required for conventional materials to produce acceptable components. Manufacturing tolerances are quite a bit narrower for refractory metals than for conventional materials. For example, the welding requirements of excellent fit-up (gaps no greater than 0.005 in.)

and extremely close control of the welding current are considerably more important for welding molybdenum and tungsten than for any other known metal.

To produce components economically from the refractory metals, whose cost per pound of material is high, it is desirable to use the chipless operations such as extruding, radial draw forming, hydroforming, press forming, manual spinning, and spin forging wherever possible rather than those machining operations that produce unusable chips.

The remainder of this chapter will present the experience of the author in the development of components from columbium, molybdenum, tantalum, and tungsten.

Columbium. The fabrication of components from columbium-base alloys has been limited because of the lack of availability of acceptable alloys in bar and sheet form. Materials which are the result of several years' development in industrial concerns throughout the country are only now becoming available for application. The columbium alloys F80 and F82, produced by the Fansteel Metallurgical Corporation, and the Du Pont alloy D31 are the only alloys that can be considered commercially available today. The other alloys whose properties are listed in Table 3.6 have only recently been announced or made available.

The combination of excellent room-temperature ductility and low room-temperature strength makes the F80 and F82 alloys very fabricable. Sheet materials can be sheared and formed at room temperature by conventional equipment and techniques. Sound welds with room-temperature ductility have been produced by using the TIG process and local gas protection. The development of the new GE alloy F48 with increased strength and lower ductility has made it desirable to apply the elevated-temperature fabrication techniques developed for molybdenum to produce shapes from this columbium alloy.

Molybdenum. Extensive fabrication of molybdenum-alloy components has been accomplished in bar, forging, sheet, tubing, and mechanical-fastener shapes. The fabrication technology of this base metal is described in detail in Refs. 5 and 6. It might be well to regress at this time to illustrate several shapes produced by various forming techniques described in Ref. 1. Figure 3.17 shows spin-forged nose cones; a stretch-wrapped structural ring segment; a manually spun cup; a hydroformed hemisphere; a spin-forged thin-wall tube made from an extruded preformed blank; and impact-formed elbow half sections. All the above parts were formed at elevated temperatures, ranging from 250°F for the radial draw-formed section to 1200°F for the impact-formed elbow half sections. It is the purpose of this section of this chapter to augment the information contained in the references with some of the later developments that have occurred in both the fabrication of new molybdenum alloys and the use of new or refined fabrication techniques on molybdenum alloys.

New Alloy Development. Development quantities of a new molybdenum sheet, containing 0.5% titanium and 0.07% zirconium, have recently been produced. Successful production of this sheet was possible only after careful refinement of present molybdenum production methods. The alloy sheet was produced in the following steps: arc-melted 8-in.-diameter ingots were extruded to 4-in.-diameter billets, and the billets

Fig. 3.17 Molybdenum-alloy fabrication test parts.

were hammer-forged to 2- by 5-in. bars which were rolled to 0.060- and 0.040-in. thickness sheet. The program resulted in a 79 per cent yield of good-quality sheet to indicate that commercial production would be feasible.

Room-temperature tensile tests on the sheet in the as-rolled condition resulted in an ultimate tensile strength of 150,000 psi and a 0.2 per cent yield strength of 130,000 psi. These properties are approximately 25% better than those of the 0.5% titanium–molybdenum sheet in the same condition. This alloy possesses about a 300°F advantage in elevated-temperature strength over the 0.5% titanium–molybdenum alloy and has an increased 1-hr recrystallization temperature of approximately 2600°F.

Other alloys suitable for reentry structures have recently become available. The 0.5% Zr alloy has been used in structural development work.   This alloy has a recrystallization temperature higher than that of the 0.5% Ti alloy, 2650°F, and is, therefore, useful to a higher service in the cold-worked condition.

Sectioning.   Sectioning of all molybdenum-base alloys should be done in a very rigid setup using a water-cooled abrasive wheel because molybdenum is very susceptible to sheet separation and edge cracking that can occur when other methods are used.   Abrasive wheel cutting does not induce a tensile stress in the thickness direction (as do other methods such as shearing) which causes laminations to open.   A thin, bonded aluminum oxide or silicon carbide wheel at a speed of 12 to 15 fpm is recommended.

Forming.   There are two types of application for sheet metal in the reentry airframe.   The principal difference between the two is the sheet thickness used.   For *hot-structure* components, the tendency will be to use heavier-gauge material in the 0.030- to 0.1-in.-thick range or sandwich-type structures.   For the *heat-shield* type of component, thicknesses in the 0.005- to 0.020-in. range will be used.   Both areas of application will require the same types of fabrication.

In both cases, joining will be one of the most critical considerations. In the hot-structure approach, joint strength will be critical.   In the *heat shield*, joints that can compensate thermal expansion will be critical. In both cases, a reliable oxidation-resistant coating for the joint area will be a major consideration.

Figures 3.18 and 3.19 show two typical structures that have been fabricated from molybdenum alloy.   They represent a typical stiffened wing surface design and a leading-edge design.   These parts were fabricated, coated, and tested to support the development of a typical glide reentry vehicle.   Their successful operation is an indication of the promise held by the refractory metals to solve the heating problem.

Recent developments in the forming of sheet molybdenum alloys have considerably advanced the state of the art in this area, beyond that described in Ref. 3.   Additional experience in manual spinning has resulted in documenting the correct number of intermediate breakdown steps with stress-relieving treatments to form various shapes.   Joggles with a ±0.005-in. tolerance have been produced by spinning in parts of revolution.   Work in hot pressing has produced corrugations from 0.010-in.-thick material such as those shown in Fig. 3.20.

Even though the new 0.07% Zr–0.5% Ti molybdenum alloy has a higher yield strength than the commercially available 0.5% Ti molybdenum alloy, the workability of the new alloy appears to be equal to or better than that of the commercially available alloy.   Figure 3.21 shows several manually spun nozzle sections of 0.5% Ti–0.07% Zr molybdenum alloy.   In the work done to date on this new alloy it appears that

Fig. 3.18   Molybdenum-alloy stiffened wing panel.

Fig. 3.19   Twelve-inch molybdenum edge segments with riveted contour stiffeners.

Fig. 3.20 Hot-pressed molybdenum parts showing corrugations.

Fig. 3.21 Hot-spun 0.040-in. 0.5% titanium–0.07% zirconium molybdenum-alloy nozzle.

the small zirconium addition has lowered the work-hardening rate of molybdenum. This decrease in work-hardening tendency allows the metal to flow freely during forming so that more metal can be displaced per forming pass.

Fusion Welding. The availability of precision automatic welding equipment with heated backup bars makes it possible to consistently produce sound longitudinal weldments in molybdenum in the open air with only local inert-gas protection using the TIG process. Inert-atmosphere boxes, which make the welding of large parts cumbersome,

Fig. 3.22   Three examples of welded molybdenum panels.

are used only where extensive fillet welding of intricate parts is required. The careful selection of individual sheets by the ultrasonic inspection technique ensures the absence of sheet separation in the joint area, which helps to produce sound, reliable, reproducible weldments. Three molybdenum weld panels are shown in Fig. 3.22. Of course, the optimum combination of hold-down pressure, preheat temperature, welding speed, and post-weld stress-relieving treatment is also required for quality weldments. Detailed welding conditions are described by Levy and Bernett [5].

Experimental evidence has indicated that the recrystallized zone adjacent to the weld in the base-metal molybdenum alloy has approximately the same degree of bend ductility and brittle transition temperature as the base metal when recrystallized in an inert atmosphere. The bend transition temperature in both cases is 150 to 175°F. This indicates that very little, if any, contaminating interstitial alloying elements are introduced into the material during the welding operation.

Fusion welds with room-temperature ductility have been made on automatic equipment with the addition of filler wire alloy of 50% Re and

50% Mo. Welds with this filler metal were bent 80° over a radius equal to the sheet thickness at room temperature. The use of molybdenum-rhenium filler rod makes repair welding of cracks in molybdenum-alloy structures feasible.

It has been observed in some preliminary work that a weld joint containing molybdenum-rhenium filler metal is severely attacked by cementation-type oxidation-resistant coatings. This factor could limit the use of molybdenum-rhenium as a ductile fusion-weld filler alloy. Additional work will have to be done to verify this effect and to determine methods of counteracting it.

Electron-beam Welding. Electron-beam welding is another method with which it might be possible to produce weldments with room-temperature ductility in molybdenum alloys. Initial experimental work utilizing this process is now in progress, and very few actual data are available on the welding of molybdenum alloys. The process employs localized bombardment of the material by a beam of electrons in a chamber having a very high vacuum. The use of electrons makes it possible to ionize embrittling interstitials, such as oxygen and nitrogen already present as compounds in the base metal. Therefore, very-high-purity weldments are obtained, with oxygen and nitrogen quantities of less than 5 ppm being reported. With a reduced contamination level of the above order of magnitude, weldments having room-temperature ductility should be possible. The disadvantage of electron-beam welding is the need for a high-vacuum chamber. This requirement will limit the size of part that can be economically welded.

Mechanical Fasteners. In many structures, mechanical fasteners are the best and most expedient means for building up sheet-metal assemblies. The refractory-metal mechanical-fastener development programs are as important as the welding programs in the application of molybdenum alloys to structural uses. In Fig. 3.23, the 0.5% Ti molybdenum fasteners developed to this time are shown. Note the internal wrenching bolts and screws, the hex-head bolt, and the flush-head rivets. The use of rivets made it possible to produce the all-riveted molybdenum-alloy combustion chamber shown in Fig. 3.24, the riveted airframe-type channel section illustrated in Fig. 3.20, and the molybdenum wing-leading-edge component shown in Fig. 3.19. A temperature of 1000 to 1200°F was necessary to hot-head and upset the molybdenum rivets. Hardware with riveted joints have performed very successfully, and this joining technique for molybdenum is well past the development stage.

Machining. Molybdenum is readily machinable. For most operations, carbide tools are recommended because of the abrasiveness of the material. However, satisfactory results can be obtained with high-speed steel-cutting tools. For drilling thin sheet, Cleveland Twist Drill

No. 973 (stove burner high-speed steel) is very satisfactory; and for drilling deep holes and areas coated with the cementation-type coating, a Cleveland Twist Drill No. 727 (carbide tip) or No. 760 (solid carbide) should be used.

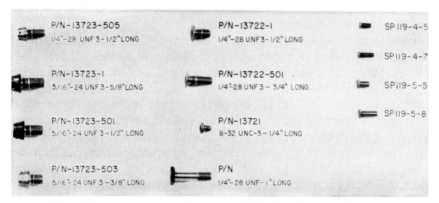

Fig. 3.23   Examples of molybdenum–0.5% titanium alloy fastener.

High-speed steel taps are adequate, but care must be taken that they are sharp and are started square to the hole.   For turning, drilling, and boring deep holes and for planing and tapping, a chlorinated cutting oil should continuously flush the chips away from the cutting area to extend

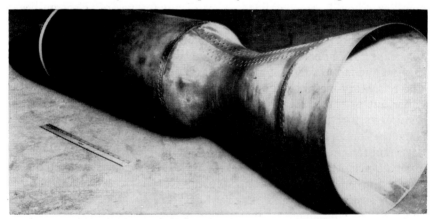

Fig. 3.24   Example of an all-riveted molybdenum-alloy combustion chamber.

tool life.   Since the material is very susceptible to chipping and flaking, care should be taken during drilling, tapping, and approaching edges during turning, boring, and planing operations.

Tantalum.   This base metal has seen limited use in flight-vehicle applications because of three primary considerations: high cost, high density, and low elevated-temperature properties.   Alloying of materials such as columbium and tungsten with tantalum, however, has proved relatively successful, and it is in this role that tantalum appears to be best suited.

Commercially pure tantalum is available in bar and sheet form and, as such, has been fabricated by using standard fabrication methods at room temperature. The metal does not show a transition from brittle to ductile fracture at a temperature as low as $-319°F$ even at high strain rates. The very low transition temperature of tantalum compared with those of molybdenum and tungsten is attributed to the higher solubility of oxygen in tantalum, which results in a lower tendency for oxides to precipitate at the grain boundaries.

Since tantalum has high ductility, low transition temperature, and low rate of strain hardening, it can be easily worked and formed at room temperature into complex shapes. The material is readily weldable by the TIG process with local inert-gas protection. If annealing is necessary, it should be done at a temperature of 2000 to 2500°F in a vacuum or in extremely pure helium or argon.

The use of tantalum in reentry structures, if it is used at all, will be restricted to the leading edge where the high melting temperature of the material will be utilized (5425°F). The availability of the 90% Ta–10% W alloy provides a material with sufficient strength to make tantalum more attractive (see Table 3.6). The attractiveness, however, lies not in its strength at high temperatures but in the combination of high melting temperature and ductility to well below $-100°F$. It is the only refractory metal that is completely ductile to very low temperatures and is readily fabricated at room temperature. Coating it to protect against oxidation remains a major problem in its utilization in reentry components.

Tungsten. The high melting temperature, usable strength at extreme temperatures, high modulus of elasticity, and promise of high-strength alloys make tungsten a very attractive base metal for extreme-temperature applications. Its commercially pure version is available in sheet, bar, and forgings, and it is beginning to see use in several rocket applications. However, its shortcomings (brittle behavior at the lower temperatures and difficult fabricability) will require considerable development effort before it can match molybdenum in actual applications. This, of course, does not include rocket-nozzle inserts where tungsten forgings are finding an important place today. It is tungsten-alloy structural assemblies that are still undeveloped. Accordingly, it will be a period of time before tungsten appears in reentry structures. However, its extreme-temperature capabilities make it the most attractive metal to widen the reentry corridor by raising the operating temperature of leading edges into the 4000 to 5000°F range. Of course, this attractiveness is predicated on the development of a satisfactory oxidation-resistant coating system.

Sectioning. The most satisfactory way to section tungsten sheet is with a water-cooled abrasive cutoff wheel. The type of wheel and speeds recommended for molybdenum can also be used for tungsten. Tungsten can be sheared when the material is locally torch-heated to about 1500°F.

Forming. The forming of tungsten sheet is accomplished at higher elevated temperatures than those used for similar forming operations to produce molybdenum shapes. An initial impact forming of tungsten sheet indicates that complex shapes can be formed by using this technique. Higher temperatures by 300 to 500°F over those used to impact-form molybdenum alloys should be used. Tungsten cups have been manually spun by heating the material to several hundred degrees higher than the 1000 to 1200°F that is required to spin molybdenum manually. For less severe forming operations such as brake forming and rolling of cylinders and cones, a temperature of 600 to 800°F is necessary, whereas only 200 to 400°F is the temperature required for forming molybdenum. However, additional development work of the various forming processes with tungsten will be necessary to establish (1) the optimum working temperatures, (2) the amount of metal that can be displaced per intermediate breakdown steps, and (3) the optimum stress-relieving cycles. Figure 3.25 shows a sheet-metal tungsten elbow that was press-formed for a rocket application. Figure 3.26 shows a tungsten rocket-nozzle insert formed from sheet by manual spinning.

Welding. The tungsten inert-gas process can be used to produce weldments in tungsten sheet. The techniques developed for welding molybdenum have been applied to fusion-welding sintered commercially pure tungsten sheet. Initial studies have shown that the problems for welding tungsten are the same ones that were initially faced for molybdenum, viz., cracking porosity and inconsistent penetration, but they are even more severe. However, some sound welds have been produced with manual automatic welding equipment. As with molybdenum, the welds in today's material are ductile only at elevated temperatures. The elevated-temperature ductility of sheet-tungsten fusion welds has been proved by forming them at elevated temperature after welding. A great deal more development work will be required to obtain the optimum conditions of the many welding variables before sound, reliable, and reproducible weldments are possible.

Mechanical Fasteners. To keep pace with the use of sheet-metal tungsten components, tungsten mechanical-fastener programs are proceeding at a satisfactory pace. One-eighth-inch-diameter flush-head rivets have been successfully produced by hot heading. Tungsten sample

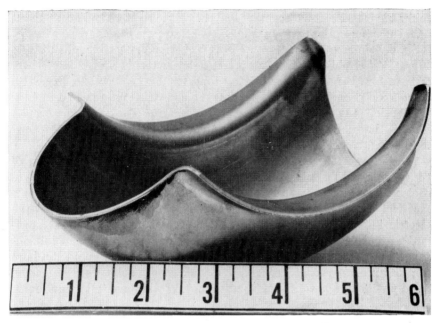

Fig. 3.25 Hot-pressed sheet-metal tungsten elbow.

Fig. 3.26 Tungsten rocket-nozzle insert formed from sheet metal by manual spinning.

joints have been riveted together by heating the rivet and adjacent sheet-metal structure prior to upsetting.   In all cases, the procedures developed for molybdenum fabrication were utilized for the fabrication of the tungsten assemblies, the only difference being that a higher fabrication temperature is required for driving tungsten rivets than is required for driving molybdenum rivets.   To date, no known attempt has been made to develop tungsten bolts, screws, and nuts.   The ability to chase threads in tungsten is the primary deterrent to producing threaded mechanical fasteners.

Machining.   The machining of tungsten is very difficult and most of the turning, boring, and planing operations are done by grinding.   Water-cooled silicon carbide wheels of 100 to 200 mesh at speeds of 10 to 15 surface feet per minute are recommended.   Drilling has been done by the electrical-discharge method.   To date, carbide and high-speed steel-cutting tools have generally proved to be inadequate in the machining of tungsten.   However, carbide cutting tools have been used to bore forged tungsten rocket nozzles.   To make the machining of tungsten more practical, a new cutting-tool technology will have to be developed.

Conclusions

The fabrication of refractory metals has reached a state of development where these materials can be worked in the manufacturing shop with several important exceptions to previously practiced shop procedures. The exceptions are particularly applicable to the fabrication of molybdenum and tungsten.   The new concepts in manufacturing that are required can be summarized as follows:

1. Material handling from the receiving dock through all phases of manufacturing to shipping of finished components must reflect the fact that these alloys are generally brittle at ambient temperatures.

2. All operations of fabrication which introduce energy into the materials, with the exception of machining, must be performed at an elevated temperature.

3. The materials engineering portion of the total input of technology and skill necessary to produce a successful component is several times that required to produce a similar part in standard materials.

Once these important facts are fully realized and practiced throughout an organization, refractory-metal fabrication can be accomplished. The use of these metals in reentry structures has reached the feasibility determination stage.   It is hoped that developments in material quality and load-carrying capability, and the fabrication of the refractory metals into experimental structural components, will make available to the designer in the near future a new class of materials suitable for service above 2000°F.

REFERENCES

1. Braun, Max T.: Materials Applications to Glide Reentry Structures, The Society of Automotive Engineers Symposium, March, 1960.
2. Braun, Max T., and Edwin G. Czarnecki: Structural Aspects of Earth Glide Reentry Vehicles, American Astronautical Society, August, 1958.
3. Report on Thermal Protection Systems, *Materials Advisory Board Rept.* MAB-151-M, June, 1959.
4. Levy, A. V., and S. E. Bramer: The Development of Refractory Sheet Metal Structures, *SAE Preprint* 56T, April, 1959.
5. Levy, A. V., and E. C. Bernett: Elevated Temperature Testing of Flight Vehicle Materials, *SAE Preprint* 104T, October, 1959.
6. Fabrication of Molybdenum, American Society for Metals, 1959.
7. Lidman, W. G., and A. R. Bobrowsky: Correlation of Physical Properties of Ceramic Materials with Resistance to Fracture by Thermal Shock, *Natl. Advisory Comm. Aeron. Tech. Note* 1918, 1949.
8. Baskin, Y., C. A. Arenberg, and J. H. Hardwerk: Thoria Reinforced by Metal Fibers, *Am. Ceram. Soc. Bull.*, vol. 38, no. 7, July, 1959.
9. Read, R. H.: Fiber Metallurgy: A Progress Report, *Mater. Design Eng.*, December, 1959.
10. Fisher, J. I., and R. L. Hodson: Development of Metal Fiber–Ceramic Rocket Nozzles, *Armour Research Foundation of Illinois Institute of Technology, Rept.* 2177-3, August, 1959.
11. Leggett, H., et al.: Development and Evaluation of Insulating Type Ceramic Coatings, *WADD Tech. Rept.* 59–102, part II, April, 1960.
12. Levy, A. V.: Thermal Insulation Ceramic Coatings, *Can. Aeron. J.*, pp. 343–346, December, 1958.
13. Sterry, W. M.: Ceramic and Composite Ceramic-Metal Materials Systems Applicable to Reentry Structures, *WADD Tech. Rept.* 60-58, presented at Society of Aerospace Material and Process Engineers National Symposium, Dayton, Ohio, March, 1960.
14. Pearl, H., et al.: Refractory Inorganic Materials for Structural Applications, *WADC Tech. Rept.* 59-342, February, 1960.
15. Scala, E.: Composite Materials, *Am. Rocket Soc., Paper* 1098-60, April, 1960.
16. Levy, A. V., S. R. Locke, and H. Leggett: Composite Ceramic-Metal Systems for 3000°–6000°F Service, *Am. Rocket Soc., Paper* 1572-60, Annual Meeting, December, 1960.

4

Materials for Thermal Protection

W. H. STEURER

CHIEF OF ENGINEERING MATERIALS
CONVAIR
SAN DIEGO, CALIFORNIA

Severe thermal environments constitute one of the most critical problem areas of space technology. Temperatures may reach magnitudes that are well beyond the solid state of any material. As the solution of the problem cannot be expected by new materials, new ways have to be sought to exploit the capabilities of existing materials.

In this attempt, it is no longer possible, as in the past, to rely solely on the passive properties of materials, such as strength or conductivity. In activating their latent properties, such as heat content or bonding energies, materials are capable of assuming active functions in the process of heat exchange.

To utilize fully these capabilities, materials will have to be tailored to the environmental requirements of a specific vehicle as well as to its design and operational requirements.

Thus, materials research is no longer a self-contained field, and the materials engineer must understand the problems as well as the language of the related disciplines.

Principles of High-temperature Design

If a structure is exposed to high temperatures, the designer has the choice of two fundamental approaches:

1. Selection of a heat-resistant structural material, which retains sufficient physical and chemical properties at the operating temperature

2. Protection of the stress-carrying structure against excessive heat exposure

The first approach is commonly referred to as the *hot structure*. It is based on the use of so-called heat-resistant materials, i.e., materials

94

that exhibit sufficient strength and oxidation resistance at the required temperature. This passive application of materials is limited by the strength decay encountered in most materials at high temperatures and, ultimately, by melting or sublimation. Further, for prolonged operation times, the hot structure will lead to considerable internal heating, which in most vehicle elements is not permissible because of heat-sensitive payloads, such as instruments or human crews. In both cases, thermal protection becomes imperative.

The material, material system, or the functional device that provides this protection is called the *thermal protection system*. It separates the heat-resisting and stress-carrying function of the structure into a non-load-carrying protection system (designed exclusively for thermal efficiency) and a load-carrying substructure. While in its ideal form the thermal protection system precludes any heat transfer to the substructure, it acts in practical cases as a high impedance to the heat flow. High mechanical properties are thus retained in the substructure.

Thermal Environment

The thermal environments encountered in aerospace vehicles are generated by either external or internal heat sources. The most probable types of external heating are the aerodynamic heating of the vehicle hull and solar heating. In addition, there are a number of other external heating sources of less significance, such as the radiant heating of the structure in the neighborhood of a propulsion exhaust, or the effect of man-made nuclear explosives. Internal heating is produced by power plants or propulsion systems and by electronic equipment.

Aerodynamic Heating. Aerodynamic heating is mainly produced by molecular impact and the adiabatic compression of the air at the vehicle surface. The magnitude of heating depends primarily on the vehicle velocity and altitude (representing air density and viscosity). However, secondary factors, such as body shape, angle of attack, and flow pattern, are important. In representing the aerodynamic heating for complete vehicle systems, certain simplifications must be made because the heating differs for various elements and locations. It is customary to relate the heat input to the stagnation areas, such as leading edges or the vehicle nose, thus eliminating a number of secondary parameters. The relationships between the stagnation heat input and the altitude and velocity are shown in Fig. 4.1. This chart is commonly used as a graphical background for the entire flight trajectory, thus identifying the entire thermal history.

For the present preliminary assessment of material requirements, it is convenient to describe the thermal environment by a few numerical terms. For level flight, the heat input can be well defined by the heat flux $\dot{q}$ (Btu per square foot per second) or by the equilibrium temperature T_e. For rapidly changing heating conditions, as in missiles or reentry vehicles, the thermal regime may be identified either by the total integrated heat input Q (in Btu per square foot) or the average heat flux (or equilibrium temperature) together with the duration t of the heat

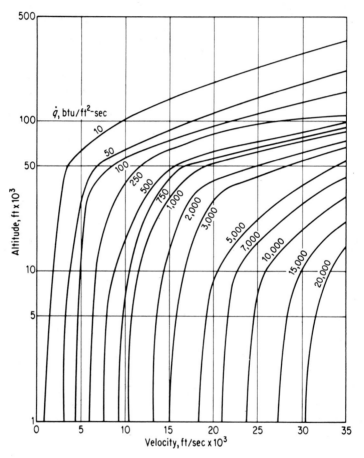

Fig. 4.1 Typical stagnation-point heat flux in relation to velocity and altitude.

input. Typical thermal data for a number of vehicles, together with the related design parameters, are complied in Table 4.1.

The heating during reentry from orbital or extra-orbital operation requires particular consideration in view of the high velocities (energies) involved. Two basic types of reentry are encountered:

1. Steep or drag reentry similar to that of an intercontinental ballistic missile (ICBM), where extreme heat fluxes in terms of hundreds or

thousands Btu per square foot per second are encountered for the exposure times of 10 to 40 sec, with a peak heat flux at a lower altitude level. Because of the extreme temperatures in the stagnation area, the radiation from the boundary layer becomes appreciable and may in some cases assume a magnitude equal to the convective heat flux.

2. The tangential or lifting reentry, primarily for human return, where for navigational reasons and for reduction of the heat flux the reentry is extended over a long trajectory. The magnitude of the heating for a wide variety of trajectories changes from heat inputs of only 20 to 30

Table 4.1 Typical Environmental Data of Atmospheric Flight

Vehicle	Maximum velocity, fps	Total Q, Btu	Average heat flux q_2, Btu/(ft²)(sec)	Time t, sec	Equil. temp. T_e, °F
Supersonic transport.....	4,000	5,000	0.5	3 hr	800
Advanced high-altitude cruise vehicle.........	6,000–10,000	50,000	5–10	3 hr	1400–1800
Low-altitude cruise vehicle..............	3,000	50,000	15	1 hr	2000
Boost glide:					
Low L/D............	35,000	11,000	30	350	3500
High L/D...........	24,000	25,000	15	2,500	2000
Tactical missile.........	5,000–9,000	4,000	10–50	10–75	1800–3000
ICBM...............	23,000	11,000	450	25	6000

Btu/(ft²)(sec) to several hundred Btu per square foot per second, and time increases from minutes to hours. In this case the heating occurs always at higher altitude levels.

Solar Heating. Heating by radiation from the sun is for all practical purposes constant from ground level throughout the entire near-space region, and it amounts to 0.12 Btu/(ft²)(sec). The wavelength spectrum of solar radiation has a peak in the visible region between 2,000 and 5,000 A.

During the passage of an orbital vehicle through the earth's shadow, only infrared radiation is encountered. Part of this is direct radiation from the earth's surface and the remainder is from the atmosphere. During the sun-exposed part of the orbit a portion of the vehicle is exposed additionally to the albedo of the earth consisting of reflected and scattered solar radiation, while another portion is exposed to direct sunlight.

Across the planetary space, the solar heat flux changes with the distance from the sun. The following heat fluxes have been calculated for the vicinity of the closer planets:

Planet	Heat Flux, Btu/(ft²)(sec)
Mercury	0.79
Venus	0.24
Earth	0.12
Mars	0.052
Jupiter	0.0044

Combined Solar and Aerodynamic Heating.   Even though solar heating is also present in atmospheric flight, it can be disregarded at lower altitude levels because it is negligible in comparison with aerodynamic heating up to an altitude of about 60 miles.   Likewise, aerodynamic heating is negligible at altitudes above 150 miles.   In the intermediate-altitude field, however, both aerodynamic and solar heating have to be taken into account.   The combined heat-flux data applying to orbital speeds in this region have been calculated as shown in the following table.

Altitude, miles	Heat flux, Btu/(ft²(sec)	
	Circular orbit	Elliptical orbit
60	1.4	13
80	0.23	1.13
100	0.14	0.24
120	0.13	0.15
150	0.12	0.13
200	0.12	0.12

Internal Heating.   Heat may be generated in the vehicle interior by propulsion systems, power plants, electronic equipment, or even the human crew.

Of foremost interest are the thermal environments of solid-propellant rocket nozzles and casings, which are exposed to the extreme combustion temperatures, chemical reactions, and erosive action of advanced propellants.   In the nozzle throat area, conditions shown in the following table are encountered.

Condition	Today	Potential
Maximum gas temperature, °F	6300	8000
Pressure, psi	200–2,000	3,000
Time, sec	30–90	180
Heat flux, Btu/(ft²)(sec)	200	500
Maximum wall temperature, °F	3500–4400	5000

The internal heating from power plants and the heat released from electronic equipment is transferred mostly by conduction. Even though of modest magnitude, it is significant in space vehicles because of the long operating times and the difficulty of heat dissipation to the environment.

Principles of Thermal Protection

Mechanism of Heat Exchange. As a vehicle is exposed to a thermal environment, heat is transferred in the skin material by conduction, convection, and/or radiation. The skin material, likewise, transmits this

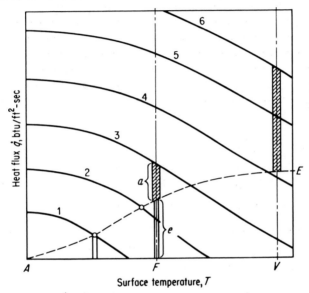

Fig. 4.2 Components of heat absorption.

heat by conduction into the substructure and by reflection and reradiation to the environment from its surface. As the process continues, the following changes in the heat exchange take place:

1. The heat absorbed by the skin material decreases as its thermal capacity is exhausted.

2. The surface temperature rises.

3. The heat dissipated by radiation increases according to the Stefan-Boltzmann law.

4. The heat of flux from the environment decreases with the reduction of the temperature differential between environment and surface.

The process of heat absorption, as related to heat flux and temperature, is illustrated in a qualitative way in Fig. 4.2 for a material with distinct melting and boiling points. The solid lines represent the heat flux transferred to the surface as related to surface temperature, for various levels of thermal environment. The starting points of those lines identify the *cold-wall heat flux* commonly used to identify the thermal environment. The dotted line indicates the heat flux dissipated by radiation, as related to the surface temperature.

At the beginning of the heating process, radiation is very ineffective and the heat absorption is provided mainly by the thermal capacity of the material near the surface and by diffusion into the bulk material. As the heat capacity of the material is gradually utilized, the surface temperature increases and radiation dominates at the surface. The temperature rise comes to a stop as soon as equilibrium is reached between the incident heat flux and radiation; this point is identified by the intersection of the two representation lines. At higher environmental heat-flux levels, the intersection point may fall outside the solid state of the material, as for line 3 in Fig. 4.2. In this case, the temperature increase comes to a temporary stop at the melting point, and equilibrium is attained in the liquid state. At higher heat-flux levels, as in lines 5 and 6, vaporization takes place before the radiation equilibrium can be reached.

The heat absorbed in the process of melting or vaporization represents only the portion of the environmental heat flux which exceeds the radiant dissipation capability. This may be expressed as

$$\dot{q}_{\text{melt}} = \dot{q}_{\text{env}} - \dot{q}_{\text{rad}} \qquad \text{Btu}/(\text{ft}^2)(\text{sec}) \tag{4.1}$$

as indicated in Fig. 4.2, if the relatively small conduction into the solid bulk material is neglected. If this portion of the absorbed heat flux is related to the heat of fusion H_f,

$$\dot{q}_{\text{melt}} = \frac{H_f \rho \cdot d}{t} \qquad \text{Btu}/(\text{ft}^2)(\text{sec}) \tag{4.2}$$

Where ρ is the density in pounds per cubic foot, the time at which the temperature remains constant can be assessed for an assumed depth of the fusion zone, d, by the relationship

$$t = \frac{H_f \rho \, d}{\dot{q}_{\text{env}} - \dot{q}_{\text{rad}}} \qquad \text{sec} \tag{4.3}$$

Fusion and vaporization are not acceptable in the conventional use of materials, which is limited to the solid state. In ablation design materials, however, one takes advantage of the high amounts of heat that can be absorbed by fusion and vaporization. In such materials, the heat-absorbing capability gradually diminishes as material is consumed. Their use is time-limited and applies primarily to transient cases of heating, typical for reentry bodies or rocket aircraft. Pure radiation systems are more adaptable to sustained flight conditions. In some cases, such as a cruising aircraft performing at high speed or a high angle of attack maneuver, a transient heating cycle may be superimposed to the steady-state condition. This provides a possibility for the use of both types of heat absorption in the same protection system. Heat flux and time are thus the basic parameters identifying both the heating characteristics of the vehicle and the heat-absorbing capability of the material.

Representation of the Heat Exchange. For the definition of the thermal environment of vehicle systems and their major components (nose, leading edges, lift surfaces, etc.), the convective aerodynamic heat input is expressed in terms of cold-wall heat flux $\dot{q}_C$ for zero surface temperature, and it is independent of the skin material or protection system. It is commonly used for flight profiles or trajectory charts, such as that shown in Fig. 4.1. Except for high-drag boosters at extreme velocities, the radiant heat input from the hot gases of the boundary layer, $\dot{q}_R$, is comparatively small and is usually neglected. For the determination of the actual net heat flux $\dot{q}_n$ to the surface at a certain point of the heating process, a reduction $\dot{q}_H$ has to be made for the respective surface temperature.

On the side of the material, the heat absorption is composed of the heat radiated and reflected at the hot surface, $\dot{q}_e$ and $\dot{q}_r$; the heat absorbed in the material or the active part of the protection system, $\dot{q}_a$; and the heat $\dot{q}_s$ transferred to the substructure.

The heat exchange is then expressed by the general heat balance

$$\dot{q}_{\text{input}} = \dot{q}_{\substack{\text{absorbed and} \\ \text{dissipated}}}$$

$$\dot{q}_C - \dot{q}_H + \dot{q}_R = \dot{q}_e + \dot{q}_r + \dot{q}_a + \dot{q}_s$$

Representation of Material Capabilities. The capability of a material for radiant-heat dissipation depends solely on its emissivity at the temperature concerned. This value remains constant for indefinite operation times, unless changed by oxidation or similar processes.

The absorptive capability of materials or thermal protection systems may be identified by its thermal capacity or heat content in Btu per pound over a given temperature range, which can be obtained from handbooks. For technical purposes a modified term has been introduced, which includes only the effective part of the thermal capacity of a material system. It has been designated as *effective thermal capacity* Q^*, in Btu per pound, and is identified by the relation

$$Q^*W = \dot{q}t$$

where W = mass of material, lb/ft^2 of vehicle surface
$\dot{q}$ = incident heat flux
t = operation time

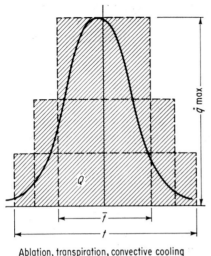

Ablation, transpiration, convective cooling

Fig. 4.3 Representation of a heat pulse.

The fundamental relationship, in spite of its simplicity, is the primary key to the entire field of thermal protection. The left side represents the two basic criteria of the vehicle design: material capability and weight requirements. The right side identifies the primary environmental and operational characteristics: heat flux and time.

While the terms $\dot{q}$ and t are clearly identified for steady-state conditions, i.e., prolonged operation times, additional definitions have to be made for transient heating as it applies, for example, to ballistic missiles. For such cases the modified sinusoidal heating characteristic is replaced by a rectangular pattern of the same maximum heat flux $\dot{q}_{max}$ and the same total heat input Q, as shown in Fig. 4.3; and the representative time is designated as $\bar{t}$.

Thermal Protection Systems

There are several ways of combining the various capabilities of materials in systems for thermal protection. In order to distinguish the various approaches, it is necessary to define the essential elements of heat absorption so that a system of classification of thermal protection systems can be established. In the first approach it should be considered that heat is energy and that the law of energy conversion has to be observed. This implies that heat can only be either removed from the place of heat input by such means as conduction, radiation, or reflection or transformed into another form of energy. According to this fundamental concept, thermal protection systems may be classified into systems based on the principle of heat dissipation and those based on the principle of heat absorption. These two categories embrace the following thermal-protection systems:

1. Systems based on heat dissipation

    a. Direct radiation
    b. Insulation
    c. Indirect radiation
    d. Convective cooling

2. Systems based on heat absorption

    a. Heat sink
    b. Ablation
    c. Transpiration
    d. Film cooling
    e. Direct energy conversion

Heat-dissipation systems may be more accurately defined with regard to the location at which the dissipation takes place. This may be either the place of heat input by *direct dissipation* (e.g., direct-radiation systems) or, by transfer of the heat, a location of low environmental heat input for *indirect dissipation;* the transfer may be accomplished either by thermal conduction or by functional means (convective cooling). Heat absorption may be either *intrinsic* (i.e., the conversion of energy is carried out within the protective material, as in a heat sink or by ablation) or *extrinsic* by the use of media supplied to the place of heat exchange by functional means, as in film cooling or transpiration.

For the application of thermal-protection systems to design, a clear definition of the primary mode of heat absorption is essential in order to arrive at highest efficiency and at the same time compatibility with secondary parameters of the environment. In the final design optimization it is necessary to adjust the thermal protection systems carefully to meet the design and operational requirements on one hand and the environmental conditions on the other. Moreover, it appears possible to increase efficiency, in some cases, by the utilization of one or more environmental influences.

In addition to these primary elements of heat absorption there are, of course, a number of secondary properties and processes which contribute to the overall thermal efficiency. Table 4.2 classifies the various thermal protection systems according to their primary and secondary elements of heat absorption. It should be noted that there may be some difference of opinion as to the relative importance of these factors.

Systems Based on the Principles of Heat Dissipation. The primary tool of all heat-dissipation systems is radiation, which, for reasons of simplicity, is preferably carried out at the point of heat input. In addition, a certain portion of the heat input diffuses into the bulk material and the substructure and is absorbed there by thermal capacity of the structure. This absorptive process is, however, only temporary. As soon as the thermal capacity of bulk material and substructure is exhausted, only as much heat will be removed from the surface by conduction as can be dissipated by radiation at interior surfaces. For any prolonged application, dissipation is provided solely by radiation.

Table 4.2   Elements of Heat Absorption in Thermal-protection Systems

System	Primary element	Secondary element
Hot structure............	Radiation	Thermal capacity of structure
Radiation...............	Radiation	Thermal capacity of substructure
Insulation..............	Radiation	Thermal capacity of insulation
Convective cooling.......	Radiation	Thermal capacity of coolant
Heat sink..............	Thermal capacity in solid state	Radiation endothermic reactions
Ablation...............	Thermal capacity to include fusion, vaporization, decomposition, dissociation	Radiation blocking action, endothermic reaction
Transpiration...........	Heat of vaporization, superheating of coolant, or dissociation	Blocking action
Film cooling............	Blocking action	Thermal capacity of coolant
Energy conversion.......	Energy conversion	

Direct Radiation.   In its most primitive form, thermal protection may be achieved by the radiation capabilities of the surface (see Fig. 4.4a). This may be achieved either by means of surface treatments or by coatings to increase the emissivity or reflectivity.   Increasing the emissivity may not always be an advantage, because the absorptivity (and thus

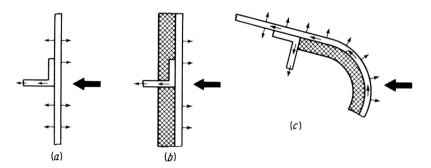

Fig. 4.4   Types of hot structures.   (a) Hot; (b) insulated; (c) dissipated.

the radiant heat input) may be increased.   For refined direct dissipation systems, the wavelength spectrum of the incident radiation and the surface emission spectrum must be well adjusted.   The ideal is to produce a surface that has a low absorptivity in the wavelength range of incident radiation and a high emissivity in the infrared region.

The efficiency of direct dissipation may be further enhanced by the application of internal insulation (see Fig. 4.4b), which leads to higher surface temperatures and thus more effective radiation. From this point of view, the internal insulation used commonly in design for the protection of payloads is, at the same time, an important part of the external protection systems.

For protection against aerodynamic heating, direct radiation has only limited application and is largely employed to extend the use of hot structure to somewhat higher heat-flux rates. Reflective surfaces are frequently used for internal protection against the radiant heat from power plants or other internal heat sources.

For the protection of space vehicles against solar heating, direct dissipation is used exclusively for several reasons: (1) the heat input is purely radiative; (2) the incident radiation spectrum can be accurately defined; (3) the system is required to function for extremely long times; (4) space has no thermal capacity, and radiation is the only means of dissipating heat. As the incident heat flux is primarily in the visible region of 3,000 to 8,000 A, highest protection efficiency is obtained with materials of low absorptivity in this region and high emissivity in the infrared. The efficiency of a surface or coating is, therefore, represented by the ratio of alpha to epsilon, i.e., of absorptivity to sunlight and the emissivity in the infrared. By the proper selection of this ratio, the vehicle skin temperatures as well as the temperature in the interior can be adjusted with a high degree of accuracy. In space, chemical changes do not occur, but the emissivity ratio of coatings may be altered by ultraviolet and higher-energy radiation. Such changes must be anticipated and allowed for in the design.

Indirect Dissipation. In most aerospace vehicles, the heating pattern is not uniform, but has *hot spots*, i.e., areas of enhanced heat input, such as the stagnation zone of vehicle noses or leading edges. In such cases, the peak of the temperature profile may be reduced by conducting a portion of the heat to places of lower heat input and dissipating it there by radiation, as illustrated in Fig. 4.4c. This requires materials or composites with directional thermal properties, such as laminates, consisting of layers of high and low conductivity, or pyrolytically deposited materials. Pyrolytic graphite has been found highly effective for this application.

Indirect dissipation may also lend itself to the temperature control of space vehicles by transferring some of the solar heat input to the shadow side for radiant dissipation.

Insulation. The common concept of insulation is the use of a low-conductivity material that acts as a high impedance to the flow of heat between the place of heat input and the components to be protected.

With the exception of the initial heating phase, where the insulation material absorbs some of the heat input until the thermal gradient has been stabilized, insulation has no capability of heat absorption and all heat has to be dissipated by radiation. Hence, insulation is merely a special case of radiation systems in which the heat dissipation at the hot surface is increased by means of a higher surface temperature. The significant material properties are, therefore, the thermal conductivity representing the impedance capability, the emissivity of the surface, and the temperature limitations of the surface material, particularly with regard to oxidation. The properties of a number of typical insulation materials are listed in Table 4.3.

Table 4.3   Properties of Typical Insulation Materials

Material	Density, lb/ft³	Thermal conductivity k		Insulation factor, density/k	Temp. limit T, °F
		Btu/(in.)(hr)(ft²)	°F		
Alumina.................	230	38.5	2000	740	3500
Zirconia................	363	14.4	1800	435	4500
Silica...................	138	13	2200	149	3050
Pyroceram..............	165	20	1000	274	1200
Firebricks..............	30–60	1.3–3.5	1500	3.2–18	1800–3000
Ceramic fiber, compacted....	12	1.87	2000	1.87	2300
Min-K 2000..............	20	0.27	1000	0.45	2000
Foamsil.................	11	1.85	900	1.70	2000
Asbestos fibers...........	15	0.63	600	0.78	1000
Glass fiber mat...........	0.5	0.52	300	0.021	400
(Vacuum panel)...........	(15)	(0.03)	(40)	(0.039)	(1000)

Insulation may be classified as either internal or external. The criterion for the distinction is the location relative to the stress-carrying structure. If the insulation is exclusively internal, the stress-carrying structure is fully exposed to the heating and its operational temperature is limited by the temperature effects on the mechanical properties and oxidation resistance of the structural metals. Materials for internal insulation, therefore, do not require high heat resistance. For convenience, they are mostly in the form of fiber mats, consisting of silica fibers, glass fibers, or even plastic fibers.

In view of the temperature limitations of structural metals, and of the increasing service temperatures of aerospace vehicles, the trend is strongly directed toward the use of external insulation. This, obviously, calls for insulation materials of high-temperature capability.

A favorable combination of the significant properties is found in ceramics, which exhibit a low conductivity, high melting or sublimation temperature, and insensitivity to chemical surface changes, even though

the emissivities of such materials are usually low. As the insulation
capability of ceramics depends solely on their conductivity, it can be
improved only by increased insulation thicknesses, and this is limited by
weight considerations. The use of monolithic ceramics is further limited
by their inherent brittleness and by their poor resistance to vibration and
sonic fatigue.

Both shortcomings point toward the replacement of monolithic ceramics
by a relatively loose aggregate of particles or fibers. In this form, the

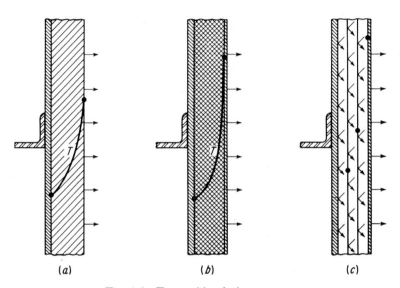

Fig. 4.5 Types of insulating systems.

insulating value and resistance to dynamic loads are greatly increased,
particularly in fibrous systems.

The lowest conductivities have been obtained by the use of particles
with sizes smaller than the mean free path of the air so that the molecular
heat transfer between particles is minimized.† All these loosely packed
composites, however, require a "cover skin" whose temperature capability determines the limitations of the system.

The ultimate insulation system is the evacuated panel. In its ideal
form, heat is transferred merely by radiation, and this can be reduced
by the introduction of radiation barriers, as shown in Fig. 4.5c. The
pressures of vacuum panels will be in the order of 10^{-1} mm Hg, because
lowering of the pressure does not offer any advantage. In practical
design, the use of low-pressure panels introduces considerable difficulty.

† Min-K, a proprietary product of Johns-Manville.

In the first place, the cover skin as well as the radiation barriers has to be supported, which cannot be done without considerable reduction of efficiency. Furthermore, the reliability depends greatly on the development of special sealing techniques that prevent catastrophic failure in case of skin damage.

The primary problem in the usefulness of high-efficiency insulation to flight systems is the capability of manufacturing and applying a highly heat-resistant cover skin. Connections to the substructure that are necessary to support the cover skin increase the thermal conductivity and present difficulties in joining. Further, ways have to be found to compensate for the differential thermal expansion to avoid thermal stresses or buckling. In spite of these difficulties, high-efficiency insulation systems of this type will necessarily find widespread application in future flight systems.

Internal insulation is widely in use for thermal protection of crew or passenger cabins, for instrumentation, or for the protection of cryogenic fuel or oxidizer tankage. External insulation is still approached with caution, yet its extensive use in vehicles operating for prolonged times at speeds above 5,000 fps is clearly indicated. The development of high-efficiency external insulation systems will necessarily become a major field of aerospace engineering, in which the designer and the materials engineer have to work hand in hand.

Convective Cooling. The effectiveness of indirect dissipation can be considerably increased if the heat transfer is provided by functional means instead of the previously described passive system. In convective cooling the heat is absorbed by a circulating liquid coolant which releases the heat for radiant dissipation at places of low heat input. In the simplest form, convective cooling may be attained by self-circulation of the coolant in a double-wall structure (Fig. 4.6a). This design is limited to components with a very localized hot spot. For the cooling of larger areas, such as the lift surfaces of reentry vehicles, it is necessary to provide heat exchangers, located at a nonheated spot, through which the heated coolant is circulated by means of a pump (Fig. 4.6b). Even though a certain amount of heat is initially absorbed by the thermal capacity of the coolant (in the temperature range between pre-entry temperature and the exit temperature of the heat exchanger), it should always be remembered that, for any length of operation, convective cooling is a purely radiant dissipation system, in which the coolant and all plumbing are merely tools for transferring the heat to the place of radiation. An exception is the two-fluid system, in which the heat exchanger is cooled by a second liquid, which, in turn, is vaporized to the environment. Water, lithium, and hydrogen have been considered for use as coolants.

While convective cooling is extensively used in power plants, its application to externally heated structures is approached with caution in view of the resulting intricate designs and the high weight requirements.

Systems Based on the Principles of Heat Absorption.   *Heat Sink.* The designer will always avoid the use of functional cooling systems as long as the heat absorption can be provided by the material itself.   A

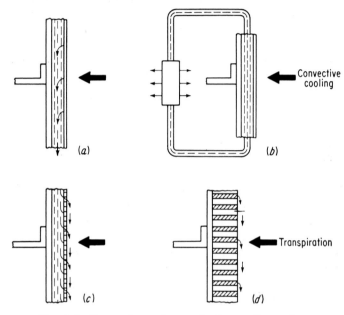

Fig. 4.6   Convective and transpiration cooling systems.

considerable amount of heat can be absorbed, in addition to the radiant-heat dissipation, by the skin itself by using a sufficient wall thickness of a material of high thermal capacity and diffusivity.

The efficiency of a material as a heat sink is determined by the heat content in the solid state, i.e., by the specific heat and melting temperature.   The thermal capacities of several metals in the solid state are listed in Table 4.4.   It should, however, be noted that these values may not be fully utilized because metals flow at temperatures below the melting point.   The maximum useful temperature may be further reduced if the heat sink is simultaneously used as a stress-carrying structure (*shell structure*), the amount of reduction depending on the strength limitations of the material at high temperatures.

The most obvious way to increase the effectiveness of a heat sink is by the use of a material of high melting temperature.   Refractory metals are not attractive because of their high densities.   Ceramics, on the other hand, exhibit poor thermal properties. Much effort has been expended to develop materials having favorable characteristics. Metal–metal oxide combinations have been found highly effective. An additional advantage of such heterogeneous systems is the possibility of adjusting the mixture to specific thermal requirements.

In certain applications, the heat-sink concept may be extended beyond the solid state, if the melting material is contained in an envelope of higher melting temperature. While this approach does not appear promising for structural applications, it may be adapted in the design of rocket

Table 4.4   Heat Contents of Several Metals at Various States
(Reference temperature, 77°F)

Metal	Heat absorbed in solid state, %	To melting point, Btu/lb	To include fusion, Btu/lb	To include vaporization, Btu/lb
Aluminum........	4.4	250	421	5,710
Beryllium........	9.5	1,090	1,560	10,540
Copper..........	6.6	176	268	2,660
Iron.............	8.6	297	414	3,440
Magnesium.......	9.0	279	439	3,083
Molybdenum.....	7.9	288	414	3,640
Silver...........	6.2	90	135	1,458
Titanium........	8.5	387	567	4,540
Tungsten........	7.8	200	279	2,643
Zirconium.......	7.7	227	322	2,915
Lithium.........	2.7	285	464	10,322

nozzles, landing gear, brakes, or similar internal elements of high, transient heat exposure.

Heat sinks in various modifications are shown in Fig. 4.7. In most cases, insulation must be used between the heat-absorption shield and the stress-carrying structure to avoid excessive heat transfer into the interior of the vehicle.

The heat-sink concept is primarily attractive for the nose cones of tactical missiles, as their heat flux–time characteristic covers the same thermal regime as the thermal capabilities of materials in the solid state. This means of thermal control has also been used extensively for nozzles of solid-propellant rocket motors, where high erosion effects and tight dimensional limitations preclude the use of nonmetallics in ablative systems.

Ablation. The heat-absorbing capability of the solid heat sink is limited by the heat content of materials in the solid state. A comparison of the figures in Table 4.4 shows that this represents less than one-tenth of the total heat-absorbing capability of a material for temperatures up to and including vaporization. This ratio would be still greater if superheating, dissociation, and ionization of the vaporized gases were included. It appears that extremely efficient thermal protection could be achieved if these phenomena were utilized for heat absorption. However, this requires that the heat-absorbing material be retained at the surface, or at least within the zone of heat exchange, until its total

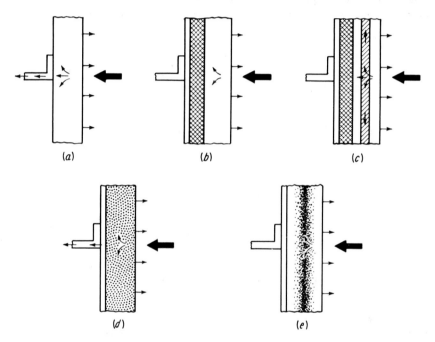

Fig. 4.7 Types of solid heat sinks. (*a*) Shell; (*b*) insulated; (*c*) composite; (*d*) heterogeneous; (*e*) composite heterogeneous.

capacity has been fully utilized. Furthermore, if this process should be required to function for any length of time, it must be orderly and uniform, to avoid surface discontinuities and excessive weight losses.

The process that combines all these parameters into a thermal protection system is called ablation. Thermal ablation may be defined as a self-controlled uniform process of heat absorption, utilizing the entire heat content of a material to include vaporization or even dissociation, and utilizing air flow for the continuous removal of the resulting products. A portion of the material is continuously expended; its use is primarily limited to transient heating conditions, such as are encountered in ballistic missiles and reentry vehicles.

The heat-exchange system of the ablation process is illustrated in Fig. 4.8. Of the total heat input, a portion of its radiant energy is reflected from the surface back to the boundary layer and may be partially absorbed, depending on the transparency of the layer to the reflected wavelengths. However, the major portion of this reflected energy is dissipated beyond the boundary layer. The remaining incident heat, representing by far the major portion, enters the surface, raising its temperature through fusion to vaporization. During this process a major part of the heat is absorbed by the heat content of the material,

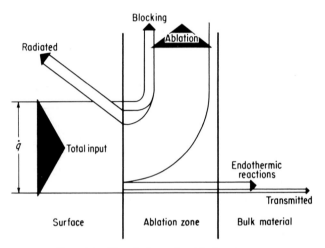

Fig. 4.8   Heat balance in ablation system.

including the changes of state, and by surface radiation, whose effectiveness increases with the surface temperature. The vaporized gases may further contribute to the heat absorption by dissociation with a reduction in the heat transfer to the surface by thickening of the boundary layer. This action is identified in Fig. 4.8 by the term *blocking action*. The heat not absorbed in the surface layer diffuses into the bulk material, where the endothermic reactions in the solid state may further contribute to the heat absorption. A small remainder of the heat flux will finally diffuse through the bulk material to the substructure, continuously changing the thermal gradient and increasing the back face temperature. In most applications of short duration, this can be neglected. For prolonged operation times, however, the efficiency and limitations of an ablation system are dependent on the diffusion characteristics in the bulk material.

The elements of heat absorption which constitute the ablation process are summarized below:

1. Primary elements of heat absorption

   a. Heat content of the active material including changes of state
   b. Surface radiation
   c. Blocking action in the boundary layer
   d. Decomposition in the ablation zone

2. Secondary elements of heat absorption

   a. Reflection of radiant heat input
   b. Endothermic reactions in the solid state
   c. Decomposition of the bulk material
   d. Heat-sink effect of the bulk material

The thermal capabilities alone, however, do not constitute an ablative material. Characteristics that ensure an orderly functioning of the process are equally important. In the first place, the utilization of all heat-absorbing phenomena can be achieved only if the material is retained at the surface long enough to vaporize. For most ablative materials this requires a framework of a material of higher refractoriness in which the ablative materials are embedded and held in place until vaporized. Secondly, for uniformity of surface removal and to ensure a continuous functioning, it is necessary that the active ablation process be confined to a minute surface layer. This is achieved by means of a steep thermal gradient, i.e., a material of low conductivity. Where ablation materials of high conductivity are required, it is necessary to provide a matrix material of low conductivity as a continuous phase, thereby reducing the overall conductivity of the composite. Uniformity can further be ensured by a heterogeneous structure of the material, as any change of state, such as melting or vaporization, is always confined in the thickness direction to the dimension of a single particle.

All these functional requirements makes a heterogeneous or composite structure imperative for ablation materials. Single homogeneous materials may perform satisfactorily for very short times (i.e., seconds). For any longer duration, heterogeneity is mandatory.

For development of ablative materials, the following primary requirements have to be met:

1. High heat content
2. Low overall thermal conductivity
3. Heterogeneous or composite structure

The temperature at which ablation takes place can be predetermined by proper selection of the two components of the heterogeneous material system. For example, if the temperature is a little above the melting temperature of the active heat-absorbing material, the process will be maintained at this temperature and will not include vaporization. However, depending on the properties of the materials, vaporization may take place as the liquid material moves downstream. Full vaporization as part of the active ablation process is ensured by selection of a highly

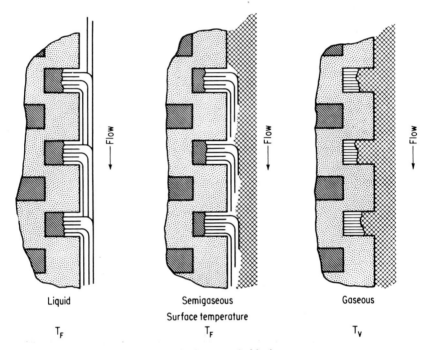

Liquid	Semigaseous	Gaseous
	Surface temperature	
T_F	T_F	T_V

Fig. 4.9 Principal types of ablation systems.

heat-resistant skeleton material. Three basic operational conditions may, therefore, be distinguished (see Fig. 4.9):

1. The liquid system, in which the ablation process takes place at a temperature level between melting and boiling point
2. The gaseous system, at a temperature at or above the boiling point
3. The semigaseous system, which is basically a liquid system, in which vaporization takes place while the liquid material is moving along the surface; in this case the original point of ablation does not benefit from the vaporization

In a well-designed ablation material, operating temperatures are attained quickly because of low thermal conductivity. From this time on, steady-state conditions exist. Unlike other protection systems, ablation does not require accurate adjustment to a certain heat-flux rate because changes are automatically matched by an increase or decrease of the ablation rates; the operating temperature remains practically constant. This explains the preference for ablative materials to resist the sinusoidal heat pulse, characteristic of ballistic missile nose-cone reentry.

Table 4.5 Effective Thermal Capacities $Q*$†

Heat sink:
Cu...	180
Fe...	308
Be...	1,105
Pyro graphite..................................	Over 4,000

Convective cooling:
Water...	1,000
Helium...	3,000
Lithium..	2,300
Hydrogen......................................	8,500

Transpiration:
Air..	1,500
Water...	2,500
Helium...	4,500
Hydrogen......................................	12,000

Ablation:
Graphite..	8,000
Silica...	6,000
Pure resins.....................................	1,500–2,000
Glass-reinforced plastics....................	2,000–3,000
Ceramic-reinforced plastics.................	3,000–5,000
Heterogeneous metal-ceramic systems........	2,000–6,000
Ceramic A.....................................	2,800
Ceramic B.....................................	4,700
Ceramic C.....................................	6,200

† As the data differ for the test method used, they should be regarded as examples.

A list of ablation materials, together with typical values for their heat-absorbing capabilities (expressed by the effective thermal capacities $Q*$) is compiled in Table 4.5.

At first glance, many of these materials appear not to fulfill all basic requirements for a perfect ablation system. In the phenolic resin–fiber glass system, for example, which has been used successfully, the phenolic is certainly not a high-heat-resistant matrix material. At high-heat-flux rates it is, however, charred instantly, thus forming a highly heat-resistant carbon skeleton in which the glass fibers are firmly held in place while melting. The glass, likewise, is not retained in its original form. During the heating process the flux constituents boil away, so that finally almost pure silica is obtained at the surface and this acts as a highly viscous shield that maintains a uniform surface while moving slowly downstream. Both useful materials are thus actually generated during flight by the very heat they are designed to counteract.   The utilization of the environmental heat to generate or modify the ultimate materials is a powerful tool in the development of ablative materials.

For some specific operational conditions, such as the reentry of a drag body at extreme velocities, the radiant heating from the boundary-layer gas, almost negligible otherwise, may assume the same order of magnitude as the convective heat flux.   Most materials become increasingly transparent at high temperatures, so it is sometimes necessary to provide an opaque heat-resistant surface.   This, again, may be generated during initial heating by a charring resin, leaving a carbonaceous surface of high opacity and emissivity.   The optimum design would provide a surface layer that combines low absorptivity in the shorter-wavelength region of the incident radiation with high emissivity in the infrared and opacity over the entire wavelength field.

The development of ablative materials for low-heat-flux rates and prolonged operation times is one of the most difficult research problems. While a number of materials have been successfully used at low heating rates [24 to 75 Btu/(ft^2)(sec)] and short times, their suitability for long-time operations has not been demonstrated.   The particular thermal and operational regime of manned reentry from orbit places increased emphasis on this requirement.   Likewise, the use of ablation in solid-propellant rocket nozzles is expected to gain considerable attention in the near future.   One of the prime obstacles is the requirement for shape integrity during attack by the highly erosive combustion products.

Transpiration.   In transpiration cooling systems (Fig. 4.6c) the heat absorption is provided by vaporization of the coolant at the surface of heat input.   The use of a liquid coolant, supplied from containers through a double wall, requires a porous skin of uniform permeability. Transpiration may be the only means to achieve absorption of extreme heat-flux rates in terms of thousands of Btu/(ft^2)(sec) for prolonged operation times, limited only by the amount of coolant which can be carried.   At very short times of operation, transpiration cooling may be provided by an oriented heterogeneous material, consisting of a heat-absorbing material embedded in a skeleton material of higher melting point (Fig. 4.6d).   As the heat is applied, the heat-absorbing components will melt and vaporize at the surface, providing a temporary transpiration cooling effect.   Data on the capability of transpiration systems may be obtained from Table 4.5.

So far, transpiration cooling has not been used except in liquid-propellant rocket nozzles, and no immediate applications are foreseen.   It may, however, be the only resort at extreme heat fluxes, where ablation is not acceptable, either because of long time requirements or in view of the ablation products.

Film Cooling. The efficiency of thermal protection provided by a liquid film at the surface is obviously limited by the thermal capacity of the coolant. It may, for transient heating, be stored in the skin material itself or supplied through a porous wall from containers. The use of the *blocking action* of a gaseous film, however, may have considerable development potential. Accurate adaptation of the gas and the injection rate to specific aerodynamic and thermal environments appears to be necessary. Gas-film *cooling* is no longer an absorptive system, and boundary-layer modification may be introduced as a new principle for thermal protection.

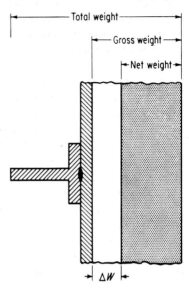

Fig. 4.10 Method of designating weight requirements.

Direct Energy Conversion. In view of the costly production of power in space vehicles, it appears desirable to utilize the solar heat input at the vehicle surface for power generation by means of a direct-energy-conversion system instead of the presently used dissipation to the environment. However, the effective application of this scheme to space thermal protection will have to await further advances in the technology of direct-energy-conversion materials.

Design Integration

Weight Requirements. The prime criterion of aerospace design is weight. In order to permit a comparison of the weight requirements of thermal protection systems, several weight definitions have to be introduced (Fig. 4.10):

W_t = *total weight* of both thermal protection system and directly connected stress-carrying substructure

W_g = *gross weight* of entire protection system, excluding stress-carrying substructure

W_n = *net weight*, representing only the portion of thermal protection system actively participating in process of heat absorption or dissipation, e.g., portion removed in ablation or expended coolant in transpiration

ΔW = *support weight*, comprising the part of protection system which supports its functioning indirectly, such as thickness remaining at end of ablation process; or coolant tanks, pumps, plumbing, and injection systems in transpiration

The most representative weight term for design is the gross weight W_g. As thermal protection systems refer to a surface, all weights are expressed per unit of surface area in pounds per square foot.

Capabilities of Thermal Protection Systems. The thermal efficiency of radiative and insulative systems can be determined satisfactorily by heat-transfer calculations. For sophisticated high-efficiency insulation systems, however, calculation becomes difficult and tests provide superior reliability.

The capability of absorptive systems is well identified by the previously defined *effective thermal capacity* Q^* (Btu per pound).

This value represents the practical absorption capability of a protection system and should include the positive or negative effects of all contributing phenomena. As these differ for the various protection systems, Q^* will likewise be different and will have to be determined for each system. Q^* may further change at certain heat-flux levels, at which new phenomena or environmental interactions are encountered. Q^* should, therefore, be always qualified with regard to the system, as well as with regard to the applicable heat-flux range, representing an environmental regime.

Q^* may be determined by analytical or experimental means. Analytical methods are fairly accurate for passive systems (heat sinks). They become extremely complicated and unreliable for active systems, particularly for ablation, because of the complex interactions of the various factors. Q^* is, therefore, preferably determined by tests under closest simulation of flight conditions. A number of test devices have been developed, such as the solar furnace, arc image furnace, rocket jet, shock tube, and finally the plasma jet—which represents the best combination of test parameters. The Q^* values of a number of typical materials are compiled in Table 4.5.

Once the value of Q^* is determined, the net weight requirements for a given heat flux $\dot{q}$ and operation time $\bar{t}$ can be easily determined from the relationship

$$Q^*w = \dot{q}t$$
$$W_n = \frac{\dot{q}t}{Q^*}$$

For ablative systems, the net thickness a expended is calculated from the formula

$$a = \frac{\dot{q}t}{\rho Q^*}$$

For the determination of the ablation rate $\dot{a}$, this relationship is modified to

$$\dot{a} = \frac{\dot{q}}{\rho Q^*}$$

For non-steady-state conditions, such as the sinusoidal heat flux–time characteristic, the values $\dot{q}$ and t are replaced by the terms $\dot{q}_{max}$ and $\bar{t}$.

For the establishment of the actual design weights, these net-weight requirements have to be converted to gross weights W_g by addition of ΔW. This value depends greatly on the specific design, yet can be

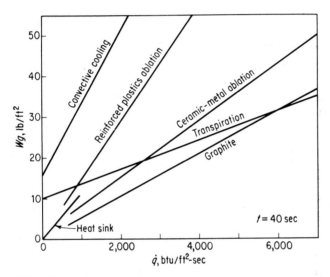

Fig. 4.11 Comparison of various types of thermal protection systems.

approximated as follows: convective cooling, 15 lb/ft²; transpiration and film cooling, 10 lb/ft²; ablation, 25 to 50% of ablated weight, depending on material.

For the ultimate representation of capabilities, the gross (design) weight requirements, W_g, of various systems are plotted in a single diagram over heat flux for one or more time limits. A typical W_g-$\dot{q}$ diagram for a constant time of 40 sec is presented in Fig. 4.11.

The crossover points in this diagram denote the changeover of weight-wise superiority from one system to another. Transpiration, for example, is inferior at low-heat-flux levels because of its high initial weight. With increasing heat flux, its relative position becomes more favorable. To assess the relative design effectiveness, this diagram should always be matched by the representation of W_g versus time for constant-heat-flux levels.

While these representations will be satisfactory for the selection of a thermal protection system and the assessment of weight and thickness requirements for preliminary design purposes, actual vehicle design will always require an accurate assessment of all parameters and their interaction with specific aerodynamic and thermal environments, supported by simulation tests. This will ultimately lead to thermal protection systems tailored to specific vehicle requirements.

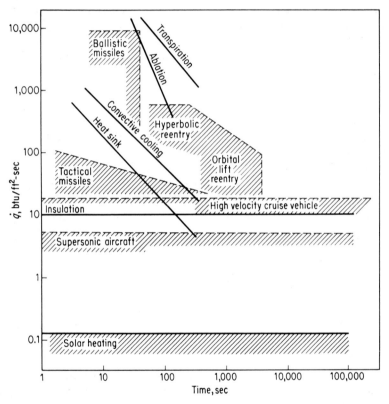

Fig. 4.12 Comparison of vehicle requirements and material capabilities.

Application to Flight Regimes.   Both vehicle environments and material capabilities have previously been defined by heat flux and time. The use of these common denominators permits a direct comparison in a single diagram.   In the heat flux–time diagram (Fig. 4.12) the capabilities of various thermal protection systems, based on equivalent weight requirements, are superimposed on the major flight regimes.   This comparison shows the adaptability of various protection systems to the vehicle classes and, at the same time, conveys a picture of the state of the art.

According to this comparison, the regimes of short exposure to high and intermediate heat-flux rates (ballistic and tactical missiles), as well as the regime of long exposure to moderate heat flux (supersonic cruise) are well within the present state of the art of ablation, heat-sink, and insulation systems.   A problem area exists in the intermediate heat flux–time regime, representing hypervelocity cruise vehicles, as well as various types of lifting reentry from space operation.   The diagram clearly indicates the potential approaches: high-velocity cruise as well as some orbital reentry problems call for the development of advanced high-efficiency insulation systems, while the problems of high-heat-flux space reentry may be attacked from the side of absorptive systems, particularly by extension of the ablation capabilities to longer times (*slow ablation*).

Conclusion

The gaps between vehicle requirements and the capabilities of protection systems show that materials play a decisive role in advanced aerospace systems; mission limitations are becoming increasingly dependent on the state of the art in materials.   Even though a continued improvement of material capabilities can be expected, sizable advancements in their performance under severe thermal environments can only be achieved by the acceptance of the following new concepts:

1. The functional role of materials in the interaction between vehicle and environment
2. The integrated development principle, representing a joint approach of the disciplines involved in vehicle design, materials, environments, and operations
3. Utilization of "active" material capabilities
4. Emphasis on material systems, such as composite or heterogeneous materials

In this approach, the dividing line between design and materials is fading.   All the related disciplines will have to join forces if the dreams of space flight are to become a reality.

5

Compatibility of Materials

E. J. ZEILBERGER

SUPERVISOR OF MATERIALS ENGINEERING
ROCKETDYNE—A DIVISION OF NORTH AMERICAN AVIATION
CANOGA PARK, CALIFORNIA

Compatibility of materials for missiles and spacecraft is a section of a larger field which might be described as the proper selection of materials. The object of this chapter is to cover the behavior of the materials in these systems, not with outside environment in mind, which is covered more rigorously in the other chapters, but rather with the fluids present in missiles and spacecraft. These fluids might be classed as propellants, pressurizers, hydraulic fluids, and heat-transfer fluids.

Many reports on compatibility of materials indicate a lack of reliable information on their subject in general and the complete absence of applicable design information in particular. There have been difficulties in obtaining desired data because conditions to be investigated are impossible to re-create on earth. On the topic of environmental conditions also, very little reliable information is available, not because of inability to duplicate the desired environment but rather because of the reluctance of the manufacturers of both the propellants and the materials of construction to allot any development effort to this area of interest. Furthermore, the military and space agencies have until recently sponsored little effort in this field, but rather have depended on the prime contractor of missiles and spacecraft to sidetrack usually insufficient funds for the investigation of compatibility problems. The answers gained in this manner are usually hidden in progress reports on weapon systems. This chapter contains a list of references, but some of the material may not be reliable. Some of the flaws and pitfalls of various investigations will be pointed out in this chapter, and these will no doubt also be discussed in the references. Investigation of these references will provide some idea of what has been done in this field and will show how little really has been accomplished.

122

Although behavior of the materials with these fluids is critical, emphasis must remain on the overall system design requirements.   Also, the selection of materials has to be made by taking into consideration the three important parameters of time, temperature, and operating characteristics of the component.   However, the most important consideration that must be understood at the beginning is that there is no universal material. There is no one material for any given service; compromises of the possible solutions have to be made.   Likewise, there is no one material that is a panacea for all problems.   Bearing these important points in mind, we consider first the behavior of materials in contact with oxidizers.   The oxidizers that will be covered are liquid oxygen (LOX), hydrogen peroxide, fluorine, chlorine trifluoride, nitrogen tetroxide, and red fuming nitric acid (IRFNA).

Liquid Oxygen

Metallic Materials.   Liquid oxygen is the most universally used oxidizer in liquid-propellant rocket engines.   Liquid oxygen is noncorrosive.   However, most materials, including some metals, become brittle at the temperature of liquid oxygen ($-297°F$) and do not possess the resistance to impact or sudden shock that they have at ambient temperatures.   The same holds true for liquid nitrogen ($-320°F$).   Some materials of construction to be avoided for this service are iron, low-carbon steels, and most organic materials.   Aside from the embrittlement of the metals, the chief cause of rupture at LOX temperatures is the presence of defects in the material in the form of inclusions or a coarse-grained structure.   The suitability of metals for use in cryogenic applications is generally related to the crystalline structure of the metal. Body-centered cubic metals are subject to brittle fracture, while face-centered cubic structures are generally suited for cryogenic service.   This will be covered in more detail in subsequent chapters.   The following metals have been satisfactorily used with LOX:

1. Nickel
2. Monel
3. Inconel
4. Copper
5. Aluminum alloys

6. 18-8 stainless steel
7. Annealed brass
8. Some precipitation-hardening stainless steels (A286)

The most commonly used construction materials for LOX tanks in missiles are stainless steel and aluminum.   For example, the LOX tank on the Atlas missile is fabricated from 301 stainless steel, whereas the LOX tanks on the Titan and Thor missiles are fabricated from 2014 aluminum.   It can thus be seen that in individual systems, other design considerations aside from compatibility govern the selection of materials. These considerations are ease of fabrication, cost, weight, weldability, workability, fabrication experience, etc.

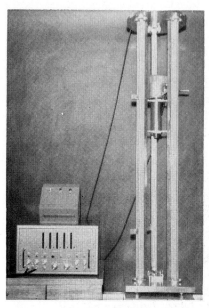

Because LOX is an excellent oxidizer most organic materials will react with it under conditions of impact, heat, friction, or other applications of available energy. There are, however, conditions under which organic materials have given good service with LOX. It is imperative that the exact service conditions be stipulated before test procedures are devised for the selection of organic materials for this service.

First, the physical properties of organic materials at the LOX temperature should be examined. Because of the brittleness of most organic materials at this temperature, a great many materials can at once be eliminated. Several other qualification tests have been devised by the industry. The most widely heralded is the impact sensitivity test.

Fig. 5.1 ABMA impact sensitivity tester.

This test is intended to measure the ease with which an explosion or detonation is initiated with a liquid propellant in contact with a test material by mechanical impact. In general, the sensitivity to impact is determined by dropping a known weight through a variable distance on a striker which sits on the sample immersed in the propellant and then measuring the energy at which a detonation occurs. The distance multiplied by the weight will provide foot-pounds of energy. The most universally accepted tester is the ABMA impact sensitivity tester (Figs. 5.1 and 5.2). No standardization of test methods or instruments has yet been accomplished.

At present there are a number of organizations trying to resolve this problem. Wright Air Development Division (WADD) has contractual efforts at Southwest Research Institute and at the Martin Company (Denver) and also conducts an industry cooperative test program. The Aerospace Industry Association is also conducting an industry-wide test program. The objective of all these groups is to eliminate all the variables of the test method and to standardize on an instrument.

At present, to be classed suitable for service, a material must not detonate when subjected to 70 ft-lb impact while in contact with the propellant. A negative test at this level on a material merely indicates nonsensitivity within the test conditions and should not be construed to mean that the material will be insensitive under all possible conditions of pressure, flow, and impact energy.

Fig. 5.2   ABMA impact sensitivity tester.

Should the aforementioned development and test efforts in eliminating variables be completely successful, only an empirical relationship between the test and the final application of the material would be realized. The industry is in need of a completely new approach to the testing of materials for LOX service.

The oxygen bomb method is another method of testing the compatibility of materials with oxygen. The test method is ASTM D-942-50. The test consists in placing a suitable sample in a bomb, which is then pressurized with oxygen to 110 psi. The bomb is closed and immersed in a fluid where it is heated to 210°F. The test then consists in observing the pressure decay over a suitable time, which may be in intervals of 100 hr. The amount of pressure decay measures the reaction of the oxygen with the test material. This test is designed specifically for lubricants, greases, and fluids.

Organic Materials. In general, the fluorinated plastics, such as Teflon, TFE and FEP, and Kel-F have been found compatible for service as seals, gaskets, diaphragms, propellant and expulsion bags, and inner liners in flexible propellant lines. These materials do not react with LOX under normal conditions and give negative results on impact testing. However, it is presumptuous to assume that all forms of these materials are satisfactory for most applications with LOX. Chemical compatibility is only part of the problem. Very little work has been done on the determination of physical and mechanical properties of plastic materials down to $-320°F$. It is essential to possess this information when components are being designed from these materials. Work is underway to determine the following properties:

1. Tensile properties (yield, ultimate, modulus, and elongation)
2. Flexural properties (ultimate and modulus)
3. Compressive properties (ultimate and modulus)
4. Impact strength (notched Izod)
5. Torsional modulus
6. Coefficient of thermal expansion
7. Cyclic load or deflection tests (fatigue tests for potential diaphragm materials)

These properties will be sought not only on the parent material but on the materials in different states of crystallinity. It has been found, for example, that Kel-F in a certain lip-seal application had to have a very low state of crystallinity to be serviceable over a temperature range of from -320 to $+160°F$. A certain heat treatment to obtain this crystallinity had to be developed. Following this, a micro-hardness test procedure was developed to check the state of crystallinity with great reliability. What is to be learned from this example is that materials should not be given only by their trade names on commercial specifications; rather, explicit rigid specifications for these materials for all critical applications must be developed.

Mylar, a polyester film, has been used in a number of applications with LOX. Although it has been determined that this material has a low impact-sensitivity threshold with LOX, by carefully evaluating the applications and selecting those where there is little chance of impact, this plastic has been successfully used as an expulsion bag and as a diaphragm in high-pressure LOX regulators. This material is the strongest unreinforced plastic, having a tensile strength of 30,000 psi at LOX temperatures as well as good flexibility.

Carbon has been used for rotating seals in LOX. Although this type of material has given good service, it should be noted that a rigorous evaluation of the many carbon-type materials has to be made for each specific application. Only carbon materials with no organic residue should be utilized for LOX service.

There are no elastomers known today that do not become brittle in LOX. However, in specific designs elastomeric materials may be included if they do not have to operate dynamically while in contact with LOX, and if they can recover their elastic behavior with higher temperatures, provided that the rather high coefficient of thermal contraction is taken into account.

Unfortunately, there are no petroleum-base lubricants satisfactory for LOX service. The closest to a lubricant for this service that we can come is MoS_2 powder. Dry-film lubricants have been used in LOX service, but the exact application must be evaluated critically.

The use of conventional lubricants in rocket engines using highly reactive propellants creates a requirement for a complex sealing system. This imposes a weight and design complexity penalty which can be avoided if the propellant is used as, or substituted for, the lubricant. Work on this problem is now being studied at Rocketdyne under WADD sponsorship.

Hydrogen Peroxide

General Comments. Concentrated hydrogen peroxide in strength of 75 per cent or greater, but usually of 90 per cent concentration, has been used as a propellant from the early days of rocketry. It has been used as a monopropellant by catalytic decomposition or as a bipropellant by direct combustion with fuel or, on the other hand, by catalytic decomposition followed by reaction with fuel. It has been used in gas generators and auxiliary power units. It may be used for attitude control in spacecraft and satellites, and it is used in high-speed high-altitude aircraft, such as the X-15 and the Century-series fighters. Concerning compatibility of materials with hydrogen peroxide, two factors must be considered. First is the effect of the decomposition of the hydrogen peroxide by the material, and second is the effect of the peroxide on the material, both effects being equally critical. Concentrated hydrogen peroxide is an extremely stable material when placed in a suitable container. In glass or 2SO aluminum containers it loses not more than approximately 1 per cent of its strength per year.

In approaching the selection of materials for a specific application, it must be considered that the compatibility test results are general in nature and must be interpreted in terms of specific conditions of the application. Naturally the material with the highest degree of compatibility with hydrogen peroxide that meets the physical property requirement should be selected. This must be done realistically so that materials of extreme compatibility are not forced into an application where less compatible materials of more suitable physical properties could be employed. Materials classed as unsuitable may even find occasional application where close control is maintained, but great care must be exercised to take into account all factors when this is under consideration. This philosophy holds true for all the propellants and fluids discussed.

The producers of H_2O_2 have classed materials for use with H_2O_2 into the following four categories based on use for long-term storage:

1. Materials satisfactory for unrestricted use with H_2O_2
2. Materials satisfactory for repeated short-time contact with H_2O_2, such contact not to exceed 4 hr at 160°F or 1 week at 70°F
3. Materials which should be used only for a short time with H_2O_2; this would be one-time or repeated use, never more than 1 min at 160°F or 1 hr at 70°F
4. Materials not recommended for H_2O_2

Passivation of Materials for H_2O_2. All metals used for H_2O_2 service should be descaled and degreased by conventional practice. Steel materials should then be immersed in 70 per cent nitric acid for 4 to 5 hr at ambient, or 1 hr at 180°F. They should then be drained and thoroughly rinsed with distilled or deionized water. The steel is then heated in air at 550°F for 2 hr and allowed to cool. This heating produces a passive oxide film on the steel.

Aluminum parts are to be passivated with 35 per cent HNO_3 for 1 to 2 hr.

After this passivation the part should be cleaned with 1 per cent detergent solution in distilled or deionized water, and after this it should be thoroughly rinsed with distilled or deionized water and dried.

Finally, the part should be checked with 90 per cent H_2O_2 for at least 2 hr. In this check the part should at no time give a temperature rise of 5°F over ambient. The gas given off is collected and measured. Each part used for an H_2O_2 system has to be calibrated for allowable gas evolution per period of time. Activity testing is a means of determining the passivity of a metal toward H_2O_2. It checks the active oxygen loss of peroxide in contact with a material. The more passive the surface, the smaller the active oxygen loss.

Test Methods for H_2O_2 Compatibility. The effect of materials on H_2O_2 decomposition and of the H_2O_2 on the materials is evaluated by *immersion* of the sample in H_2O_2 with a standard wetted surface of H_2O_2 volume ratio of 0.33 in.^{2}/in.^{3} at controlled standard temperatures of 86 and 151°F for standard periods of time of 4 weeks and 1 week, respectively. Where the surface-volume ratio of the final application is known, this should be used in preference to the standard ratio because the decomposition of the peroxide is surface-area-dependent. The surface-volume ratio must be included with the test result. All surfaces of the samples and test containers shall be thoroughly cleaned and passivated. Passivation of a metal consists in generating a passive oxide on the surface of the metal as described above. This film is not visible.

Table 5.1 Materials Compatible with H_2O_2

Aluminum		Other Metals
Wrought	*Cast*	Silicon
1060	150	Tantalum
1100	214B	Tin
1160	214F	Zirconium
1260	356F	
3003	4043	*Plastics*
5054	5052	Polyethylene, unplasticized
5056	6066	Polyvinyl chloride
5652	6363	Dacron
5654	B356	Kel-F
6061		Teflon
6063		Mylar
7072		Viton A
		Kel-F elastomer
Stainless Steel		Silicones (some)
Wrought or forged AISI 300 with exception of 303 and 316 17-7 PH		Fluorinated silicone

The results of the immersion compatibility tests for effect of the material on the rate of decomposition of the peroxide are reported as the per cent of active oxygen loss from the H_2O_2. This is measured as volume of gas per unit area per period of time. The effect of H_2O_2 on the test material itself is determined visually or mechanically, such as corrosion, staining, pitting, swelling, bleaching, blistering, or disintegration. *Impact sensitivity* tests with H_2O_2 are performed in the same manner as described previously in the section on materials for use with Liquid Oxygen.

Materials compatible with H_2O_2 are shown in Table 5.1. Most other metallic elements tend toward catalytic action on contact with hydrogen peroxide. This is especially true of silver, lead, cobalt, copper, bronze, brass, gold, and platinum. Iron after exposure forms iron oxide rust which is catalytic. Titanium and zinc are severely attacked by hydrogen peroxide. When H_2O_2 is being stored in aluminum vessels for extended periods of time, care must be taken to have the chloride content of the H_2O_2 below 1 mg/liter or corrosion of the aluminum will occur. A high chloride content might be partially offset by an equivalent NO_3 concentration. This latter course of action, however, is still under investigation. In any case, care must be taken to have all trace impurities in H_2O_2 kept at an absolute minimum or deleterious effects on H_2O_2 decomposition catalysts will result. However, this is a subject too lengthy to discuss in this chapter.

Although it was mentioned that H_2O_2 is compatible with 300-series stainless steel, it should not be stored in stainless vessels for more than a day or two if the peroxide is to be subsequently catalytically decomposed. A phenomenon known as chromium leaching occurs, especially in rough-cast surfaces. As a result the chromium in the stainless is preferentially dissolved in the peroxide. The occurrence can be readily detected because it produces a pink color in the H_2O_2. The reason this phenomenon is undesirable is that it will poison H_2O_2 decomposition catalysts.

All storage vessels for hydrogen peroxide should be equipped with a temperature-sensing device so that one can notice when there is a temperature rise in the hydrogen peroxide. Any temperature rise over 5°F above the ambient would immediately cause the venting of the tank. All storage containers or pressure vessels containing hydrogen peroxide should, therefore, be equipped with a fast-venting device.

The process of H_2O_2 decomposition is exothermic and the rate of decomposition is exponential with temperature. Therefore, it may easily be seen that when H_2O_2 starts to decompose the temperature rises and the decomposition rate increases. This process, once started, can propagate so rapidly that vessels with 2-in. openings have been completely destroyed because the decomposition accelerated to such a rate that the opening was unable to let the decomposition products escape. This is the reason for the 5°F above ambient temperature rule.

Plastic or elastomeric materials should never be used with hydrogen peroxide at temperatures in excess of 200°F. Laboratory observations show that plastic materials tend to cause fires and detonations when they are exposed to hydrogen peroxide at approximately 200 to 250°F. Polyethylene can react spontaneously when close to its softening point of 160°F.

When an elastomeric material is being selected for service for H_2O_2, it is not sufficient to designate the material by its trade name. Different fabricators vary sufficiently the recipe of the compound to cause a marked difference in the degree of compatibility of like compounds. The material should always be thoroughly identified. The difference in a filler, oxidation inhibitor, color, or rubber catalyst can make one compound compatible and another totally unsuitable. This applies to all compatibility testing, not merely to H_2O_2.

Liquid Fluorine and Chlorine Trifluoride

Liquid fluorine and chlorine trifluoride are two very potent oxidizers. The materials problems with these two exotic oxidizers, as far as metallic materials are concerned, are not too serious. Metals when thoroughly cleaned and free of organic materials are satisfactory in general for this service. The one exception is possibly the use of titanium with liquid fluorine or chlorine trifluoride, which severely attacks titanium and molybdenum. The problem of titanium with fluorine and oxidizers in general will be covered in a subsequent section of this chapter. Stainless steel is another problem area and one which requires some discussion of testing philosophy. North American Aviation, Inc., has been working with liquid fluorine since 1948. Materials have been tested by immersion for various times and temperatures, by flow testing, and by use in actual components for a short period under controlled conditions. In these tests NAA determined that 300-series stainless steels and many other metals were not attacked by fluorine when properly cleaned. This inertness to corrosion and the fact that no fires resulted when the metals were exposed to the oxidizer were the only criteria for acceptability.

Based on this experience, a stainless-steel fluorine transfer system was built by NAA for one of their large engine test facilities. After a very short period of time, this system contained a buildup of loosely adhering red and green corrosion products $\frac{1}{16}$ in. thick on the walls of pipes and valves, which were termed stainless-steel fluorides. This caused no end of problems in operation. The factor overlooked in the evaluation was that the helium pressurant contained minute traces of moisture which, combined with residual propellant, created havoc with the system. When actual hardware testing is undertaken, it is next to impossible to keep the oxidizer system free of minute traces of moisture. Therefore, it is strongly recommended that all compatibility testing closely simulate the actual operating conditions of the final service, or the test results will be next to meaningless or, more important, they will be misleading. Any system for use with liquid fluorine or chlorine trifluoride must be leaktight and must be thoroughly cleaned of all organic materials or scale. After it is thoroughly cleaned, all weld scale is removed, and all rough surfaces are polished, the system must be passivated. Passivation consists in first purging the system of all moisture. Following this it is flushed with increasing concentration of gaseous fluorine in nitrogen. Finally, gaseous fluorine at 390°F is introduced and held in the system from 2 to 4 hr. Where heating is impractical, longer periods of exposure to gaseous fluorine are necessary. This passivation will not "take" on stabilized stainless steels, and they should not be used where other materials can be utilized. The passive coating in this case is a fluoride.

The result of contact of organic materials or moisture with fluorine is one of instant reaction causing fire and total destruction. The behavior of fluorinated plastics with this oxidizer has been found to be only marginal. These plastics have been successfully used with gaseous fluorine and chlorine trifluoride at low pressures and low flow rates; however, with liquid fluorine at high pressures and high flow rates they have been found unreliable to date in the sense that reactions may or may not occur. Work is now in progress to treat these materials in several ways to make them suitable for liquid fluorine systems, since they seem to offer the only hope for satisfactory resilient or elastomeric seals.

The lines of attack take three separate paths. First, it is postulated that the attack on the plastic starts by fluorine reacting with impurities in the materials included in the fabrication processes. To remedy this situation, research on new and unique cleaning techniques is being carried on. Second, in the present commercial fluorinated plastics the chain endings are not completely fluorinated, and the possibility exists that liquid-fluorine reactions start at the chain ends and proceed rapidly when started. Here the line of attack is to modify the chain endings of the fluorinated polymers.

The third line of work starts with the premise that this attack proceeds because of the poor heat transfer of these materials. It is postulated that fluorine reacts with minor impurities on the surface of the plastic, and because of the poor heat transfer of the material the resultant heat of reaction is sufficient to decompose the rest of the material. The present investigation includes designs where good conductors of heat, such as copper or other metals, are incorporated in the plastic in powder, wire, or foil form to carry the heat of the reaction away from the plastic part and, in this manner, prevent a runaway reaction. Thus, it can be seen that in a present system for fluorine or chlorine trifluoride no non-metallic seals of any type can be utilized. The system, therefore, will have to be fully brazed or welded. Thin aluminum or copper gaskets and lip seals made of tin or silver have been used. Since fluorine is a cryogenic liquid similar to liquid oxygen, only the metals listed in the first section under liquid oxygen can be used, since they also have to stand the very low temperature ($-300°F$). In particular, monel, nickel and nickel alloys, aluminum alloys, and in some cases copper alloys are recommended.

Red Fuming Nitric Acid

Metallic Materials. The oxidizer red fuming nitric acid (RFNA) has been used in small ballistic air-to-air missiles, as well as in such defense missiles as the Corporal and Bomarc. Nitric acid can be stored in proper containers for rather long periods of time. The nitric acid corrosion problem with less suitable materials has presented one of the major problems in the use of this very superior oxidizer. Because of the magnitude of this problem, the literature is full of corrosion data on nitric acid–metal systems. Interpretation of these data is extremely difficult, and their correlation is virtually impossible. Since most of the tests were performed under different experimental conditions, i.e., varying times, temperatures, and acid compositions, it is difficult to make quantitative comparison. In addition to these variables, the method of preparing the sample and its previous metallurgical history are important to interpreting the results. Many times these details are poorly described or are not even reported. In 1951, during experiments at Rocketdyne to add a vapor-pressure-reduction agent to RFNA, in the course of the investigation it was determined that one such additive, anhydrous hydrofluoric acid, materially reduced the corrosive effect of red fuming nitric on steels, stainless steels, and aluminum alloys. Mason, at the Jet Propulsion Laboratory, did additional work on the corrosion inhibition effect of the addition of hydrofluoric acid to RFNA and substantially confirmed Rocketdyne findings. Since that period this inhibitor has been universally used, with RFNA modified to IRFNA.

The preferred metals for IRFNA are aluminum alloys and 300-series stainless steels, although 400 series and 17-7 PH have been used. In general, the statement can be made that at ambient temperatures aluminum is the preferred material, while at elevated temperatures stainless steels are preferred since the copious amounts of aluminum nitrate corrosion product formed may cause operational difficulties. This does not imply that no sludge is obtained with stainless steels. In fact, unless the proper cleaning and passivation procedures have been accomplished, sludge will become a serious problem. The problem with IRFNA is further complicated because there are four types of MIL-Spec acids differing by their NO_2 concentration. Further, it is difficult to give data on corrosion except of a general nature because the rate of attack depends on the NO_2 concentration and the H_2O concentration. Even these are not defined in a given acid since there is an equilibrium established which can be expressed as

$$4HNO_3 \rightleftharpoons 4NO_2 + 2H_2O + O_2$$

which is constantly shifted by the corrosive attack on the container.

It can also be stated in general that the noble metals such as gold and platinum are suitable. Chrome plate is a good protection for inferior materials. It must, however, become quite obvious that under the conditions described tests must be based on each specific requirement.

It should be pointed out that corrosive attack of IRFNA is quite critical at the weld areas. The vapor-liquid interface is a serious trouble spot. Galvanic corrosion between dissimilar metals can be seriously aggravated in contact with IRFNA. Also, concentration-type cell corrosion, which arises from having fluid at different concentrations in contact with metal, may become very serious.

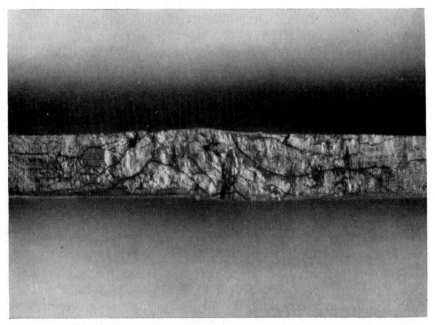

Fig. 5.3   Titanium sheet after exposure to RFNA.

In 1953, titanium was investigated for use with RFNA. It was found that titanium reacts pyrolytically with nitric acid and may react spontaneously with other oxidizers if conditions are right. The following are experiences with this material and RFNA.

1. Titanium 75A inert-gas-welded specimens were partially immersed in RFNA in bombs. Temperature was maintained at 165°F for a period of 6 weeks. An insignificant weight loss was noted with very slight discoloration. The specimens were placed in a desk and upon examination about 1 month later it was noted that cracks had occurred on the sheared edges of the specimens. The cracking occurred only in areas which had been in the liquid phase of the RFNA. It is possible that the cracking was present after the 6 weeks' immersion test, but it is believed to have occurred during the ensuing month. This condition is illustrated by Fig. 5.3, which is an enlarged view of the

edge of a 0.060-in. sheet.   This photo is in the weld area; however, the cracking was also found away from the weld area, but to a lesser degree.

2. The effect of bimetallic couples with RC 130A titanium alloy was investigated by using slotted specimens of titanium, 2S aluminum, and stainless steel Type 347.   Figure 5.4 illustrates, from left to right, 2S aluminum in contact with RC 130A, RC 139A which was

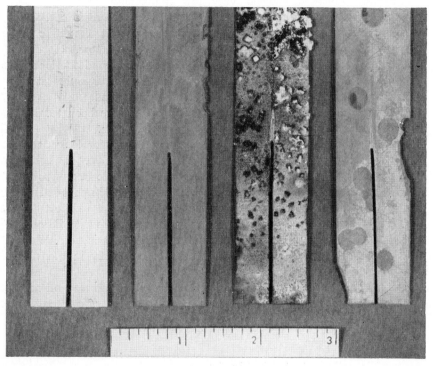

Fig. 5.4 Samples of 2S0 aluminum, 130A titanium, 347 stainless steel, and 130A titanium after exposure to RFNA.

coupled with 2S aluminum, stainless steel Type 347 which was coupled with RC 130A, and RC 130A which was coupled with stainless steel Type 347.   The specimens shown in Fig. 5.4 were placed together by means of the slots so as to form a cross with bimetallic contact established the length of the specimen.   They were then immersed in RFNA in bombs at 165°F for 14 days.   At this time it was noted that darkened areas had appeared on the titanium alloy. When probed with a scribe, one of the darkened areas was found to be spongy in nature and subsequently exploded after further probing. The nature of the spongy material thereafter was the subject of much speculation, and considerable work was conducted in an attempt to explain the explosion phenomena. The information gathered can be summarized as follows:

a. Metallographic examination indicated that one phase of the alloy had been attacked while the other phase remained in a finely divided form in the spongy mass. Spectrographic analysis of the spongy material showed very low manganese content, which indicated that the manganese-rich phase had been attacked.

b. This type of corrosion has been produced without bimetallic contacts, thus proving that galvanic action is not a factor.

c. There seems to be no correlation between stress and the location of the attacked areas. Corrosion usually accompanies stress; however, it is found frequently in areas not stressed.

d. Several different heat numbers of RC 130A have been tested to illustrate that the results were not an isolated case.

e. When the spongy material was allowed to dry for long periods (several weeks), it was no longer impact-sensitive. This dried material, if again wet with RFNA, would explode upon probing. It was found that the dry spongy material was impact-sensitive with LOX when tested in an impact apparatus.

f. The corrosion has been produced in glass containers with RFNA at 165°F, without pressure, exposed for 7 days. It is notable that corrosion under these conditions has occurred only in the vapor phase when the specimen was partially immersed.

g. This type of corrosion has subsequently been produced on many occasions. It has been characterized by the following three types of occurrences:

(1) Random spots which are only slightly darkened in color and resemble a stain, but are "rotten" when probed. This type is well illustrated in Fig. 5.4.

(2) An overall attack which makes the entire sheet "rotten." In several instances this condition changed the appearance of the material so little that it was believed that corrosion had not occurred; however, upon moderate pressure the specimen would crumble.

(3) Another type of attack observed has been the "doughnut" type of corrosion, which is illustrated in Fig. 5.5. This attack is characterized by the formation of large crystals and also ringlike corrosion products under which the metal was found to be spongy. This differs from previous types noted, in that corrosion products previously were not deposited on the surface of the specimen, and a dark blue discoloration of the metal was developed.

3. During observation of the effects of annealing on stress-cracking behavior of RC 70, the following sequence of events occurred:

   a. RC 79 annealed at 1000°F for 30 min, followed by a descaling pickle in 5 per cent HF, 15 per cent HNO_3 for 3 min, was tested in bombs at 165°F with RFNA. After 6 weeks of exposure, the specimens were not attacked except for stress cracking on sheared edges of the specimens that were not annealed.

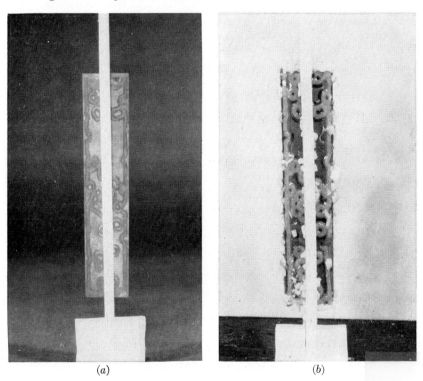

(a)   (b)

Fig. 5.5 Titanium sheets (a and b) after exposure to RFNA.

   b. The constant-temperature water bath used in the test failed mechanically and the test was therefore abandoned. It was believed that the specimens might have been slightly overheated when this occurred. The bombs containing the test pieces were set aside, and after 2 months it was discovered that corrosion had occurred. The corrosion was distributed in small areas resembling pitting which occurs on aluminum alloys; however, the darkened spots were not pits but rather small areas of dark spongy material. Four specimens were included in this test; the test pieces which were not annealed both corroded; and one of the annealed specimens corroded so badly that immediately adjacent to the inert-gas weld the specimen fell apart. The other annealed specimen had no corrosion, being only slightly discolored.

4. The effect of mixed oxides of nitrogen only on RC 130A have been observed. Mixed oxides consisting of 70 per cent NO_2 and 30 per

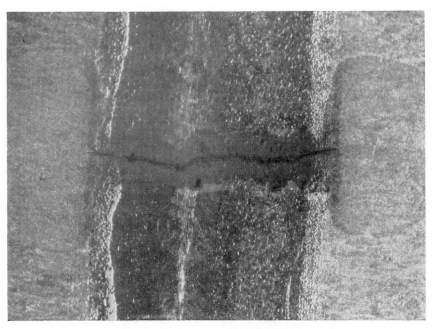

Fig. 5.6   Titanium sheet after exposure to RFNA.

cent NO were placed in bombs with RC 130A at 165°F for 3 weeks. No corrosion was noted. A slight iridescent discoloration had occurred.

5. Titanium 100A and RS-80 alloys have been tested in RFNA in bombs at 165°F with no appreciable corrosion noted.

6. Figure 5.6 illustrates a stress crack across a weld terminated by dome-shaped spongy areas at the ends of the crack. Figure 5.7 illustrates cracking which occurred adjacent to a stamped numeral on a specimen.

There have been several accidents when titanium was used with RFNA. It is emphasized that *this metal should never be used in contact with RFNA*.

Several titanium vessels have been ruptured when they contained LOX. It is postulated that when an inherent protective film is penetrated there is then an immediate reaction between gaseous or liquid oxygen and the metal. Studies of this phenomenon with gaseous oxygen were carried out at Stanford Research Institute. Studies are currently being conducted with titanium and LOX at Battelle Memorial Institute.

In any case, it is advisable to investigate thoroughly all ramifications of the problem before selecting titanium for use with an oxidizer.

Nonmetallic Materials. The fluorinated plastics have been found suitable for use with RFNA. The oxidizer does not chemically attack

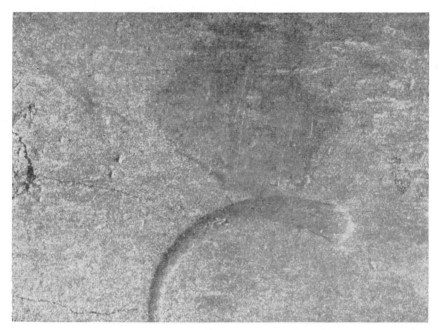

Fig. 5.7   Titanium sheet after exposure to RFNA.

the plastic. It should, however, be noted that these plastics are permeable to RFNA. The rate of this permeability depends on the plastic and, to some extent, on the fabricating conditions; in general, Kel-F is less permeable than Teflon. The protection of inferior metals by fluorocarbon coatings is not recommended.

The two elastomers that have some compatibility with RFNA are Viton compounds and fluorosilicone elastomers. The exact data depend on the formulation of the elastomers, but it can be stated that these materials swell and their strength deteriorates in contact with RFNA. Therefore, contact up to several weeks only can be recommended.

Nitrogen Tetroxide

Materials and Reactions. Nitrogen tetroxide (NTO) is a storable oxidizer. It is being employed as oxidizer in the second-generation liquid-fueled missiles. Its great advantage over LOX is that it can be stored for long periods of time and can be fully utilized, when required, with little sacrifice in performance. It is a liquid at ambient temperature but has a rather high freezing point (11°F). Its compatibility problems are similar to those of IRFNA, but there are some important differences. The propellant, when dry, can be shipped in carbon-steel containers.

Table 5.2   Materials for NTO Service

Aluminum alloys
  1100
  5052
  6061
  6066
  356
  B356
  Tens 50
Corrosion- and/or heat-resistant alloys
  AISI 300-series stainless
  17-7 PH
  A286
  Haynes 16-25-6
  Inconel-X
Plating
  Chromium (microplate, electrolyzing, etc.; care
  must be taken to avoid cracks or pinholes)
Other
  Teflon-filled Flexitallic gaskets
Lubricants
  DC-11
  LOX-Safe (Aroclor and graphite)
  Graphite
  Molykote Z (without binder)

However, in practice of handling the propellant in the field it is almost impossible to keep the system dry. It is for this reason that more exotic materials of construction are necessary.

In testing materials for NTO service the first to be attempted are immersion tests. Since the oxidizer has a low boiling point (70°F) and picks up water easily, immersion tests and accelerated immersion tests at 165°F have to be carried out in high-pressure containers of the same or similar material of construction as the test material. Most of the following information resulted from static testing or from examination of hardware that had undergone test firing. Almost no dynamic testing has been done to date, but work is getting underway on this problem at Bell Aircraft. An example of the requirement for dynamic testing is as follows: Materials with very low static corrosion rates can lose several

Table 5.3   Materials Unsatisfactory for Nitrogen Tetroxide

Materials	Remarks
Metals:	
2024 aluminum	Pitting, corrosion products buildup
7075 aluminum	Anodize removed, severely etched
K-Monel	
Brass	Dissolves
Bronze	Dissolves
Silver	Dissolves
Zinc	Dissolves
Cadmium	Dissolves
Nickel	Fourteen-mil-per-year corrosion rate, static and ambient temperature
Copper	Slow dissolving
Hastalloy	Etching
EZ Flo 45 braze	Dissolves
Plating:	
Electroless nickel	Severely attacked
Cadmium	Severely attacked
Copper	Severely attacked
Anodizing of Al alloys	Anodizing removed by NTO; preliminary work shows that sodium silicate impregnation of anodized parts looks promising
Nonmetallics:	
Cotton-base phenolic laminate (bearing retainers)	Disintegrates and swells
JM 60	Softens
JM 70	Cracks and embrittles
Viton A	Hardens and disintegrates
Kel-F elastomer	Becomes soft, stringy, and tacky
Mylar	Dissolved
Buna-N (AN and MS O rings)	Embrittles and cracks (rapidly)
AN 6246 leather backup ring	Complete disintegration
Hypalon	Embrittles and cracks
Lubricants:	
DC-55 (MIL-G-4343)	Chars, solidifies
Oxylube (M_0S_2 coating)	Moderate reaction, bubbling
MIL-L-6068	Forms precipitate
MIL-L-25336	Forms precipitate

mils per hour under flow and elevated-temperature conditions. Nickel, for instance, has a corrosion rate of 15 mils/year at ambient temperature in NTO. In NTO vapor at 500°F, it has a corrosion rate of approximately 20 mils/min. Both are without flow. Static tests determine only unsatisfactory materials; they do not necessarily show good materials for service conditions. Tables 5.2 and 5.3 list materials for NTO service and materials unsatisfactory for NTO service.

Since a liquid-propellant engine is static-fired many times before the final launching, the problem of removing residual propellant from the system is critical in the case of fluids such as IRFNA, NTO, F_2, ClF_3, and hydrazine-type fuels. Residual amounts of these fluids mixed with moisture are more deleterious to the materials of the system than are the original propellants. The attempts to flush an engine with inert gases under high pressure have been completely unsatisfactory because the molecular weight of the flushing gases is usually lower than that of the propellants. Aqueous fluids are obviously unsatisfactory. Most organic fluids react with the propellants. Oxidizers such as NTO, F_2, and ClF_3 have a habit of being partially absorbed in the materials of construction or creeping into crevices in the system where they cannot be readily removed by pneumatic flushing. The attempts to neutralize chemically the residual propellants have been doomed to failure because resulting by-products of neutralization contaminate the system, or because of undesirable heats of reaction. Investigations are now under-way to attempt flushing with inert fluorinated organic fluids.

Impact Testing of Lubricants and Sealants. Impact testing of lubricants and sealants with LOX is widely used for deriving the LOX compatibility properties of the material. With the advent of NTO as an oxidizer for rocket engines, it was questionable whether impact testing would work as a selection tool for that propellant. Therefore, a short impact test program with NTO was used on the drop-hammer tester to obtain the validity of this test for judging NTO compatibility of materials.

It appears that a few materials can be detonated with NTO under impact, but the method is far less selective than when used for LOX compatibility evaluation. In comparisons of immersion tests with impact tests using NTO there are some discrepancies. DC-55, a silicone grease, was reacted with NTO in an immersion test but did not detonate with it under impact. MIL-L25336, a diester-base oil, detonated once in 40 trials showing only slight sensitivity; but it can be reacted with NTO by immersion. These results illustrate that any impact testing with materials with an oxidizer like NTO should be accompanied with an immersion test or other test to verify the compatibility. It has recently been determined that titanium metal and alloys are impact-sensitive in the presence of NTO.

Compatibility of Nonmetallic Materials. The compatibility data available for nonmetallics with storable propellants, such as NTO, have until very recently all been of a qualitative nature in that materials have been listed as compatible or noncompatible as a result of visual observations after immersion testing. Those materials that dissolve, swell excessively, or disintegrate in the environmental media have been classed as noncompatible, while those that appear much the same as before their immersion have been classified as compatible. Materials that appear unchanged after short periods of time and then rapidly deteriorate have been grouped into short-term-usage classifications. This type of test can give only negative results. The designer can determine what materials he cannot use, but he cannot determine what physical properties can be expected from materials after the various exposure times to the different propellants. Because of urgent design schedules, parts have been designed and made with materials listed as compatible on the assumption that they can work to the physical properties for these materials as given in a design manual. This assumption can lead and has led to large problem areas. Some preliminary work at Rocketdyne has attempted to show the change of physical properties after exposure to the oxidizer. Most of the plastics and elastomeric materials lose a portion of their initial mechanical properties after exposure to the oxidizer. The ultimate

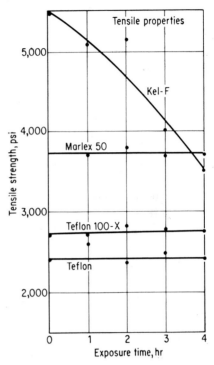

Fig. 5.8 Effect of nitrogen tetroxide on Kel-F, Teflon, Teflon 100-X, and Marlex 50.

amount lost and the rate at which these losses occur vary with the exact conditions.

The tests described here were conducted at ambient temperature under static conditions. The effect of temperature can and will be investigated in the near future. An elaborate system would have to be set up to pump and control the flow of storable propellants; therefore, the effect of flow on materials was not determined. The effect of short-term contact with NTO on the tensile strength of plastic materials is shown in Fig. 5.8. The tensile strength of Kel-F was reduced from 5,500 to 3,500 psi in 4 hr. The other materials were unaffected by this short exposure time. The short- and long-term effects of NTO on the hardness of Kel-F are shown in Fig. 5.9. A decrease of 14 hardness points occurred after 4 hr exposure and a 30-point decrease to a reading of 50 after a 1-month exposure. This value is as low as can be obtained with a hardness test.

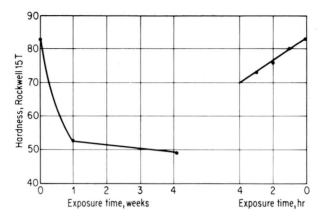

Fig. 5.9   Effect of nitrogen tetroxide on Kel-F (hardness).

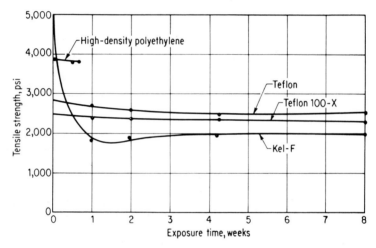

Fig. 5.10   Effect of nitrogen tetroxide on Kel-F, Teflon, Teflon 100X, and high-density polyethylene (tensile properties).

The long-term effects of NTO on Kel-F, Teflon, Teflon 100X, and Marlex 50 are shown in Fig. 5.10.

The short-term effect of NTO on elastomers is shown in Figs. 5.11 and 5.12.   The resistance of a modified fluorosilicone rubber to NTO is shown in Figs. 5.13 to 5.16.   After a 1-hr exposure the tensile strength is reduced to 800 psi from 950 psi.   No further reduction in tensile properties occurs between a 1-hr and a 1-week exposure to NTO.

A comparison of some of the applicable mechanical properties of the plastic materials evaluated with NTO is presented in Table 5.4.   It can be seen that the physical properties of Kel-F are superior to those of the

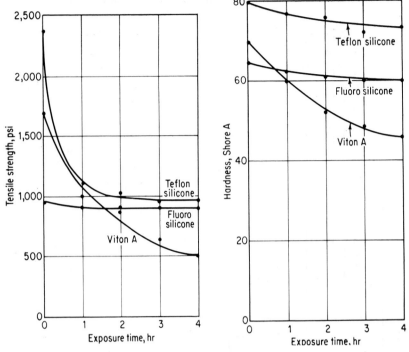

Fig. 5.11 Effect of nitrogen tetroxide on Teflon modified silicone, Viton A, and fluorosilicone rubber (tensile properties).

Fig. 5.12 Effect of nitrogen tetroxide on Teflon modified silicone, Viton A, and fluorosilicone rubber (hardness).

Table 5.4 Comparison of Some Physical Properties of Plastic Materials Evaluated with NTO

Property	Kel-F	Marlex 50	Irradiated Marlex 50	Teflon	Teflon 100X	Polypropylene
Tensile strength, psi....	4,600–5,700	4,400	4,630	1,500–3,000	2,700	5,000
Elongation, %..........	125	40–400†	40–400	100–200	250–330	60
Flexural modulus, psi...	182,000	140,000	155,000	50,000–80,000	80,000–85,000	170,000
Impact strength, ft-lb/in.	3.62	3.0	2.8	2–3	....	1
Hardness, Rockwell 15T	80	68	70	50–60	55	
Heat distortion, temperature, 66 psi, °F...	....	165–175	175–185	250	162	22

† Varies with strain rate.

other materials in almost every respect. Of the three properties that
are probably most important for a lip-seal material—tensile strength,
flexural modulus, and impact strength—Kel-F is superior to all the other
materials tested. Unfortunately, however, the mechanical properties of
Kel-F are more grossly affected by NTO than are those of either Teflon or Teflon 110X. After less than
1-week's exposure to NTO, Kel-F has
lost 60 per cent of its original tensile
strength and an estimated 90 per
cent of its flexural modulus. Teflon
and Teflon 100X after similar exposure conditions are almost unaffected
by NTO.

Because Teflon and Teflon 100X
are weaker than Kel-F, more material
will have to be used if lip seals are
designed to the maximum properties
of Kel-F. These design changes
would usually amount to an increase

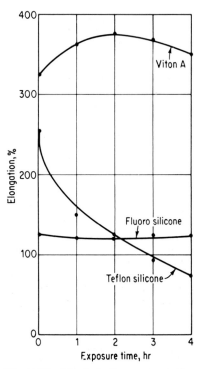

Fig. 5.13 Effect of nitrogen tetroxide on Teflon modified silicone, Viton A, and fluorosilicone rubber (elongation properties).

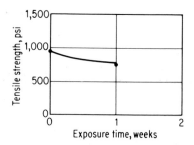

Fig. 5.14 Effect of nitrogen tetroxide on fluorosilicone rubber, Stillman rubber TH1080 (tensile properties).

in thickness to compensate for weaker material. Teflon 100X is more
truly a thermoplastic than is Teflon and, when molded, has more uniform
properties than regular Teflon. It can be postformed in the lip seals at
a much lower temperature without the toxicological danger encountered
when Teflon is hot-formed. It is more translucent than opaque, making
it easier to detect imperfections and impurities. There are fewer processing vendors for Teflon 100X than for Teflon at the present time, but
most of these are more quality-control-conscious than the average Teflon
molder. Because of its high price and semitransparency, more precautions are being taken to avoid contaminants which would be cause for

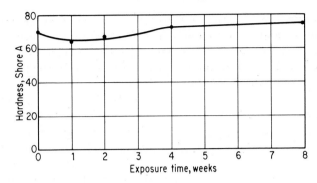

Fig. 5.15 Effect of nitrogen tetroxide on fluorosilicone rubber (hardness).

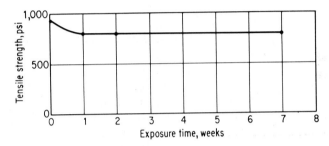

Fig. 5.16 Effect of nitrogen tetroxide on fluorosilicone rubber (tensile properties).

rejection of the finished part.   Work done at Aerojet-General, Sacramento, has shown that the attack of NTO on fluorinated plastic materials such as Kel-F, Teflon, and Teflon 100X is not a chemical attack on the polymer chain but acts by a method of absorption.

In this method of attack the NTO acts as a sort of plasticizer on the polymer which gets in between the molecular chains and causes softening and swelling.   This softens and weakens the polymer.   It has been shown that by extensive vacuum-drying methods that the NTO can be completely removed from the polymer after a period of time and then the polymer regains almost all its original mechanical properties.   This vacuum-drying method has been useful in explaining the mechanism of attack of the NTO.   It is, however, not recommended that vacuum drying be used on hardware systems, because this method is too impractical and time-consuming.   Hypalon, a chlorosulfonated polyethylene polymer, was evaluated for NTO service because it has a quite polar molecular structure.   Anhydrous NTO is essentially a nonpolar fluid.   The chemical attack of polar compounds by nonpolar solvents is usually less than that of nonpolar compounds.   This hypothesis was proved to be fairly valid.   The Hypalon was not disintegrated by short-term exposure to NTO.   However, much of the NTO was absorbed in the Hypalon.

When the samples were immersed in water, the NTO immediately reacted with the water and thus turned it into nitric and nitrous acids. These reacted violently with the Hypalon. The elastomer samples blistered and swelled to three times their size. Viton A was evaluated because published reports showed that it was resistant to red fuming nitric acid. As shown in Fig. 5.17, Viton samples did not disintegrate in NTO, but they swelled to approximately twice their original size after 7 days' exposure. The tensile strength was also reduced to almost one-fourth of its original value after a 4-hr exposure to NTO. The Teflon modified

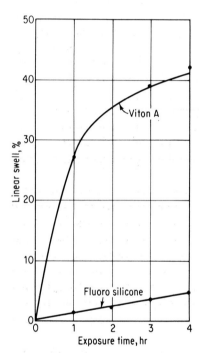

Fig. 5.17 Effect of nitrogen tetroxide on Viton A and fluorosilicone rubber (linear swell).

silicone rubber was evaluated and found to have possibilities as a static seal for NTO service. The compound did not swell to an appreciable degree in NTO, but it did tend to delaminate when exposed to NTO. The bond between the Teflon fibers and the silicone rubber was attacked by the NTO; for dynamic service this would be very detrimental. The physical properties of the fluorosilicone polymer LS-53 were affected less by NTO than were those of any other elastomeric material tested. It is not a particularly strong elastomer, but it maintained over 75 per cent of its original strength after 7 days' exposure to NTO. The compound does not swell to any appreciable degree, nor does the hardness change by exposure to NTO. It is the only compound tested to date that could possibly be used as a dynamic O ring for NTO service. It is not an optimum compound, but it will have to be used until something better is developed. At the present time, there is some investigation in modifying the basic fluorosilicone polymer LS-53 so that it can better resist the reaction of NTO.

Amine-type Fuels

This section discusses the compatibility of materials with amine-type fuels such as anhydrous hydrazine, monomethylhydrazine, unsymmetrical dimethyl hydrazine (UDMH), and diethylene triamine. Hydrazine is one of the newer fuels in rocketry.   It is currently employed as a fuel in a storable propellant combination of NTO and hydrazine.   Sometimes a 50-50 mixture of hydrazine and UDH is employed.   A fuel consisting of a mixture of UDMH and diethylene triamine was used in the booster rocket that put the first American satellite Explorer I in orbit.   Hydrazine is also used as a monopropellant in auxiliary power units and as a gas-generator propellant.

Hydrazine is a colorless, somewhat hygroscopic liquid which boils at approximately 230°F and is quite corrosive to certain metals.   Its vapors are toxic and explosive in air.

Hydrazine is a strong reducing agent which reacts violently with the oxides of iron and copper, particularly at elevated temperatures.   Hydrazine forms explosive compounds (azides) with silver and with mercury. Molybdenum oxide is extremely catalytic to N_2H_4.   Copper, brass, bronze, nickel, and steel cause hydrazine to decompose rather rapidly at high temperatures.   Hydrazine, being basically an amine and acting as a fairly powerful solvent and/or reducing agent, can be generally considered as detrimental to other organics.   This action is typified by blistering and stripping of organic finishes, dissolving of dye from color-anodized aluminum, swelling of O rings, and disintegration of other organic materials.

Anodized aluminum is darkened and sometimes the anodized film is stripped by hydrazine, but no evidence of appreciable weight change was detected after 5 days' static immersion.   Cadmium-plated parts discolor and show some blistering after a 2-week exposure to hydrazine.   Type 4130 steel has been observed to be severely corroded by hydrazine, and after several days' static immersion it begins to crumple away at the surface.   It is fairly safe to assume that metals satisfactory for hydrazine will also be good for UDMH or monomethylhydrazine because they are no more corrosive than hydrazine and are not so subject to catalytic decomposition.

Metallic Materials for Amine-type Fuels.   It must be understood that any metal recommended is to be used with the fuel in the anhydrous condition.   Furthermore, since metals tend to become catalytic toward hydrazine at higher temperatures, these metals are recommended for use only below the boiling point of hydrazine without further testing.   Metals that have been found satisfactory for amine-type fuel service are listed in Table 5.5.   Unsatisfactory metals are listed in Table 5.6.

In general, it is recommended in the literature that metals be passivated for hydrazine service.   In practice, however, no appreciable benefit could be observed by using this procedure.   This passivation consists in taking the cleaned system and exposing it to a 10 to 40 per cent aqueous hydrazine solution at about 120°F for some period of time before intro-

Table 5.5   Metals for Use with Amine-type Fuels†

Aluminum alloys	Corrosion-resistant steels	Others	Plating
1100	AISI 300 Series†	Inconel	Chromium (only)
5052	17-7 PH	Titanium 6AL-4V	
4043	A286‡		
6061			
6066			
356			
B356			
Tens 50			

† Steels, copper, and nickel may be used if free of oxides and at ambient temperatures of 100°F or less.   Not recommended for use other than propellant transfer or similar service.

‡ The materials 316 and A286 contain 0.5% Mo, and usage should be restricted to below 160°F with hydrazine.

ducing hydrazine into the system.   The purpose of this procedure is to remove from the system any deleterious oxides that might have formed since the cleaning cycle.   However, unless the system is dried immediately after passivation and then filled with hydrazine, the oxides will tend to reform.

Nonmetallic Materials with Hydrazine-type Fuels.   Kel-F, Teflon, and Teflon 100X may be used in hydrazine, UDMH, or mixtures of UDMH and hydrazine in the same manner as they are presently used in RP-1 fuel systems.   The properties of these materials are unaffected by exposure to these fuels as determined by laboratory tests.   However, lip seals used in experimental engines fired with hydrazine have developed radial cracks around the circumference of the lip area, causing excessive leakage.   The exact cause and nature of this failure has not been determined.   It is, however, postulated that Kel-F is subject to stress crazing when in contact with hydrazine-type fuels. Some plastics are checked for residual stresses by applying small amounts of specific liquids to the surfaces of the plastics; and when the plastic is highly stressed, immediate crazing will occur.   It appears that a delayed mechanism of this sort is taking place with Kel-F lip seals in contact with hydrazine.

Certain butyl rubbers are the best elastomeric materials tested for service with hydrazine-type fuels.   Two out of four butyl compounds tested were severely attacked by a 50-50 mixture of UDMH and hydrazine. For this reason no blanket recommendation for butyl rubber compounds for service with hydrazine-type fuels is given, but the following two particular compounds are recommended: Stillman Rubber Company SR 613-75 and Enjay Company, Inc., Compound 6297.   Their physical

Table 5.6   Materials Not Satisfactory for Use with Amine-type Fuels

Materials	Remarks
Metals:	
40E aluminum	Causes decomposition, particularly above 100°F
2024, 2014, and 7075 aluminum tested at 160°F	Corrosive to lead, zinc, cadmium, magnesium, and 4130 and 4340 steel; free copper appears on 2024 aluminum after 2 days
4130 steel	
Other iron and steel	
Brass	
Bronze	
Lead	
Zinc	
Cadmium	
Magnesium	
Copper	
Nickel tested at 160°F	
Monels	
17-4 PH tested at 160°F	
Silver	
Inconel-X	Pits after 1-week immersion
Plating:	
Cadmium	Dissolves (particularly in UDMH)
Copper	Catalytic
Zinc	Dissolves and pits
Nickel (electroless)	Some pitting
Electroless gold	Catalytic
Silver	
Nonmetallics:	
Mylar	Dissolves
Viton A	Brittle and flakes
LS-53	Disintegrates
Neoprene	Swells and blisters
Buna-N	Swells and is softened and gummy after extended exposure
Saran	
PVC (Tygon)	
PVA	
PT201-G coating	Blisters, particularly in vapor
Kel-F 5500 elastomer (composition 89)	Blisters and becomes sticky
Fluorolube	Corrodes both aluminum and stainless in presence of N_2H_4
MIL-L-6086	Precipitation even in 0.1% N_2H_4 concentrations; forms wax with higher concentrations tions of N_2H_4

properties are affected less by hydrazine fuels than are those of the other materials evaluated. These compounds have been in testing for about $1\frac{1}{2}$ years and still have 70 per cent of their original tensile strength and an elongation of about 150 per cent. These compounds are the best materials available at the present time for O rings and rubber seals. Standard AN and MS O rings can be used in hydrazine-type fuels for very short exposure periods, i.e., less than 1 day. They are softened and blistered when exposed for longer periods. The effect of UDMH and hydrazine and of mixtures of UDMH and hydrazine on elastomers is quite severe. Generally, UDMH has a greater effect on elastomers than does hydrazine. A greater loss of tensile strength, more softening, and more absorption of liquid into the elastomers were found when samples were exposed to UDMH. After approximately a 2-day exposure to UDMH or mixtures of UDMH and hydrazine, the silicone rubbers tested were so plasticized by the fluid that they had lost all their resilience. O rings made from these materials would develop such poor compression-set properties after short-term exposures to UDMH that they would be completely useless. Silicone rubbers, even high-strength silicones, are quite a bit weaker than the average elastomer. A 30 per cent reduction in tensile properties caused by exposure to propellants results in an ultimate tensile strength much lower than that obtained for two butyl compounds. The best elastomeric materials tested were two butyl rubber compounds, as previously stated. After approximately a 20 per cent reduction of tensile properties during the first 2 days' exposure to a 50-50 mixture of hydrazine and UDMH, there was little further drop-off in tensile properties throughout the remainder of the exposure period.

DC 5 and DC 6 lubricants have been found suitable for use with N_2H_4 and with NTO.

Alkali Metals

In the advanced propulsion systems, such as nuclear electrical power plants and ion rocket engines, the use of such alkali metals as sodium, potassium, rubidium, and cesium is planned as heat-transfer fluids and propellants. One difference between these systems and the present power plants is that these new engines are designed to operate from a period of weeks to years. Therefore, contact of the fluids at elevated temperatures with materials of construction becomes a serious compatibility problem. The first approach to this problem should be to run static corrosion tests at elevated temperatures under both boiling and quiescent conditions, using a great variety of promising materials. Special emphasis should be placed on testing coated and uncoated refractory metals and alloys. Static tests of duration as long as 2 years are anticipated. Because these tests are conducted at elevated temperatures, it is not probable that accelerated corrosion tests can be devised. In general, however, static corrosion tests by themselves are insufficient for positive answers to materials compatibility problems, but even in these cases they are mandatory for screening materials before attempting dynamic testing. The effects of various impurities, such as oxygen, nitrogen, or other trace elements, in the liquid metals and in the metal of construction are most readily investigated during static tests. These tests offer a good possibility of controlling the corrosive media and utilizing small laboratory-size samples.

For dynamic corrosion tests some form of thermal-convection loop is generally used for low velocities, and forced convection is used for high velocities. Dynamic corrosion tests are used primarily to amplify small differences in solubility of the construction material in the molten fluid. The most general type of corrosion that takes place in any heat-transfer system is a result of a very small solubility of the container material in the liquid at the highest system temperature, and even smaller solubility at the lowest temperature. This results in mass transfer. That is, container material is dissolved at the high temperature and deposited or precipitated at the low-temperature region. Even though the solubility difference may be measurable only in parts per million, the container can be almost completely transferred from the hot zone to the cold zone over a long period of time with the resultant plugging of passages at the cold temperature.

Isothermal dynamic corrosion is useful only in revealing the corrosion effects of the fluid at a given temperature. If the container material has a certain solubility in the fluid and the dynamic corrosion loop is isothermal, the container will merely dissolve to the limit of its solubility and the saturated solution will be circulated with little subsequent corrosion or precipitation. For this reason it is important that dynamic tests maintain a temperature difference between one portion of the circuit and another. This is realistic in view of the power systems and propellant feed systems being designed.

Another factor of dynamic corrosion which must be considered is the probable lack of carry-over of the container material through the vapor. In general, the vapor is much less corrosive than the liquid at the same temperature because of its lower density. For this reason material tested in vapor will generally show less attack than that tested in liquid at the same temperature. In addition, mass transfer is severely limited when there is a vapor barrier between the high and low temperatures of the circuit. However, the most critical point in any system is the liquid-vapor interphase, if any, or any point where vapor is allowed to condense.

It is believed that dynamic corrosion tests should utilize a minimum velocity. It is felt that low-velocity circuits can indicate mass transfer much faster and more simply than a high-velocity circuit. Turbulence exposes more of the liquid to the container walls, but it does not leave any two molecules in contact sufficiently long to permit diffusion or reaction to reach equilibrium and does not promote precipitation of the container material in the cooler regions.   Any dynamic test loop must provide a relatively quiescent cool region for precipitation to occur.   For these reasons quasi-dynamic corrosion tests should be used initially to further screen materials from static test data.   This quasi-dynamic test is a simple yet very severe test of materials.   Briefly, it consists in heating a single capsule, similar to that used in static tests, in the testing furnace so as to create both axial and diametrical temperature gradients. The temperature gradients so established will promote thermal circulation within the capsule and allow mass transfer to occur if solubilities permit.

Cesium

Tungsten shows little or no reaction with cesium at 1830°F over a 100-hr period.

Molybdenum is quite compatible with cesium at 1290 and 1830°F over 100-hr.

Nickel is quite compatible with cesium at 1290°F, but at some temperature between 1290 and 1830°F intergranular attack by cesium becomes important.   At 1830°F the attack is pronounced so as to give a distinct etched appearance to the nickel.   Even at this temperature, however, the attack takes place with little or no mass transfer and appears to be essentially a surface feature.

Stainless steel (321) is compatible at 1290°F, but is definitely corroded at 1830°F over a 100-hr period.   At the latter temperature a substantial weight increase, combined with pitting and scaling, of the sample was observed.

Work is just now beginning on testing of Na, K, and NaK and Li at high temperatures (2000°F and above).

The following are typical methods of liquid-metal corrosion:

1. Simple solution
2. Alloying
3. Intergranular penetration and selective solution
4. Impurity reaction
5. Temperature-gradient mass transfer
6. Concentration-gradient mass transfer

Liquid Hydrogen

The subject of structural materials for liquid hydrogen is covered in Chap. 2.   In general, it appears that some aluminum alloys, some titanium alloys, and some 300-series stainless steels look promising.

One area that needs investigation is the chemical effect on metals exposed to hydrogen for extended periods of time.

Very little work has been done on nonmetallic materials with liquid hydrogen. The materials that have proved satisfactory with liquid oxygen and nitrogen have been used. Work is just beginning at the Bureau of Standards at Boulder, Colorado, to investigate mechanical properties of nonmetallics. Work will also start at Rocketdyne to investigate the mechanical properties, mentioned before in the section on materials for Liquid Oxygen, of such plastics as Teflon, Kel-F, Nylon, and Mylar.

There are no compatible lubricants for use with this fuel; work is in progress at Rocketdyne to investigate liquid hydrogen as a lubricant for bearings and gears.

Fluorinated Greases

In the early stages of liquid rocket engine development (in the period from 1948 to 1953), lubricants consisting of fluorinated polymers were used. These materials were Kel-F grease and Fluorolube. In 1953 several detonations occurred in systems using fluorinated polymers on aluminum parts at the General Electric Company and the Buffalo Electro Chemical Company. Investigations since that time in various laboratories have shown the following: a number of halogenated materials were tested by placing the test material on the blunt end of a rotating drill press and forcefully pulling it down on a sheet of aluminum. Although this test does not simulate service conditions, it is a test method that will show which materials are sensitive to shear reactions with aluminum. All materials that detonated contained both chlorine and fluorine. Materials containing only one of these elements alone did not cause a reaction. It is reported that all these materials are polymers of chlorotrifluoroethylene, although they are marketed under various trade names. Kel-F was made to react in oil, powder, and sheet form. Teflon and Aroclor 1254, examples of compounds containing fluorine and chlorine alone, respectively, could not be made to react. It should be pointed out that reactions did not occur with all the Al alloys tested. The reason for this is not clear, but only points out the fact that further work needs to be done. Dr. R. Hauser of the Martin Company did some unpublished work on this problem in 1958, in which he attempted to correlate the occurrence of reaction with the speed of rotation of the drill and the load on the drill.

Permeability Testing

Whenever a material is considered as a liner material, as an expellant bladder, or as a protective coating, it is not enough to test the chemical reaction of the material with the fluid. It is necessary to test the material for permeability of the fluid in both the gaseous and the liquid state and also to establish the rate of this permeability. The rate of permeability is dependent on the material, the temperature, and the pressure.

Conclusion

In this chapter an attempt has been made to relate some of the experiences of compatibility investigations with certain propellants and other missile fluids. The following several points are emphasized:

1. Service conditions should always be specified as closely as possible when a material is being selected.

2. Material should be tested under conditions as close as possible to the service requirements.

3. Rigorous specifications should be established for the material selected.

4. All conditions must be taken into account when material is finally selected.

Many occasions have arisen where compatibility information has been requested or vigorous tests have been undertaken on materials with propellants that in actual operating conditions never will come in contact. Examples of this are ground-handling equipment, test-stand equipment, electrical checkout systems, etc. This type of equipment will be in contact with the propellant only in case of accidental spillage. In cases of this type it should only be determined that no spontaneous reaction will take place between the construction materials and the propellant. To design all this equipment with compatible materials would necessitate paying a high penalty in design and cost.

One tendency on the part of the design or development engineer is to spend considerable time thinking out all ramifications of the design and then, when he thinks he has everything worked out, to approach the materials engineer as an afterthought to request the right materials. Generally, he wants a question answered, such as whether a given metal will be good with a certain propellant for a 5-year storage period. It is necessary to emphasize strongly that accelerated compatibility tests are difficult, if not impossible, to obtain. The engineer should contact the materials engineer at the very beginning of a design so that he can begin his materials test immediately. It takes as long, if not longer, to develop the material as it does to design and fabricate the component.

REFERENCES

1. Baldrige, J. H.: Research on Rubberlike Materials for Applications Involving Contact with Liquid Rocket Propellants, WADC TR 57-651, parts I, II, and III, May, 1960.

2. Singleton, A. H., and E. J. Sterner: Compatibility of Liquid Fluorine with Various Structural Materials and Carbon, Progress Reports on WADD Contract AF33(616)-6515, Air Products, Inc., 1960.

3. Liberto, R. R.: Research and Development on the Basic Design of Storable High Energy Systems and Components, Progress Reports AFFTC-EAFB Contract AF33(616)-6689, Bell Aircraft, 1960.

4. "Liquid Propellants Handbook," Battelle Memorial Institute.

5. "Field Handling of Concentrated H_2O_2 Handbook," NAVAER 06-25-501, Bureau of Aeronautics, July 1, 1955.

6. Mason, D. M.: Properties of Fuming Nitric Acid Affecting Its Storage and Use as a Rocket Propellant, *Am. Rocket Soc.*, *Paper* 237-55, presented at Annual Meeting, Nov. 14–18, 1955.

7. Materials of Construction for Equipment in Use with H_2O_2, *Becco Bull.* 104.

8. Nitrogen Tetraoxide Corrosion Studies by Allied Chemical Corporation, WADD Contract AF33(616)-6588, 1960.

9. Weatherford, W. D., J. C. Tyler, and P. M. Ku: Properties of Inorganic Working Fluids and Coolants for Space Applications, WADC TR59-598, Southwest Research Institute, December, 1959.

10. Research on Elastomeric and Compliant Materials, RMD 2028-Q1, WADD Contract AF33(616)-7227, Thiokol Chemical Corporation, July, 1960.

11. Rittenhouse, J. G.: Corrosion and Ignition of Titanium Alloys in RFNA, *California Institute of Technology, Jet Propulsion Laboratory Rept.* 26-2, Nov. 30, 1955; *Rept.* 26-4, Mar. 30, 1956; *WADC Tech. Rept.* 56-414, February, 1957, Contract AF33(616)-3066.

12. Mowers, R. E.: How New Propellants Affect Plastics and Elastomers, *Mater. Design Eng.*, vol. 50, no. 3, pp. 89–91, 1959.

6

Choice of Materials and Fabrication Techniques for Pressure Vessels

A. HURLICH

RESEARCH GROUP ENGINEER, MATERIALS RESEARCH GROUP
CONVAIR-ASTRONAUTICS, SAN DIEGO, CALIFORNIA

Low weight and high reliability are primary requirements for airborne pressure vessels; they must therefore be fabricated from materials having high strength-weight ratios and uniform and reproducible mechanical properties such that unexpected failures cannot occur at stresses lower than the design operating conditions. Before considering a specific high-strength material that may be employed in pressure-vessel applications, it would be well to discuss some of the factors that govern the mechanical properties and behavior of metallic alloys.

The strength of metals is determined essentially by their alloy contents and microstructures, and a large variety of alloy combinations and heat treatments have been devised to yield high-strength steels, and aluminum-, titanium-, and magnesium-base alloys, as well as alloys of other metal systems. If the strength were the only limiting design parameter, it would be a simple matter to select a high-strength material for use in a pressure vessel or other engineering structure. Unfortunately, however, many widely used engineering alloys can and do, under specific environmental conditions of temperature, loading rate, and stress distribution, undergo failure at nominal stress levels well below their yield strengths.

During and after World War II an epidemic of brittle fractures occurred in the welded Liberty ships that were constructed to augment the merchant marine of the Allied Nations. These ships were fabricated from low-carbon steel plates which, when tested in tension with standard 0.505-in.-round tensile specimens, showed very high ductility, with 60 per cent reduction in area at the fracture. Nevertheless, the fractured ship plates of the same steel exhibited no deformation whatsoever, and the broken pieces could be reassembled like pieces of a jigsaw puzzle.

158

Investigation disclosed that many of the brittle ship fractures initiated at flaws such as weld defects and arc strikes that acted as notches or stress concentrators.   Others initiated at hatch corners, reentrant angles cut in plates, and other discontinuities.   Hence, in the presence of notches, steels and other metals may exhibit a tendency toward brittle fracture at stresses well below the nominal yield strength; this characteristic is termed *notch sensitivity*.   The effect of notches is to increase the ratio of maximum tensile to maximum shear stress, a condition that promotes brittle, cleavage-type fracture.

Another factor that greatly influences the deformation and fracture behavior of metals is temperature.   Again with reference to the mild-steel ship-plate material, a tensile test at room temperature shows a yield strength of approximately 40,000 psi, a tensile strength of 60,000 psi, and a reduction in area of 60 per cent.   A tensile test conducted at a temperature of $-320°F$ results in fracture at a stress of approximately 120,000 psi with no measurable yield point, and a completely brittle fracture with 0 per cent reduction in area.   Notched-bar tests show equally dramatic differences in fracture behavior over a much smaller range in temperature.   In the Charpy V-notch impact test, for example, a test at $+100°F$ will require 60 to 80 ft-lb of energy to rupture the specimen and the fracture will show considerable deformation and evidence of toughness, whereas a similar test conducted at 0°F requires only 5 ft-lb of energy to fracture the specimen; a completely brittle fracture with no evidence of deformation in the vicinity of the fracture is observed.   A transition from a ductile to a brittle fracture behavior with reduction in test temperature is exhibited by many alloy steels as well as many nonferrous alloys.

A third factor influencing the fracture behavior of metals as well as many nonmetallic materials is the rate of loading.   A rod of solder can be placed over the edge of a table and bent a considerable amount before it breaks.   If the same rod is struck sharply against the edge of the table, it breaks into several pieces with little or no bending of the pieces evidenced upon their reassembly.

Thus, notches or multiaxial stress distributions, low temperatures, and high rates of loading all act to promote brittle fracture of many high-strength engineering alloys.   If two or more of these factors are simultaneously operative, catastrophic brittle failures of critically stressed structures such as pressure vessels can occur at stress levels considerably lower than the design service stresses.

As indicated in the discussion on the welded-ship fracture problem, welded joints also pose a critical problem in pressure vessels.   Minute weld defects such as cracks, voids, undercutting, and incomplete fusion act as notches to provide stress concentrators.   In addition, the metallurgical changes produced during welding may cause grain coarsening, grain-boundary precipitates, and other effects that tend to embrittle the material. The weldability characteristics of metals must, therefore, be carefully evaluated as well as their strength and fracture characteristics when materials are selected for pressure-vessel applications.

A great variety of tests have been developed to evaluate the resistance of metals to brittle fracture. At this point it would be well to clarify some definitions of terms which are often incorrectly taken as synonymous. *Ductility* is a characteristic evaluated in terms of per cent elongation and reduction in area of a smooth tensile test specimen that is generally slowly and uniaxially loaded to failure. Ductility is of considerable significance in evaluating the formability or malleability of metals. *Toughness* refers to the ability of a material to resist the propagation of a crack, particularly in the presence of notches, reduced temperatures, high rates of loading, etc. A tough material will absorb energy through plastic deformation, and a crack once started in a tough material will propagate only through continued application of energy. Unfortunately, the term *brittle* means the opposite of both ductile and tough and has contributed to the loose usage of the latter terms. A material can be simultaneously ductile in a tensile test and brittle (i.e., show a lack of toughness) in a notched-bar impact test.

Notched-bar Tests

Notched-bar impact tests were developed at the beginning of the century to evaluate the tendency of metals to behave in a tough or brittle manner in the presence of notches. While it is true that such tests involve impact loading, the rate of loading is moderately low and is not particularly significant. It is the notch, which acts as a stress concentrator as well as a source of multiaxial stress, that is the important feature of these tests. The most commonly used notched-bar impact test specimen is the Charpy V-notch specimen which is illustrated in Fig. 6.1. This specimen is 0.394 in. square and approximately 2 in. in length. A 0.079-in.-deep 60° V notch with a root radius of 0.010 in. is machined across one face of the specimen. The bar is broken by being supported at both ends and struck by a pendulum-supported weight impacting the face opposite the notch. The energy absorbed in rupturing the bar is determined by measuring the loss in kinetic energy of the pendulum. These tests may be performed over a range in temperatures to determine the tough-to-brittle transition behavior of the material.

While the notched-bar impact test is very useful for evaluating the toughness of forgings, plate, and bar stock, it is not applicable to very thin sheet materials such as are often employed in airborne pressure vessels. Another type of test specimen that has been employed to evaluate the brittle-fracture tendency of heavy sections of steel, and more recently of sheet alloys, is the notched tensile test specimen, such as depicted at the right in Fig. 6.1. In round specimens, the notch is circumferential; and in sheet materials, the notches are machined in both edges, as shown in the figure.

A variety of notches are employed by various investigators, with stress concentrations ranging from 3 for mild notches to as high as 18

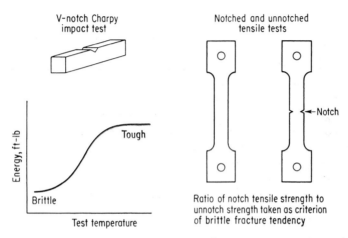

Fig. 6.1 Examples of types of specimens used to evaluate notch toughness of metals.

for severely notched specimens [American Society for Testing Materials (ASTM) and National Aeronautics and Space Administration (NASA) standard specimens]. With materials that are notch-tough, the effect of the biaxial stress distribution at the notched section is to increase the effective strength of the material, and the notched tensile strength may range from 1.0 to approximately 1.5 times the smooth tensile strength. In notch-brittle or notch-sensitive steels, the effect of the notch is to induce premature brittle fracture, and the notched tensile strength will be less than the smooth tensile strength. In notch-sensitive steels, the higher the stress concentration factor the lower will be the notched tensile strength and the notched-unnotched tensile-strength ratio. This ratio thus serves as an index of the brittle-fracture characteristics of materials.

Precaution must be taken to compare the stress concentration factors employed by different investigators when comparing notched tensile data and notch-sensitivity data reported from different laboratories.

While there are many different tests to evaluate the toughness of metals, most of them succeed in classifying various alloys in generally the same relative order of toughness.   An illustration of this is shown in Table 6.1, where two low-alloy steels heat-treated to approximately

Table 6.1   Toughness Evaluation Tests Applied to Alloy Steels

Steel	Smooth tensile properties				Notched‡ tensile strength psi	Notched-unnotched strength ratio	Charpy V-notch impact energy ft-lb
	F_{ty}, psi	F_{tu}, psi	Elong., %	R.A.,† %			
SAE 4160..	194,500	224,000	10.0	30.0	200,100	0.89	7.5
Hy-Tuf....	198,600	233,700	16.3	42.3	316,200	1.35	29.5

† Reduction in area.
‡ Stress concentration factor K_t = 6.3.

the same strength were subjected to both notched tensile and notched-bar impact tests.   SAE 4160 is a commercial Cr-Mo steel, and Hy-Tuf is a Mn-Si-Cr-Mo-V steel which was specifically developed to possess optimum toughness at a tensile strength of approximately 240,000 psi.   The SAE 4160 shows both a low notched-unnotched tensile-strength ratio and low Charpy V-notch impact energy as compared with that of the Hy-Tuf

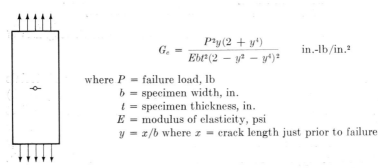

$$G_c = \frac{P^2 y (2 + y^4)}{E b t^2 (2 - y^2 - y^4)^2} \quad \text{in.-lb/in.}^2$$

where P = failure load, lb
b = specimen width, in.
t = specimen thickness, in.
E = modulus of elasticity, psi
$y = x/b$ where x = crack length just prior to failure

Fig. 6.2   Type of specimen and method of calculating critical crack-extension force.

steel.   Note also that the smooth tensile properties of the two steels show no really significant difference between the two alloys.   It is true that Hy-Tuf displays somewhat higher tensile ductility, but the differences are almost within the scatter obtainable upon replicate testing.

Another type of toughness evaluation test is the center-notched tensile test, often performed on a wide sheet having either very sharp machined notches or fatigue cracks developed at the ends of machined notches to provide high stress concentrations.   This test was developed by Irwin and coworkers at the Naval Research Laboratory and was designed to measure the critical crack-extension force G_c necessary to develop a running crack. The center-notched specimen and the calculation of G_c are illustrated in Fig. 6.2. Basically, the critical crack-extension force is given by the following equation:

$$G_c = \frac{\pi \sigma^2 a}{E}$$

where σ = gross stress

a = one-half length of crack at transition from slowly growing to running crack

E = elastic modulus

Various corrections and modifications are made to this equation to take care of finite dimensions of the test specimen, bending or lipping of the specimen in the vicinity of the crack, etc.

The G_c test has several notable advantages over the other toughness evaluation tests. It not only provides a quantitative evaluation of toughness, but it permits the calculation of the limiting crack lengths or defect sizes that will propagate catastrophically at various stress levels. One method of using the center-cracked wide-sheet tensile test is illustrated in Fig. 6.3, which shows plots from tests performed on various aluminum alloys. Tensile tests were performed on specimens having various lengths of cracks machined in them. Alloys displaying notch sensitivity failed at stress levels considerably lower than would have been predicted from their uncracked cross-sectional areas. The 6061-T6 alloy, which is tough, is only slightly degraded in strength even in the presence of cracks extending across half the section width. On the other hand, the 2020-T6 alloy evidences extreme sensitivity to the presence of cracks and loses almost all its strength. This use of the center-cracked tensile test permits the evaluation of the relative crack or notch sensitivity of various alloys

Another use of the G_c test is demonstrated by the data in Table 6.2, which classifies the same alloys in terms of the critical crack-extension forces required to propagate running cracks. With the exception of the interchange of position of the 6061 and 7079 alloys, both series of tests identically evaluated the relative toughness of the aluminum alloys.

Table 6.3 contains calculated limiting defect sizes in the X-200 high-strength steel as a function of G_c level and gross stress. The G_c values of a steel or any other metal can be influenced by heat treatment and microstructure. In the case of steel, temper embrittlement or other grain-boundary precipitation reactions will reduce the resistance to brittle-fracture propagation and the G_c level will be reduced. Note that at low G_c values, the length of crack or defect that could propagate to catastrophic failure is small and could escape detection by even refined

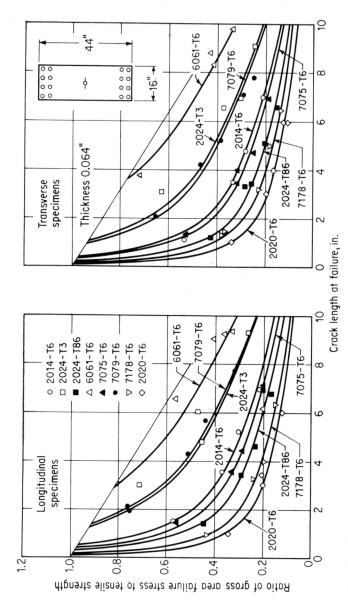

Fig. 6.3 Relation between crack length and failure stress for some aluminum alloys. (*Courtesy Aluminum Company of America, New Kensington, Pennsylvania.*)

nondestructive test techniques.   At higher G_c values, defects must be $\frac{1}{4}$ to $\frac{1}{2}$ in. in size before running cracks will develop.   Such defects are

Table 6.2   Critical Crack-extension Force G_c for Various Aluminum Alloys†
(Tests conducted on 0.064-in. sheet)

Alloy	G_c, in.-lb/in.^{2}	
	Longitudinal	Transverse
7079-T6	935	713
6061-T6	640	714
2014-T6	397	321
7178-T6	218	207
2020-T6	122	106

† Data from Aluminum Company of America.

sufficiently large to be readily detected by radiography, ultrasonic inspection, or other nondestructive tests.   In brittle materials, therefore, minute defects that will not be revealed by careful inspection may nucleate cracks resulting in failure of the part.

Table 6.3   Relation between Crack-extension Force G_c and Critical Defect Size in X-200 Steel†

G_c, in.-lb/in.^{2}	Limiting defect size, in.	
	At 200,000 psi stress	At 230,000 psi stress
200	0.095	0.075
300	0.14	0.11
400	0.19	0.145
600	0.29	0.22
1,000	0.48	0.37

† Calculations from U.S. Steel (reprinted with permission of Materials Advisory Board).

High-strength Materials

Consideration of high-strength metals for possible use in airborne pressure vessels is generally limited to alloy steels and alloys of aluminum and titanium.   Although some of the high-strength magnesium alloys compare favorably with these on a strength-to-weight basis, magnesium alloys are not usually considered for pressure-vessel application because of their general low toughness.   The steels will be discussed under two categories: the low-alloy heat-treatable martensitic steels and the high-alloy austenitic or semiaustenitic steels which may be either or both cold-worked and heat-treated to high strengths.

Steels. A typical variety of high-strength steels that are correctly being used or considered for the manufacture of airborne pressure vessels is listed in Table 6.4. Note the absence of standard SAE grades of steel such as 4340 and 8640, which have for a long time been employed for highly stressed critical components. The commercially standardized grades (SAE steels) are generally unsuitable for applications at strength levels above approximately 200,000 psi because of their susceptibility to

Table 6.4   Chemical Compositions† of Low-alloy Ultrahigh-strength Steels for Airborne Pressure Vessels

Alloy	C	Mn	Si	Ni	Cr	Mo	V	Co
AMS 6434	0.35	0.70	0.30	1.80	0.80	0.35	0.20	
D6A	0.46	0.75	0.20	0.55	1.00	1.00		
UCX2	0.40	0.70	1.00	....	1.10	0.25	0.15	1.00
X-200	0.43	0.85	1.50	....	2.00	0.50	0.05	
300 M	0.42	0.80	1.60	1.80	0.80	0.40	0.05	
Super Hy-Tuf	0.40	1.30	2.30	....	1.40	0.35	0.20	
Vascojet 1000	0.40	0.40	0.90	....	5.00	1.30	0.50	

† In per cent.

temper embrittlement, quench cracking, and other factors that reduce their resistance to brittle fracture. As a consequence of this, it became necessary to develop special alloy steels for ultrahigh-strength applications.

These new high-strength steels have carbon contents generally in the range of 0.35 to 0.45 per cent, contain molybdenum in the amounts of 0.35 to 1.0 per cent to reduce the susceptibility to temper brittleness, and many contain from 0.15 to 0.50 per cent vanadium for the purpose of promoting secondary hardening and to increase the resistance to tempering so that high tempering temperatures may be employed without excessive reduction in strength. Silicon is also employed as an alloying element in many of these steels because it is a ferrite strengthener and also does not deleteriously affect toughness. The total alloy content of the ultrahigh-strength steels is considerably higher than that of many of the standard SAE grades, and therefore they possess high hardenability. Since the section sizes employed for airborne pressure vessels are low, the ultrahigh-strength steels may be fully hardened by air cooling or oil quenching from elevated temperatures.

The mechanical properties of some of the ultrahigh-strength martensitic alloy steels are shown in Table 6.5   Note the high notched-unnotched tensile ratios and high notched-bar impact properties of these steels when heat-treated to tensile strengths in the range of 230,000 to 300,000 psi. By way of comparison, the properties of SAE 4160 are listed in the same table to show the reduced toughness of the standard grade. Of course, the higher carbon content of the SAE 4160 (0.60% carbon) contributed to its poor toughness properties, but even at 0.40% carbon this steel would be inferior to the ultrahigh-strength steels at comparable strength levels.

In addition to the development of new alloy steels, the overall quality of high-strength steels has also been improved by refinements in steel-making practice. The use of vacuum-melted steels for critically stressed

Table 6.5   Mechanical Properties of Ultrahigh-strength Steels

Alloy	Yield strength, ksi	Tensile strength, ksi	Notched tensile strength, ksi	Notched-unnotched tensile ratio	Charpy V-notch energy, ft-lb
D6A	241	256	320†	1.25	13.0
300 M	241.7	296.1	303†	1.02	18.0
Hy-Tuf	193	234	315‡	1.35	31
Vascojet 1000	226	268	300§	1.12	20.4
4160	194.5	224	200.1§	0.89	7.5

† $K_t = 3.0$.
‡ $K_t = 11$.
§ $K_t = 6.3$.

applications has been increasing. Vacuum melting greatly reduces the oxygen, nitrogen, and hydrogen contents of steel and results in a much cleaner steel with fewer and smaller nonmetallic inclusions. A comparison between the ductility of air-melted and vacuum-melted heats of the same steel (the 5% chromium H 11 hot-work die steel) is shown in Table 6.6. The per cent elongation and reduction in area in the transverse direction has been greatly increased in the vacuum-melted heat. While the effect upon resistance to crack propagation may not be so marked as the effect upon ductility, the consensus of data indicates an improvement in overall properties of vacuum-melted over air-melted steel.

Typical chemical compositions of highly alloyed austenitic and semi-austenitic steels used in pressure-vessel applications are included in Table 6.7. Type 301 is a 17% Cr–7% Ni austenitic stainless steel which is not hardenable by heat treatment, but which can be hardened by cold rolling. Strengthening in this alloy is achieved by two mechanisms: cold working of the austenite and partial transformation of the metastable austenite to martensite as a result of the cold working. The resulting

Table 6.6   Vacuum Arc Remelt Improvements: Tensile Properties of
$4\frac{3}{4}$-in. Round Corner Squares, SAE H 11 Billet†

(All tests transverse)

Test location	Air melt				Vacuum arc melt			
	F_{tu}, ksi	F_{ty} (0.2 % offset), ksi	Elong., % in 2 in.	R.A.,‡ %	F_{tu}, ksi	F_{ty} (0.2 % offset), ksi	Elong., % in 2 in.	R.A.,‡ %
Top first ingot:								
Mid-radius.................	289	242	1.1	6.0	296	248	7.5	25.0
Center....................	287	240	5.7	13.5	298	254	6.4	19.6
Mid-radius.................	291	241	1.7	6.6	296	250	8.6	31.7
Bottom first ingot:								
Mid-radius.................	287	240	1.8	6.0	287	241	9.6	33.9
Center....................	285	240	3.2	9.8	291	242	7.2	21.1
Mid-radius.................	287	239	2.1	7.0	288	242	9.6	34.9
Magnaflux cleanliness:								
Top.......................	$F/S = 7/7$ per square inch				$F/S = 0/0$ per square inch			
Bottom....................	$F/S = 1/1$ per square inch				$F/S = 0/0$ per square inch			

† Data from Ladish Company, Cudahy, Wisconsin.
‡ Reduction in area.

Table 6.7   Chemical Compositions† of High-alloy Ultrahigh-strength Steels
for Airborne Pressure Vessels

Alloy	C	Mn	Ni	Cr	Mo	N	Al
301	0.10	1.0	7.0	17.0	....	0.05	
AM 350	0.10	0.75	4.25	16.5	2.75	0.10	
AM 355	0.15	0.75	4.25	15.5	2.75	0.10	
17-7 PH	0.07	1.0	7.0	17.0	....	....	1.20
15-7 Mo	0.07	1.0	7.0	15.0	2.25	....	1.20
410	0.15	1.0	0.5	12.5			

† In per cent.

low-carbon martensite is both strong and tough.   The next four steels—
AM 350, AM 355, 17-7 PH, and 15-7 Mo— are variants of the Cr-Ni
stainless steel where the Cr and Ni contents have been adjusted to permit transformation of austenite to martensite upon heat treatment, and
other alloying elements have been added to promote precipitation-hardening mechanisms.   The heat treatment of these steels is fairly complex,
sometimes involving refrigeration after quenching from elevated temperatures as well as duplex tempering cycles.   The last steel, Type 410,
does not really belong in this classification since it is a martensitic heat-

treatable alloy, but its high chromium content puts it among the stainless steels, although its corrosion resistance is much poorer than that of the austenitic steels, which have higher chromium and often lower carbon contents.

Upon cold working or heat treating, the high-alloy steels of the types described above can achieve strengths in the range of 200,000 to 250,000 psi with good resistance to brittle fracture. Type 301 stainless-steel sheet can be cold-rolled 70 to 75 per cent and achieve tensile strengths up to 300,000 psi, and AM 355 sheet can be subjected to combinations

Table 6.8   Notched and Unnotched Tensile Properties of High-strength Stainless Steels

Test temp., °F	Unnotched tensile strength, psi	Elong., %	Notched† tensile strength, psi	Notched-unnotched tensile ratio
301 Stainless Steel (60% Cold-rolled)				
+350	216,900	1.0	217,000	1.01
+70	221,000	3.9	233,700	1.06
−320	309,000	18.0	305,300	0.99
AM 350 Steel Heat-treated to Strength				
+70	206,750	13.0	227,750	1.13
−320	286,750	8.0	132,900	0.46

† Stress concentration factor $K_t = 6.3$.

of cold rolling and heat treatment to develop tensile strengths up to 350,000 psi, but both steels will suffer considerable loss in toughness as compared with the lower-strength conditions.

Unfortunately, many engineers still regard ductility (per cent elongation or per cent reduction in area) as an index of brittle-fracture susceptibility. Data on the mechanical properties of 60 per cent cold-rolled Type 301 and of heat-treated AM 350 are presented in Table 6.8 in an attempt to dispel this notion. Type 301 steel has the unusual characteristic of a minimum in per cent elongation at a temperature of 350 to 400°F, with the elongation increasing with decreasing temperature down to at least −320°F (liquid nitrogen), as well as increasing at temperatures above 350 to 400°F. Both notched and smooth tensile tests performed at temperatures of +350, +70, and −320°F showed a relatively constant resistance to fracture, with notched-unnotched tensile ratios remaining substantially unity, even though the per cent elongation ranged from a high of 18 per cent to a low of 1 per cent.

The AM 350 steel has an elongation of 13 per cent at room temperature and a high resistance to brittle fracture as manifested by a notched-unnotched tensile ratio of 1.13. At −320°F this steel still displays a respectable elongation of 8 per cent, but the notched-unnotched tensile ratio at this temperature has fallen to 0.46, the notched specimen fracturing at less than 50 per cent of the smooth tensile strength and well below the yield strength of the material!

Table 6.9   Chemical Compositions† of High-strength Titanium Alloys
Used for Airborne Pressure Vessels

Alloy	Al	V	Cr	Ti
6Al-4V	6	4	. . .	Balance
120 VCA	3	13	11	Balance

† In per cent.

Table 6.10   Mechanical Properties of Titanium Alloys

Alloy	Condition	Yield strength, psi	Tensile strength, psi	Elong., %	Charpy V-notch energy, ft-lb
6Al-4V	Annealed	125,000	135,000	20	25
6Al-4V	Heat-treated	147,000	164,000	20	17
120 VCA	Annealed	135,000	145,000	23	6
120 VCA	Heat-treated	185,000	203,000	5	1.5

In spite of the accumulation of many data of the above type, most design and materials engineers nevertheless take comfort behind high elongation values and write materials specifications containing minimum acceptable elongation requirements. This again points up the confusion that exists in equating ductility with toughness. Toughness is the characteristic required in critically stressed engineering structures, not ductility. Engineers may specify steels with a minimum of 10 per cent elongation; yet the part fabricated from this steel may be inoperable if it deforms more than half of 1 per cent.

Titanium Alloys. Up to the present time, only two titanium alloys have been either used or considered for use in airborne pressure vessels: the 6Al-4V-Ti alloy and the all-beta 120 VCA alloy listed in Table 6.9. The 6Al-4V-Ti alloy is of the alpha-beta type and can be hardened by a solution quenching and aging heat treatment to achieve tensile strengths in the range of 160,000 to 180,000 psi, as shown in Table 6.10. The

120 VCA alloy is hardened by a precipitation-hardening mechanism by aging for 20 to 50 hr at temperatures in the range of 850 to 950°F. While the 120 VCA alloy is stronger than the 6Al-4V-Ti alloy, the former is much more notch-sensitive and poorer in toughness (see Table 6.10). The 6Al-4V-Ti alloy retains a high level of toughness at temperatures down to −320°F, having a Charpy V-notch impact resistance

Table 6.11   Chemical Compositions† of High-strength Aluminum Alloys Evaluated for Airborne Pressure Vessels

Alloy	Cu	Mn	Mg	Zn	Cr	V	Zr	Ti
2024	4.5	0.65	1.5					
7075	1.6	....	2.5	5.7	0.25			
7178	2.0	....	3.0	6.6	0.25			
2219	6.0	0.30	...	...	....	0.10	0.15	
7079	0.7	0.15	4.3	3.3	0.15	....	....	0.06

† In per cent.

Table 6.12   Mechanical Properties of Aluminum Alloys†

Alloy	Yield strength, psi	Tensile strength, psi	Elong., %	Notched‡ tensile strength, psi	Notched-unnotched tensile ratio
6061-T6	40,800	44,000	13.8	46,200	1.03
2014-T6	65,800	70,200	10.3	65,300	0.93
2219-T62	39,000	58,300	11.0	47,900	0.82
7079-T6	72,300	77,500	11.5	70,800	0.91
7178-T6	83,600	90,000	12.2	51,800	0.58

† Data from Ref. 30.
‡ K_t = 18 (NASA specimen).

of 10 to 12 ft-lb at this temperature and a notched-unnotched tensile ratio of essentially unity, with notched specimens with a K_t of 6.3. The 120 VCA alloy should not be employed in critically stressed applications at temperatures below approximately −40°F since it becomes almost glass-brittle and exceedingly notch-sensitive at reduced temperatures.

Aluminum Alloys.   Several high-strength aluminum alloys are being used or evaluated for use in airborne pressure vessels. Those listed in Table 6.11 represent the higher-strength alloys and include some, such as 7075 and 7178, whose restricted weldability would limit their use in pressure vessels even if low toughness were not a factor. The mechanical properties of some of the aluminum alloys are listed in Table 6.12, which includes notched tensile data obtained with the very sharp notched NASA specimen that has a K_t of 18. While the 6061, 2014, 2219, and 7079 alloys have reasonably high notched strengths, the 7178 alloy exhibits a notched-unnotched tensile ratio of only 0.58. While the NASA notched specimen tends to yield low notched strengths because of the extreme severity of its notch, less severely notched specimens (K_t of 6.3) also show the 7178 alloy to be very notch-sensitive. Tests with a specimen having a K_t of 6.3 show that the 2219 and 7079 alloys retain considerable notch toughness at temperatures down to $-320°F$ and that the 6061 and 2014 alloys are notch-tough at temperatures down to $-423°F$.

Table 6.13   Physical and Mechanical Properties of Filament-wound Plastic Laminate†

Material . . . .   Fiber glass filament bonded with 15% by weight of epoxy resin
Density . . . .   0.075 lb/in.³
Modulus of elasticity . . . . 4.5×10^{-6} psi
Tensile strength:
    Unidirectional windings . . . .   180,000 psi
    Helical windings . . . .   130,000 psi
    Flexural strength . . . .   100,000 psi
Strength-density ratios:
    Unidirectional windings   2,400,000
    Helical windings   1,735,000

† Courtesy Lamtex Industries, Inc., Encino, California.

Glass-filament Composites. The final class of materials to be considered for pressure-vessel applications consists of resin-bonded glass-filament constructions. Glass in massive form is very hard and should be strong, but the occurrence of a large number of minute flaws causes glass to fracture in a brittle fashion when it is stressed to a very small proportion of its true strength. Glass can, however, be spun into very fine filaments containing relatively few flaws; these filaments can develop tensile strengths up to several million pounds per square inch.

Glass filament can be wound on a mandrel to form any desired shape and can be resin-bonded to develop a strong pressuretight vessel. Depending upon the orientation of the filaments with respect to the direction of the stress application, resin-bonded laminates can develop strengths up to approximately 180,000 psi, as shown in the data contained in Table 6.13. Cylindrical pressure vessels are generally produced with a helical winding which develops hoop tensile strengths in the range of 100,000 to 130,000 psi. Since glass-filament laminates have low densities, corresponding to that of magnesium, the strength-density ratio of this class of material is extremely high, and exceeds those of all high-strength metallic alloys currently being considered for pressure-vessel applications.

Strength-weight Ratio. Table 6.14 lists the strength-weight characteristics of some of the higher-strength materials including glass laminates and titanium, aluminum, and steel alloys. Note that the strength-weight ratios of aluminum alloys are considerably lower than those of the

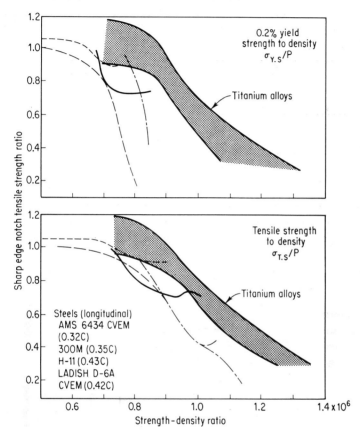

Fig. 6.4 Notched-unnotched strength ratios versus strength-density ratios for titanium alloys and some high-strength steels. (*Courtesy W. F. Brown, Jr., National Aeronautics and Space Administration, Lewis Research Center, Cleveland, Ohio.*)

other materials listed, and it is for this reason that aluminum alloys are not generally used for pressure vessels when weight is of paramount importance. While the highest-strength steels are competitive with the titanium alloys on a strength-weight basis, the titanium alloys are generally tougher (more resistant to brittle fracture) than the steels at strength-weight ratios above approximately 800,000 in.-lb/lb as shown in Fig. 6.4. These curves of yield strength–weight and tensile strength–weight ratios versus notched-unnotched strength ratios were obtained

Table 6.14   Comparison of High-strength Materials

Material	Tensile strength, psi	Density, lb/in.³	Elastic modulus, psi	Strength-weight ratio, in.
Glass epoxy helical-wound filament.	120,000	0.075	4×10^6	1,600,000
Titanium:				
120 VCA....................	200,000	0.173	14.8×10^6	1,150,000
6Al-4V-Ti	160,000	0.160	15.8×10^6	1,000,000
Steel:				
AM 355 SCCRT.............	325,000	0.282	29×10^6	1,150,000
300 M.....................	290.000	0.280	30×10^6	1,040,000
AMS 6434..................	240,000	0.280	30×10^6	860,000
Aluminum:				
7079......................	75,000	0.102	10.3×10^6	740,000
2219......................	60,000	0.102	10.3×10^6	590,000

from tests with the sharp-notched ASTM-NASA specimen having a stress concentration factor of 18. The notched-unnotched strength ratios of steels decrease very markedly at yield strength–weight ratios above approximately 800,000, while titanium alloys remain reasonably tough at ratios up to about 1 million.

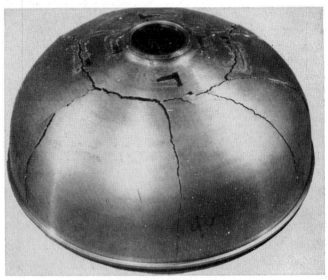

Fig. 6.5 Fourteen-inch-diameter dome forging ruptured in burst test; wall stress at 223,000 psi. (*Courtesy Pratt and Whitney Aircraft Company, East Hartford, Connecticut.*)

The high toughness of a titanium-alloy pressure-vessel component is illustrated in Fig. 6.5, which shows a 14-in.-diameter hemispherical dome forging made from the fully aged 13V-11Cr-3Al (120 VCA) titanium alloy. Upon burst testing, this dome forging ruptured at a wall stress of 223,000 psi. The biaxial loading resulted in a rupture stress considerably higher than the uniaxial tensile strength of the alloy, which was approximately 205,000 psi.

Fabrication Techniques

Following a discussion of the various materials that can be employed for lightweight missile and spacecraft pressure vessels, a review of fabrication techniques is presented in this remaining section of this chapter.

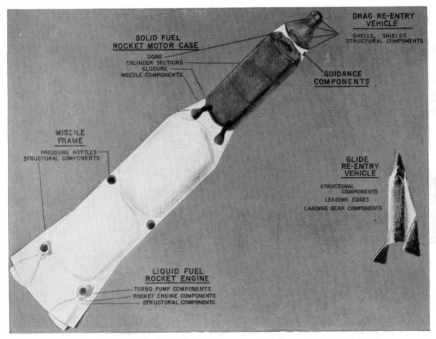

Fig. 6.6 Examples of missile and space-vehicle forgings. (*Courtesy Wyman-Gordon Company, Worcester, Massachusetts.*)

Examples of various types of pressure vessels encountered in missiles are shown in Fig. 6.6, which illustrates a composite two-stage rocket with a solid-propellant upper stage and a liquid-propellant first stage. The rocket-motor case of the upper stage is an example of one of the most important classes of missile pressure vessels. The first stage may contain a variety of pressure vessels, ranging from the large fuel and oxidizer tanks (one or both of which may contain cryogenic propellants and hence involve special materials problems due to extreme subzero temperature performance requirements) to high-pressure-gas storage bottles containing helium or other gases required to operate pneumatic systems or to provide gas required to maintain pressure in the propellant tanks during flight of the missile.

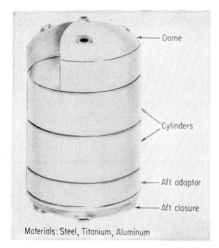

Materials: Steel, Titanium, Aluminum

Fig. 6.7 A typical rocket motor case. (*Courtesy Wyman-Gordon Company, Worcester, Massachusetts.*)

A more detailed view of a solid-propellant rocket motor case is shown in Fig. 6.7. This type of pressure vessel normally consists of a cylindrical body section and two hemispherical end closures, the latter containing flanged bosses or openings for attachment of nozzles and control devices. The motor case illustrated in Fig. 6.7 shows the end closures attached to the cylindrical body section by circumferential welds, with the wall thickness increased in the area of the welds to decrease the stresses in the critical weld areas. This is to offset any lowering in strength caused by the metallurgical changes inherent in the welding process as well as the effect of minute weld defects that may escape

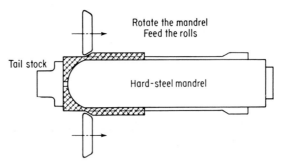

Fig. 6.8 Roll spinning of a cylinder on a mandrel.

detection. In the case of alloy steels, heat treatment of the motor case to develop its full strength is performed after welding. In the case, for example, of the 120 VCA titanium alloy, the individual components are first age-hardened to final strength; then the assembly is welded, with the reinforced weld zones left in the low-strength but tough condition. Aged welds in this alloy are extremely brittle and may initiate fracture at low stress levels.

Initially, the cylindrical body sections of rocket motor cases were made by roll-forming steel sheet or plate into cylinders and then welding the seams, these welds being oriented longitudinally with respect to the axis of the rocket motor case.   The welds were thus transverse to the

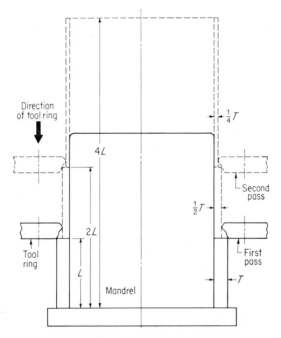

Fig. 6.9   Backspin forging.

direction of the highest stresses and were the source of many premature failures.   Many techniques were developed to overcome the deficiency introduced by the longitudinal weld.   One method involved hot-forging the weld to refine its structure and make it homogeneous with that of the base metal.   The most successful methods completely eliminated the need for longitudinal welds by forming seamless cylindrical body sections. In one of these methods (Fig. 6.8) the metal is spun over a rotating mandrel.   The workpiece is placed at one end of the mandrel and forced over the mandrel by a tool advancing over the workpiece.   This method is variously designated as flow turning, hydrospinning, or spin forging. A variant of this method, designated as backspin forging, is shown in Fig. 6.9.   In this method, the tool is forced down upon the workpiece, extruding it out into a cylindrical shape over the mandrel.   Figure 6.10

(a)

(b)

Fig. 6.10 Process of spinning of rocket motor cases for the first stage of the Polaris missile. (*a*) Hydrospinning first-stage motor-case shell; (*b*) large missile lathe machining first-stage chamber. (*Courtesy Kaiser Fleetwings, Inc., Bristol, Pennsylvania.*)

represents the spinning of rocket motor cases for the first stage of the Polaris missile and shows the type of tooling involved in this operation.

Another method which was successfully developed for the production of large seamless cylindrical body sections is ring rolling. In this method, a cylindrical billet is heated to forging temperature; a hole is forced in the center of the billet by means of a piercing tool; and the resulting

Fig. 6.11   Fifty-four-inch-diameter ring-rolled body section of a rocket motor case. (*Courtesy Ladish Company, Cudahy, Wisconsin.*)

doughnut-shaped section is then ring-rolled to final dimensions, using cylindrical rolls very much like those on a conventional steel rolling mill, except that the rolls are oriented vertically rather than horizontally. A large ring-rolled section is shown in Fig. 6.11.

Since ring rolling is performed hot, the cylinder is formed oversize on both OD and ID dimensions and is then machined to the final wall thickness. This practice is not entirely wasteful, since it readily permits contouring and thickening of the walls at the ends of the cylinder where circumferential welds are made for attaching the end closures.

End closures for large rocket motor cases may also be formed in a variety of ways. One method consists in hot-forging the end closures by using large presses or forging hammers. Figure 6.12 illustrates the largest counterblow forging hammer in the United States, the 125,000 m-kg (approximately 750,000 ft-lb) machine installed at the Cudahy, Wisconsin, plant of the Ladish Company.   Both the top and bottom forging dies move toward each other, permitting the delivery of high energy to the metal being forged, making it possible to form large thin-walled sections, and getting complete filling of the die throughout the

Fig. 6.12   The 125,000 m-kg (750,000 ft-lb) counterblow forging hammer of the Ladish Company.

forging.   An end closure for a 54-in.-diameter rocket motor case, forged on the counterblow hammer, is shown in Fig. 6.13.   This forging shows the integral bosses for end attachments and, after stress-relief heat treatment, is contour-machined inside and outside to the final dimensions. Figure 6.14 shows an alignment of ring-rolled body sections and forged end closures prior to assembly by welding.   Note that all welds are circumferential and are hence oriented across the direction of minimum stresses resulting from internal pressurization.

Fig. 6.13   Large end closure of D6A steel forged on counterblow hammer.   (*Courtesy Ladish Company.*)

Fig. 6.14   Ring-rolled cylinders and end-closure forgings for 54-in.-diameter rocket motor case.   (*Courtesy Ladish Company.*)

Another more recently developed method of forming end closures has the advantage of eliminating the large presses and forging hammers of the type shown in Fig. 6.12. This method is explosive forming, illustrated by Fig. 6.15. An explosive charge is detonated over the flat workpiece while both are immersed in a pool of water. The energy is transmitted through the water, forcing the workpiece down into the die cavity. The die cavity may be formed in cement, plaster, or other inexpensive material, and the entire explosive forming process involves

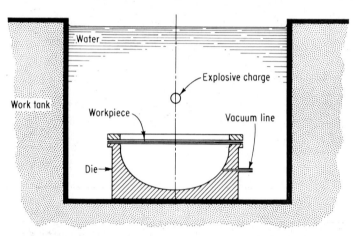

Fig. 6.15 Setup for explosive forming operation. (*Courtesy Aerojet-General Corporation, Downey, California.*)

relatively little investment in equipment and facilities. Explosive forming may be performed in stages with intermediate anneals or stress relief of the workpiece. An explosively formed bulkhead for a 54-in.-diameter rocket motor case is shown in Fig. 6.16, while Fig. 6.17 shows a similar end closure in which four flanged bosses have been integrally formed by this technique, which was developed by the Aerojet-General Corporation.

As has been previously mentioned, the various sections of solid-propellant rocket motor cases are circumferentially welded together. Typical tooling for this operation (Figs. 6.18 and 6.19) consists of jigging and fixtures to hold the adjacent sections in place and capable of rotating them under the heads of automatic welding machines. Gas-fired preheating rings, which may be placed inside or outside of the assembly, are used to preheat the metal adjacent to the welds to minimize the danger of weld cracking. Another method of welding pressure-vessel components which is finding increasing application is pressure welding. In this process (Fig. 6.20), the two sections to be welded together are carefully machined to develop flat mating surfaces, the surfaces are pressed together, and then the assembly is heated by means of an oscillating gas-fired ring burner. When the metal reaches forging temperatures, pressure is applied to the mating sections and a complete fusion weld is achieved. Some metal is forced outward on both the inside and

Fig. 6.16   Explosively formed 54-in.-diameter $\frac{3}{8}$-in.-thick semielliptical steel head. (*Courtesy Aerojet-General Corporation, Downey, California.*)

the outside surfaces of the weld to form a thickened section. The outside protuberance is generally machined off, while that on the inside of the pressure vessel is left in the as-welded geometry. The pressure-welding machine shown in Fig. 6.20 was developed by the Menasco Manufacturing Company, Burbank, California.

A 14-in.-diameter 8-ft-long pressure vessel made from the annealed 6Al-4V-Ti alloy and used in the X-15 airplane is shown in Fig. 6.21. This vessel was fabricated from a seamless cylindrical body section to

Fig. 6.17 Explosively formed end closure for 54-in.-diameter pressure vessel. (*Courtesy Aerojet-General Corporation, Downey, California.*)

which forged end closures were attached by pressure welding as described above.

The design of large, long-range solid-propellant rockets necessitated the development of special heat-treating furnaces for the processing of motor cases that could be as large as 75 to 100 in. in diameter and up to 25 ft in length. One such furnace, designed and constructed by the Lindberg Engineering Company, Chicago, Illinois, is shown in Figs. 6.22

Fig. 6.18 Girth welding of body section of 54-in.-diameter case. (*Courtesy Aerojet-General Corporation, Downey, California.*)

to 6.24. Since no machining is performed on assembled motor cases, excessive scaling and decarburization must be prevented by means of careful control of heat-treating atmospheres. The referenced figures show an alloy-steel case for the first stage of the Minuteman being prepared for heat treatment. This case has been fabricated from seamless cylindrical body sections and formed end closures attached by means of circumferential welds. Figure 6.24 shows the special holding fixture designed to suspend the cases in the heat-treating furnace so that the thin-walled structure will not be deformed. The furnace depicted in Figs. 6.22 to 6.24 can accommodate cases up to 84 in. in diameter and 24 ft in length and operates over the temperature range of 300 to 1450°F. A molten salt bath containing 240,000 lb of salt at temperatures in the range of 350 to 850°F is located in front of the furnace and is employed

(a)

(b)

Fig. 6.19 Photographs of (a) circumferential welding machine and (b) process of assembling parts for welding. (*Courtesy Kaiser Fleetwings, Inc., Bristol, Pennsylvania.*)

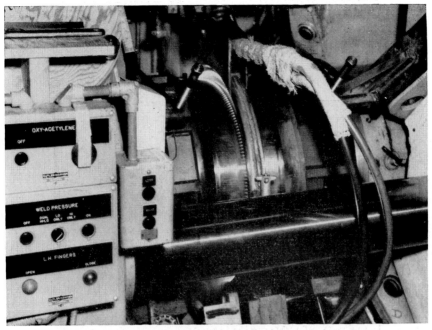

Fig. 6.20 Equipment used for pressure-welding vessel components. (*Courtesy Menasco Manufacturing Company, Burbank, California.*)

Fig. 6.21 Fourteen-inch-diameter by 8-ft-long pressure vessel for X-15 airplane fabricated by pressure welding. (*Courtesy Menasco Manufacturing Company, Burbank, California.*)

for the martempering quench after the case is removed from the high-temperature furnace.

Another type of pressure vessel that is widely used in many missiles and spacecraft consists of spherical (or other shapes) gas-storage bottles for the containment of high-pressure helium, nitrogen, and other gases.

Fig. 6.22 Large gantry furnace for heat-treating rocket motor cases. First-stage Minuteman case shown being prepared for heat treatment. (*Courtesy Lindberg Steel Treating Company, Melrose Park, Illinois, and Lindberg Engineering, Chicago, Illinois.*)

Figure 6.25 shows a spherical helium-storage bottle used in the Vanguard. This pressure vessel is made from a high-carbon modified Type 410 steel (12% chromium) and is heat-treated to a minimum yield strength of 150,000 psi. This spherical pressure vessel is welded into place between two cylindrical liquid-propellant tanks, and the finished assembly is then heat-treated to strength by a hardening and tempering operation.

A spherical pressure vessel made from the 6Al-4V titanium alloy is shown in Fig. 6.26 after it had been burst-tested at a temperature of

−320°F, failing at a pressure of approximately 10,000 psi. This bottle is employed on the Atlas missile to contain helium gas required for the pressure stabilization of the thin-skinned fuel and oxidizer tanks. In order to increase the gas-storage capacity of the pressure vessels, they are chilled to −320°F by a surrounding envelope of liquid nitrogen which

Fig. 6.23   Heat-treating furnace for rocket motor cases; molten salt tanks are shown in front of furnace. (*Courtesy Lindberg Steel Treating Company, Melrose Park, Illinois, and Lindberg Engineering, Chicago, Illinois.*)

is dumped when the missile is launched. Pressure vessels required to contain a pressure of 3,000 psi at a temperature of −320°F must be fabricated from high-strength, tough materials; and the 6Al-4V-Ti alloy, heat-treated to tensile strengths in the range of 155,000 to 165,000 psi, retains excellent toughness at temperatures down to at least liquid-nitrogen temperature.   The vessel shown in Fig. 6.26 was fabricated by the pressure-welding technique, employing forged hemispheres with integrally forged bosses.   The rough forging is machined inside and outside, leaving a heavier section at the mating surface and a raised shoulder (see Fig. 6.27) for the application of pressure during pressure welding. After pressure welding, the shoulder area is machined off and faired into the surface contour of the spherical vessel.

Fig. 6.24   First-stage Minuteman case being inserted in furnace for heat treatment, with special holding fixture developed to minimize distortion of case. (*Courtesy Lindberg Steel Treating Company, Melrose Park, Illinois, and Lindberg Engineering, Chicago, Illinois.*)

After this machining operation, the titanium-alloy pressure vessels are heat-treated to strength by a solution-quenching and aging treatment using inert atmospheres or protective coatings followed by chemical milling to remove contaminated surface layers. Similar pressure vessels are also fabricated by the fusion-welding process whereby prior solution-quenched and fully machined hemispheres are welded together, using unalloyed or alloyed titanium filler metal. After welding, the completed pressure vessels are aged, the aging treatment serving the twofold purpose of achieving the desired strength and stress-relieving the weld joint. The section at the weld is increased approximately 50 per cent in thickness to offset the lower strength of the unhardened weld zone.

Still another type of pressure vessel is illustrated in Fig. 6.28, which shows an experimental airborne pressure vessel made by the Boeing Company from 2219 aluminum alloy (see Tables 6.11 and 6.12). This

Fig. 6.25 Spherical helium storage bottle used in the Vanguard; made of Type 410 steel heated to a yield strength of 150,000 psi. (*Courtesy A. O. Smith Corporation, Milwaukee, Wisconsin, and Aerojet-General Corporation, Azusa, California.*)

pressure vessel was welded by using the 2319 alloy filler metal, which has essentially the same composition as the 2219 alloy except for the addition of 0.15% titanium to control grain size. The 2219 aluminum alloy combines moderately high strength with good weldability and excellent resistance to brittle fracture and may be used successfully at temperatures down to at least −320°F.

The Atlas ICBM incorporates unique airborne pressure vessels not only in the area of high-pressure-gas storage bottles but also in its liquid-propellant tanks. The liquid oxygen and kerosene fuel tanks of the Atlas are fabricated from Type 301 cold-rolled stainless-steel sheet and are of monocoque construction with no internal stiffening or supporting members. The two tanks share a common intermediate bulkhead, and are kept rigid through internal pressurization, with higher pressure in the fuel (bottom) tank to support the liquid oxygen and keep the intermediate bulkhead convex upward in shape. The requirements for the tank skin are many: high strength-weight ratio, formability, corrosion resistance, weldability, and retention of high resistance to brittle fracture in both

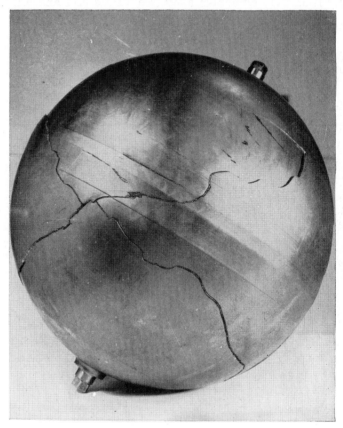

Fig. 6.26   Pressure-welded titanium-alloy gas-storage bottle after burst test at −325°F.   (*Courtesy Menasco Manufacturing Company, Burbank, California.*)

base metal and weld joints at extreme subzero temperatures.   Type 301 stainless steel, cold-rolled 60 per cent, meets these requirements (see the data contained in the upper portion of Table 6.8).

Various steps in the fabrication of the Atlas tanks are shown in Figs. 6.29 to 6.31.   The cold-rolled stainless steel, produced on Sendzimir mills to approximately one-third AISI thickness tolerances, is purchased in coiled-sheet form.   The sheet is uncoiled and inspected, then wrapped around a 10-ft-diameter mandrel to establish the lengths needed for ring segments. After cutting to length, the ends are butted together and welded by the inert-atmosphere tungsten-arc process. The longitudinal butt weld is roll-planished to smooth the surface of the weld down to the original sheet thickness; and a doubler strip, approximately 4 in. wide, is spot-welded to either side of the butt weld to provide a joint having essentially 100 per cent base-metal tensile strength.

Fig. 6.27 Machined forging for titanium-alloy pressure vessel. (*Courtesy Menasco Manufacturing Company, Burbank, California.*)

Adjacent ring segments are overlapped approximately 1 in. and welded together with roll seam welds to produce pressuretight joints. These welds are reinforced by means of rows of spot welds on each side of the seam welds. The tank walls are developed in this fashion, with V-shaped aluminum rings containing water-pressurized flexible hose inside the rings placed both inside and outside the stainless-steel sheet segments to maintain them in circular form.

The Atlas bulkheads are stretch-formed in gore segments from $\frac{1}{2}$ to $\frac{3}{4}$ hard cold-rolled stainless sheet and are contour butt-welded together to form complete bulkheads. All butt welds are also reinforced with spot-welded doublers. After the tanks are completed, they are pulled in tension so that the aluminum supporting rings can be disassembled and removed from the tanks, after which the tanks are sealed and pressurized

Fig. 6.28   Missile fuel tank made from 2219-T6E46 aluminum alloy. (*Courtesy The Boeing Company, Seattle, Washington.*)

Fig. 6.29   Overlapping ring segments of Atlas missile tank being spot-welded. Note temporary supporting rings inside sheet-steel segments.

Fig. 6.30 Segments of stretch-formed stainless-steel sheet being contour butt-welded to form Atlas missile tank transition section.

Fig. 6.31 Double reinforcement strip being spot-welded on inside of Atlas bulkhead. Bulkhead fabricated from $\frac{3}{4}$ hard Type 301 stainless steel, stretch-formed into gores and contour butt-welded with inert-gas tungsten electrode process.

Fig. 6.32 Spot-welding head attachment to Ryan-Wrap body section. (*Courtesy Ryan Aeronautical Company, San Diego, California.*)

Fig. 6.33 Large-diameter Ryan-Wrap chamber after hydrostatic burst test. (*Courtesy Ryan Aeronautical Company, San Diego, California.*)

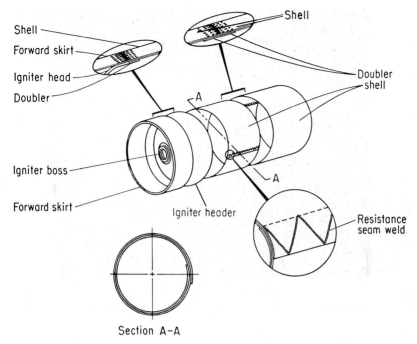

Fig. 6.34 Multilayered wrapping technique developed by the Budd Company, Philadelphia, Pennsylvania.

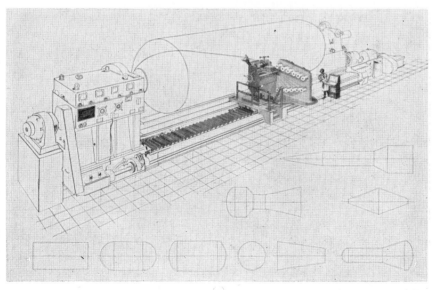

Fig. 6.35 Projected design of large filament-winding machine for fabrication of rocket motor cases.

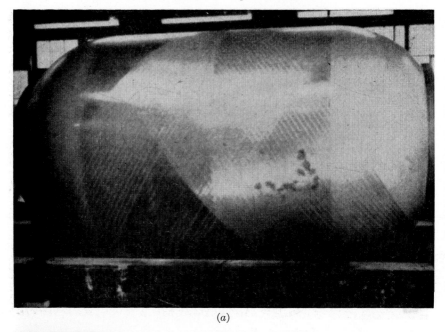

(a)

(b)

Fig. 6.36 Pictures of filament-wound cases. (a) Six-foot-diameter tank; (b) 8-ft-diameter by 17-ft-long propellant tank made by filament winding; (c) filament winding

(c)

(d)

of large case; (d) filament-wound cases. (*Courtesy Lamtex Industries, Inc., Encino, California.*)

with dry nitrogen gas.   The pressure is maintained just high enough to permit the tanks to remain taut and stable enough to support the empty missile structure in a rigid condition, the pressure required to achieve this being quite low.

The final type of metallic pressure vessel to be discussed is also fabricated from thin sheet material.   As pointed out previously, the problem of brittle fracture is a limiting design factor in lightweight high-performance pressure vessels.   Up to now, the metallurgical factors involved in toughness have been primarily stressed.   Toughness is also affected

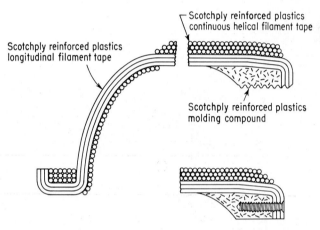

Fig. 6.37   Fiber orientations and reinforced sections of fiber-wound rocket motor case.

by geometry; everything else being the same, thin sections of steel or other alloys are inherently more ductile and tougher than thicker sections of the same materials.   This is so because thicker sections involve greater degrees of constraint upon deformation as well as permit greater multiaxial stress distributions than do thin sections.   These factors indicated that a pressure vessel built up of concentric layers of thin sheets of a high-strength metal would be more reliable than a vessel made from a single thickness of the same alloy.   Furthermore, a defect or crack in a homogeneous material could readily propagate through the wall thickness, whereas a crack started in one layer of a multilayered construction could not propagate so readily.   To rupture a multi-ply pressure vessel, a new crack must be initiated in each ply.   In very-high-strength materials it generally requires more energy to initiate a fracture than to propagate it once it is started.   For these reasons, a pressure vessel made from several layers of very-high-strength sheet metal would be expected to perform in a tougher fashion than one made from a single solid thickness of metal.

Spiral-wrapped pressure vessels made from very thin (0.008 to 0.010 in. thick) cold-rolled and heat-treated stainless sheet alloys, such as AM 355-SCCRT (see Tables 6.7 and 6.14), have been developed by several manufacturers including the Ryan Aeronautical Company and the Budd Company. The stainless-steel sheet is wrapped around a mandrel and successive layers are spot-welded together as shown in Fig. 6.32. The attachment of bulkheads to multilayered wrapped motor

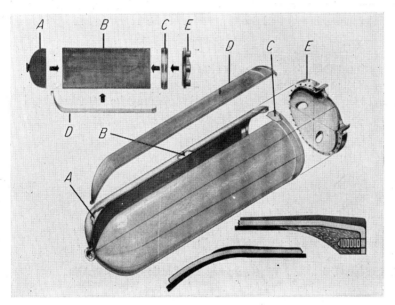

Fig. 6.38 Proposed design of filament-wound rocket motor case to permit bolted attachments of metallic end closure.

cases is a problem, and most companies regard the design and fabrication details involved as proprietary. A burst-tested spiral-wrapped pressure vessel is shown in Fig. 6.33. Burst pressures corresponding to stresses in the range of 290,000 to 325,000 psi have been consistently obtained by these means.

The multilayered wrapping technique and weld-joint design developed by the Budd Company are shown in Fig. 6.34, and good results have also been achieved by this process. While no production motor cases are being made by these techniques, the results obtained to date have been very promising and show evidence of achieving very high strength-weight ratios combined with reliable and reproducible performance.

The final type of airborne high-performance pressure vessel to be discussed is the resin-bonded filament-wound chamber now coming into production use. A filament-winding machine for the fabrication of large rocket motor cases is shown in Fig. 6.35, and other views of winding machines and completed cases are shown in Fig. 6.36. The glass filaments are precoated with resin and then wrapped around the mandrels. Metal flanges and parts are placed in position on the mandrel and are incorporated into the finished case by having filaments wound over their flange sections.

The mandrels are made from soluble plaster compositions and are dissolved out upon completion of the filament winding, sometimes after a partial curing is applied to the resin. The resin is finally cured at a temperature in the range of 300 to 350°F.

The filaments are wound in a number of different geometrical patterns to develop the desired strength characteristics in the various portions of the rocket motor case. A typical pattern is shown in Fig. 6.37, while Fig. 6.38 shows how a metal end closure may be attached by bolting into a filament-wound resin-reinforced case.

REFERENCES

1. Hodge, J. M.: Summary of U.S. Steel's Experience with Crack Propagation Testing, *National Academy of Sciences, Rept.* MAB-156-M, Nov. 15, 1959.
2. Bernstein, Harold: Fracture Toughness Tests of High-strength Sheet Metals, *National Academy of Sciences, Rept.* MAB-156-M, Nov. 15, 1959.
3. Howard, Edward: Huge Gantry Furnace to Aid Missile Industry, *Western Metalworking*, September, 1960.
4. Crane, C. H., and W. G. Smith: Application of 2219 Aluminum Alloy to Missile Pressure Vessel Application, American Welding Society, 41st Annual Meeting, Apr. 26, 1960.
5. Irwin, G. R.: Onset of Crack Propagation in High-strength Steel and Aluminum Alloys, *Naval Research Laboratory Rept.* 4763, May 24, 1956.
6. Anonymous: Unpublished data from Alcoa Research Laboratory, provided by Aluminum Company of America.
7. Kalpakcioglu, Serope: A Study of Shear-spinability of Metals, presented at ASME Annual Meeting, New York, Nov. 30, 1960.
8. High Strength High Temperature Steels, Unimach I and Unimach II: High Strength 5% Chromium Steels for Airborne Vehicles, Universal Cyclops Steel Corporation Brochure.
9. Hall, A. M.: Some Considerations in the Use of High Strength Steels, *ASME Paper* 60-MD-9, Design Engineering Conference, New York, May 23–26, 1960.
10. Mayer, L. W.: Heavy Presses in the Space Age, ASME Annual Meeting, New York, 1960.
11. Voth, R. J.: Hydrostatic Testing of Strip-wound Rocket-motor Chambers, presented at Missiles and Astronautics Division Meeting, American Ordnance Association, Ft. Bliss, Texas, Apr. 14–15, 1960.
12. Shank, M. E., C. E. Spaeth, V. W. Cooke, and J. E. Coyne: Solid-fuel

Rocket Chambers for Operation at 240,000 psi and Above, *Metal Progr.*, parts I and II, November and December, 1959.

13. Mayer, L. W.: Aluminum Propellant Cases, Aluminum Company of America, Sept. 30, 1959.

14. Applications of High Energy Rate Forming and Compaction, Aerojet-General Corporation, October, 1960.

15. Ladish D6A, High Strength Steel, Ladish Company, Oct. 4, 1957.

16. Wilson, William J.: Effects of Forming, Kaiser Fleetwings, Inc., presented at Seventh Sagamore Ordnance Research Conference, Raquette Lake, N.Y., August, 1960.

17. Espey, G. B., M. H. Jones, and W. F. Brown, Jr.: Sharp-edge-notch Tensile Characteristics of Several High-strength Titanium Sheet Alloys at Room and Cryogenic Temperatures, *ASTM Spec. Tech. Publ.* 287, June, 1960.

18. Irwin, G. R., J. A. Kies, and H. L. Smith: Fracture Strengths Relative to Onset and Arrest of Crack Propagation, *Proc. ASTM*, vol. 58, 1958.

19. Watson, J. F., and J. L. Christian: Low-temperature Properties of Cold Rolled AISI Types 301, 302, 304 ELC, and 310 Stainless Steel Sheet, *ASTM Spec. Tech. Publ.* 287, June, 1960.

20. Fracture Testing of High-strength Sheet Materials, *ASTM Bull.*, 243, p. 29, January, 1960.

21. Hurlich, A.: Titanium Pressure Vessels, *J. Metals*, February, 1960.

22. Hurlich, A.: Metals and Fabrication Methods Used for the Atlas, *Metal Progr.*, November, 1959.

23. Watson, J. F.: Mechanical Properties of High Strength 301 Stainless Steel Sheet at 70°F, −320°F, and −423°F, *Proc. Cryog. Eng. Conf.*, Berkeley, California, 1959.

24. Ultra-high Strength Steel, Unimach UCX2, Universal Cyclops Steel Corporation Brochure, 1960.

25. Coyne, J. E.: Manufacture of Pressure Vessels from Titanium Alloys, SAMPE National Symposium, Dayton, Ohio, Mar. 9, 1960.

26. Canal, J. R., and W. C. Kunkler, Jr.: Forgings for Missiles and Space Vehicles, ASME Annual Meeting, New York, November, 1960.

27. Sharp, W. H.: B-120VCA Titanium Alloy for Rocket Cases, *Crucible Titanium Rev.*, vol. 8, no. 2, March, 1960.

28. Powell, R. C.: High Alloy Ferritic Steels for Rocket Casings, Seventh Sagamore Ordnance Research Conference, Raquette Lake, N.Y., August, 1960.

29. Symposium on the Testing and Evaluation of Materials for Solid Propellant Rocket Motor Casings, *National Academy of Science, Materials Advisory Board Rept.* MAB-156-M, Nov. 15, 1959.

30. Hanson, M. P., G. W. Stickley, and H. T. Richards: Sharp-notch Behavior of Some High Strength Sheet Aluminum Alloys and Welded Joints at 75, −320, and −423°F. *ASTM Spec. Tech. Publ.* 287, Symposium on Low Temperature Properties of High Strength Aircraft and Missiles Materials, June, 1960.

7

Fracture of Pressure Vessels

GEORGE R. IRWIN

SUPERINTENDENT OF MECHANICS DIVISION
U.S. NAVAL RESEARCH LABORATORY
WASHINGTON, D.C.

The extension of a crack is a locally discontinuous process. In the over-stressed zone ahead of the main crack, local inequalities of strength cause nonuniform patterns of plastic strain. New openings are formed in regions of greatest tensile weakness. The extension and joining of these with neighboring openings and with the main crack constitute the complex process of crack extension. Figure 7.1 shows parabola-shaped markings on a fracture of Plexiglas. The arms of the parabolas open out in the direction of crack propagation. The new openings ahead of the main crack are not coplanar. Thus, as the outward spread of the crack from a new origin is overtaken by the main crack, the level difference is progressively broken through. In this way curved tear lines are formed whose appearance suggests a parabola although no exact correspondence to that mathematical contour actually exists.

The extension of tear lines from new initiation points is a prominent feature of fracture appearance. This feature is used to trace the direction of crack propagation and thus to permit determination of the region from which crack propagation developed.

When the leading edge of a crack extends after an arrest period due to unloading, the alignment of new initiation points along the arrest position is indicated by new tear lines as shown in Fig. 7.2. The starting crack attained final critical size relative to fast propagation during three loading cycles.

Except for local irregularities, a tensile crack traversing a plate follows a path normal to the direction of maximum tensile stress. Similarly, a flat tensile crack severing a thick section follows a locus plane normal to the maximum tensile stress. As such a crack approaches a free sur-

204

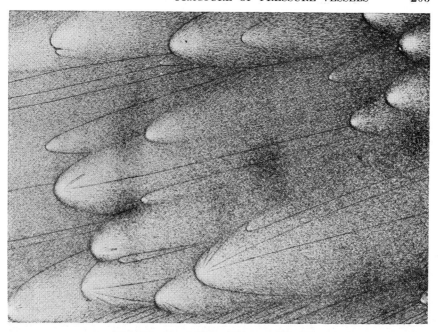

Fig. 7.1 Parabola markings on Plexiglas.

Fig. 7.2 Fracture origin showing arrest lines.

face, the greatest tension is parallel to the free surface, and so the approach to the free surface is at right angles.   However, as the unsevered section becomes relatively small, the reduction of constraint coupled with stress elevation results in rapid development of large plastic strains.   Because of these plastic strains the character of the final breakthrough to the free surface usually takes the form of an oblique shear separation.   Figure 7.3 shows a fracture originating at the intersection of a keyway with

Fig. 7.3   Fracture originating at the intersection of a keyway.

snap-ring groove of the aft snap-ring boss on a rocket-engine chamber of outmoded design.   Figure 7.4 shows a fracture through a similar section of another chamber in which the fracture markings clearly indicate the opposite direction of crack propagation.   Note in Fig. 7.4 that the snap-ring groove is completely framed by a lip of oblique shear fracture.

In the solution of existing fracture problems, fracture examinations are of primary importance.   Fracture appearance features indicate where the primary crack opening developed as well as the subsequent run and branching events which produced the final fractured condition.   The amount of oblique shear fracture gives a rough indication of the toughness of the material.   The presence and degree of general yielding near the primary-origin crack suggests the general level of stress governing starting-crack development.   Since fracture origins develop at regions of greatest tensile weakness, a flaw of some nature can usually be discerned at the origin of the starting crack. A study of the nature of this flaw, assisted where appropriate by metallographic examinations, is always of interest. The path of the running crack frequently reveals secondary-fracture origins of sufficient prominence to deserve study and consideration. Auxiliary analytical studies to provide better estimates of stresses near the starting crack are helpful. A complete picture of

Fig. 7.4 Fracture originating through a section similar to that shown in Fig. 7.3 but ending at a keyway.

the fracture event consistent with all known facts provides a sound basis for discussion of remedies.

Problem of Crack Growth

Important Factors. Three principal factors influence service fracture failures. These are:

1. Stress level abnormally high
2. A flawed condition or prior crack of unusual severity
3. An unexpectedly low degree of crack toughness

The character of the remedy appropriate to a given situation differs depending upon how the responsibility for failure is assigned relatively among these factors. To assist this determination it is desirable to have a concept of crack toughness closely related to starting-crack size and stress level.

From past fracture examinations of pressure vessels it may be concluded that the following behavior pattern is typical. When the starting-crack size is very small, say a few hundredths of an inch, the stress supported by the section prior to fracture is invariably equal to or greater than the yield stress. Sections which support only a fraction of the yield stress at failure always contain starting cracks of substantial size.

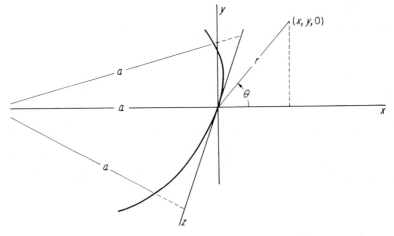

Fig. 7.5 Rectangular coordinates x, y, and z and polar coordinates r and θ at the edge of a penny-shaped interior crack.

Model for Analysis of Crack Extension. Our primary aim is to describe, understand, and control the conditions that cause fractures at stresses below the yield stress of the material. In this region of primary interest, the stress level is too low to cause general yielding of the section and, secondly, the starting crack is of substantial size. This suggests that the basic mathematical model should, at first, neglect the influence of plastic strains and regard the crack simply as an inferior free surface in an elastic solid. The model choice is influenced by the fact that the events at the leading edge of the crack are complex. A careful allowance for the influence upon the stress field of plastic strains and advanced initiations is not practical. This cannot be done with enough accuracy so that the payoff is worth the effort. Later it will be seen that a crude adjustment for inelastic strains at the edge of the crack is possible and can be helpfully employed.

An examination is in order of what is implied by the suggested mathematical model and what can be done with it. In its general aspects the leading edge of a crack will be represented mathematically as a smooth though possibly curved line, shown in Fig. 7.5 as a section of a circle of radius a. Although in later equations it may be convenient to shift the origin of the xyz coordinate system, the y direction is always taken as perpendicular to the crack, and the x direction is always the line of expected crack extension. The coordinates r, θ are used only at the leading edge in the xy plane, as shown in Fig. 7.5.

In the discussion of the extension of a through crack in a sheet, it is assumed that all stresses and strains are averaged through the thickness (z direction), as is customary for generalized plane stress.

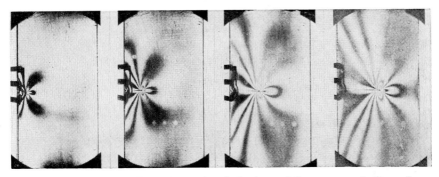

Fig. 7.6 Isochromatic fringes; four microflash views of the same crack traversing a sheet of Columbia resin [1].

Figure 7.6 shows the isochromatic fringes near a running crack traversing a plate of Columbia resin. The loop pattern designates the elevated-stress zone, and the spread of this pattern is proportional to the square of the stress elevation factor. The stresses near the leading edge have been measured in terms of fringe orders and distances in experiments of this kind. The crack-extension process in all its complexities is confined to a small region from which the isochromatic loops emerge. In order to state the stress environment which surrounds and controls this process, it is necessary to determine only the relatively simple stress pattern which pertains to the region close to the leading edge of the crack.

A complete study of the stress analysis methods applicable to crack stress fields cannot be given herein. The remarks in this chapter must be brief and somewhat incomplete. Applicable mathematical procedures have been set forth by Neuber [2], Muskhelishvili [3], Green [4], Sneddon [5], and Westergaard [6]. For two-dimensional problems, the Westergaard procedure, which will be described, is possibly the simplest.

As in most such methods, potential functions are used. A potential function is any solution of the Laplace differential equation and can always be represented as the real or the imaginary part of a function, say Z, of the complex variable $x + iy$. These are written Re Z and Im Z, respectively. With respect to derivatives, Westergaard [6] used an odd notation. Z' is the derivative of Z, Z is the derivative of $\bar{Z}$, and $\bar{Z}$ is the derivative of $\bar{\bar{Z}}$.

If we assume that the Airy stress function has the form

$$F = \text{Re } \bar{\bar{Z}} + y \text{ Im } \bar{Z} \tag{7.1}$$

the stresses are given by

$$\sigma_y = \frac{\partial^2 F}{\partial x^2} = \text{Re } Z + y \text{ Im } Z' \tag{7.2}$$

$$\sigma_x = \frac{\partial^2 F}{\partial y^2} = \text{Re } Z - y \text{ Im } Z' \tag{7.3}$$

$$\tau_{xy} = -\frac{\partial^2 F}{\partial x \, \partial y} = -y \text{ Re } Z' \tag{7.4}$$

For plane strain problems

$$\sigma_z = \nu(\sigma_x + \sigma_y) \tag{7.5}$$

where ν is Poisson's ratio.

Now the idea of the Westergaard procedure is to solve a specific problem by an appropriate choice of the stress function Z. For example, the choice

$$Z(\zeta) = \frac{K}{\sqrt{2\pi\zeta}} \tag{7.6}$$

where

$$\zeta = x + iy \tag{7.7}$$

solves the problem of the stress pattern represented by the region of isochromatic loops near the crack shown in Fig. 7.6.

Crack-extension Forces. Mechanics is the reaction of bodies to forces. Correspondingly, in fracture mechanics the force concept is of central importance. For the mathematical model we are using, the appropriate force concept is the rate of loss of strain energy with crack extension, the same energy-loss rate which was basic to the Griffith crack theory [7]. For the stress field corresponding to the preceding equations the crack-extension force is [8]

$$G_{\text{I}} = \frac{K^2}{E} (1 - \nu^2) \tag{7.8}$$

where E is Young's modulus and ν is Poisson's ratio. The subscript I indicates that the force G pertains to a stress system which pulls the crack walls directly apart, the opening mode of crack extension.

There are, conceptually, two sliding modes of fracture [9], for which the force values are written as G_{II}, for the forward-sliding mode, and

G_{III}, for the parallel-sliding mode. These correspond directionally to the edge and screw type of crystalline dislocations. For a crack travers-ing a plate, crack extension is discussed in terms of the average effective crack-extension force for the whole crack, taking no account mathe-matically of the fact that the fracture is, say, the opening-mode type in central regions and principally the sliding-mode type near the free surfaces. The convention used is to designate the total effective crack-extension force by the symbol G with no Roman-numeral subscript. For simplicity, consider that the G value for mixed-mode fractures always corresponds to generalized plane stress. Calculation of the strain-energy release rate, as shown in Ref. 8, then gives the result

$$G = \frac{K^2}{E} \tag{7.9}$$

Substituting the stress function of Eq. (7.6) into Eqs. (7.2) to (7.4) gives

$$\sigma_y = \frac{K}{\sqrt{2\pi r}} \cos \frac{\theta}{2} \left(1 + \sin \frac{\theta}{2} \sin \frac{3\theta}{2} \right) \tag{7.10}$$

$$\sigma_x = \frac{K}{\sqrt{2\pi r}} \cos \frac{\theta}{2} \left(1 - \sin \frac{\theta}{2} \sin \frac{3\theta}{2} \right) - \sigma_{0x} \tag{7.11}$$

$$\tau_{xy} = \frac{K}{\sqrt{2\pi r}} \sin \frac{\theta}{2} \cos \frac{\theta}{2} \cos \frac{3\theta}{2} \tag{7.12}$$

In these equations the influences of applied loads and geometry con-tribute to the crack-edge stress pattern only through two stress field parameters. One of these is K, which represents $\sqrt{EG}$. The other is the uniform stress σ_{0x}, directed parallel to the crack surface, that can be altered without changing the free-boundary conditions along the crack surfaces. The important parameter is K. From observations we find that the speed of crack extension is quite sensitive to the value of K (or the value of G) but is relatively insensitive to σ_{0x}. From the mechanics viewpoint, the central problem is to establish significant relationships between crack movement and the values of K or G. As we might intuitively guess, the degree of elastic constraint is also impor-tant. This is discussed later.

In order to perform and analyze experiments, it is necessary to be able to determine values of K (or G) for various loads, crack lengths, and geometries. This can be done with the assistance of experimental or theoretical stress analysis. As an example of the theoretical approach, consider the stress function

$$Z(\zeta) = \sigma \left[1 - \left(\frac{a}{\zeta} \right)^2 \right]^{-\frac{1}{2}} \tag{7.13}$$

This stress function represents a central crack of length $2a$ in an infinite plate with uniform tension σ acting in the y direction remote from the crack. Along the line of expected crack extension

$$\sigma_y = \sigma \left[1 - \left(\frac{a}{x} \right)^2 \right]^{-\frac{1}{2}} \tag{7.14}$$

For $x = a + r$ and $r \to 0$,

$$\sigma_y = \sigma \frac{a + r}{\sqrt{r(2a + r)}} \to \sigma \sqrt{\frac{a}{2r}} \tag{7.15}$$

By comparison with Eq. (7.10),

$$K = \lim_{r \to 0} \sqrt{2\pi r}\, \sigma_y \tag{7.16}$$

Thus

$$K = \sigma \sqrt{\pi a} \tag{7.17}$$

and

$$G = \frac{\pi \sigma^2 a}{E} \tag{7.18}$$

A. A. Griffith was aware of the above value for strain-energy release rate from a stress analysis due to Inglis [10]. Assuming G equal to twice the surface tension, he was able to represent approximately the influence of small cracks on the fracture strength of glass. However, as will be explained later, resistance to crack extension is much too complex to permit reliable estimates on this basis even for glass.

A useful variation of the stress function of Eq. (7.13) is [6]

$$Z(\zeta) = \sigma \left\{ 1 - \left[\frac{\sin(\pi a/W)}{\sin(\pi \zeta/W)} \right]^2 \right\}^{-\frac{1}{2}} \tag{7.19}$$

Here the position variable ζ is expressed in such a way that the whole stress pattern is periodic across successive strips of width W in the x direction. The above stress function represents an infinite periodic sequence of cracks of length $2a$ along the x axis. The shear stress τ_{xy} is zero along y direction lines of symmetry, those through the crack centers and those bisecting segments between cracks. To represent a central crack in a tensile strip of finite width, two y direction lines, bisecting segments between cracks, may be selected as the side boundaries. The model then differs somewhat from the real situation because a distribution of normal forces on the side boundaries exists which should be removed. However, these forces are directed parallel to the crack and their removal has only a small effect on the values of K and G. In a similar way, an approximate representation of a tensile strip having a pair of edge cracks of equal depth, a, can be obtained. In this case, y direction lines through the crack centers serve as side boundaries.

In either case, use of Eq. (7.16) leads to

$$K^2 = \sigma^2 W \tan \frac{\pi a}{W} \qquad (7.20)$$

Figure 7.7 shows two standard types of sheet tensile specimens, either of which may be used for a measurement of crack toughness.

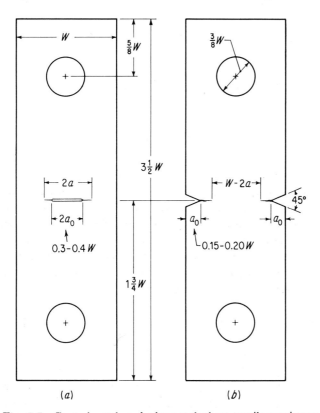

(a) (b)

Fig. 7.7   Central-notch and edge-notch sheet tensile specimens.

Crack-toughness Evaluation. The resistance of a material to crack extension is the dissipation of energy in inelastic strains which opposes the applied crack-extension force. In the modifications of the Griffith theory suggested by Irwin [26] and by Orowan, [27] it was implied that this resistance could be assumed constant, but observations do not substantiate this assumption. The resistance to crack extension measures energy dissipation in the total of the inelastic straining in progress in the crack-extension process zone. With certain reservations for strain-rate effects, this zone expands with the stress elevation, that is, with the G value. Thus, normally the crack-extension resistance increases steadily with crack-extension force. The discussion of abnormal behavior due to strain-rate sensitivity is omitted for two reasons: (1) metals with a strength-weight ratio equivalent to 200,000 psi in steel have only a relatively small dynamic elevation of the yield strength (a large fraction of current interest is in materials of this type); and (2) for clarity we should consider normal behavior first.

Since the resistance to crack extension is not constant, it is appropriate to ask next whether there are special values of the resistance that are of sufficient significance to deserve primary attention. Observationally there are only two relatively abrupt process change point. One is the change from slow to fast crack extension, in which the crack speed increases several orders of magnitude during only a few per cent change in the value of G. The other is the point of onset of forking in a sheet, or hackle in a thick section, when the average crack speed reaches a critical value. In the fracture failure of pressure vessels, engineers are more concerned with "whether they break" than with "number of fragments." Therefore first attention is given to crack-toughness evaluation based upon the resistance to onset of rapid crack propagation.

From comparison of onset of general yielding to onset of general fracturing, we can see that measurement of the critical force for the change from slow to fast crack extension is, in various ways, like measurement of yield strength. In both types of measurement certain arbitrary conventions of testing methods are advisable so that results obtained in different laboratories can be compared.

The specimens shown in Fig. 7.7 were recommended in an ASTM committee report published in January, 1960 [11]. A typical specimen might be in the range of 1.5 to 3.0 in. in width and possess other dimensions in proportion as shown in the figure. The ends of the notch are intended to represent actual cracks. A root radius of 0.001 in. does this well enough for metals of moderate toughness but not well enough for some very brittle materials. In order to be sure that the initial slots act like actual cracks it is helpful to initiate fatigue cracks at the notches. Reverse bending is probably the simplest procedure. The fatigue cracks thus started extend across the notch corners. In the tensile test, at a relatively small load, these corner cracks join and thus form an initial crack of normal shape. With additional increase of tension, slow crack growth occurs as indicated in Fig. 7.7. From the tension and crack length at onset of rapid fracture the critical values K_c (or G_c) can be calculated by using procedures of theoretical stress analysis [11].

Normally the maximum load serves well enough as the critical tensile load measurement. The other measurement needed is the crack length at onset of rapid crack extension. Currently the use of ink staining is recommended. Either india ink or a staining fluid of similar viscosity is daubed into the notches. With some precautions to prevent splashing and post-fracture creeping of the ink, the ink follows and stains just the slow part of the crack extension. For central crack specimens the recommended stress analysis provides the equations

$$K = \sigma \sqrt{W q_1} \tag{7.21}$$

$$q_1 = \tan u \tag{7.22}$$

$$u = \frac{\pi}{W}\left(a + \frac{K^2}{2\pi\sigma_{YS}^2}\right) \tag{7.23}$$

From these equations

$$\tan^{-1} q_1 = \frac{\pi a}{W} + \frac{1}{2} q_1 \left(\frac{\sigma}{\sigma_{YS}}\right)^2 \tag{7.24}$$

which can be solved graphically for q_1 when a/W and σ/σ_{YS} are given.

If Eqs. (7.21) to (7.23) are compared with Eq. (7.20), we note that the crack length appearing in the argument of the tangent function has been increased by the amount

$$a^1 = \frac{1}{2\pi}\left(\frac{K}{\sigma_{YS}}\right)^2 \tag{7.25}$$

The symbol σ_{YS} is intended to represent the resistance of the material to plastic yielding and is, for definiteness, taken to be the 0.2 per cent offset uniaxial tensile yield stress. The term a^1 is a correction to the stress analysis for local yielding near the crack. In the procedure followed here, we must express the stress elevation near the crack-extension process zone in terms of a single number K. The one-parameter degree of simplification permits only a limited kind of allowance for plastic flow. Essentially the influence of stress relaxation by local plastic flow upon the surrounding stresses is assumed equivalent to stress relaxation from an increment of crack length. From dimensional considerations, the size of the plastic zone and the crack-length correction are proportional to the length factor $(K/\sigma_{YS})^2$. When this length factor exceeds half the specimen width, general yielding of the net section occurs prior to crack propagation. If we assume the net section stress, as conditions of general yielding are approached, would approach the value 1.15 σ_{YS}, then the crack-length correction has the value shown in Eq. (7.25).

The stress analysis recommended for use with edge-notched specimens contains, in addition to the correction for local plastic yielding, an adjustment for the influence of free surface conditions along the side boundaries [11]. The equations for computation of K are

$$K = \sigma \sqrt{W q_2} \tag{7.26}$$

$$q_2 = \tan u + 0.1 \sin 2u \tag{7.27}$$

and u is given by Eq. (7.23).

Use of the plastic-zone crack-length correction removes from results a substantial portion of a trend with specimen size which would otherwise be present and which would tend to give values of K_c which increase with the size of test specimen. Contributing to this trend, however, is another effect quite different in nature from the influence of local plastic yielding.

Figure 7.8 shows schematically a relationship fundamental to onset of fast fracture in crack-toughness testing. The crack-extension resistance R is based on consistency considerations, not actual measurements.

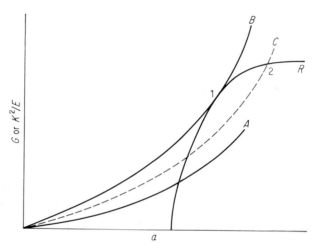

Fig. 7.8 Schematic curves showing growth of resistance to crack extension, curve R, and three G versus a curves (each for a different fixed tensile load σ).

It is assumed that measurements of the resistance for a fixed speed of crack extension, say 20 ips, can be represented by a curve rising and leveling off as shown in the figure. The initial crack extension starting from a very sharp notch or a fatigue crack does not possess a plastic zone of typical size. Thus expansion of the plastic zone and increase of R accompanies the first increments of crack extension. Eventually R must become constant for consistency with a fixed crack-extension speed. The curved lines A, B, C represent the relation of the force to crack length for a finite-width test plate. Each curve is for a different fixed load. After a small crack extension the G value acting is the intersection of curve A with R. To obtain more crack extension the load must be increased until this intersection finally becomes a tangency as shown by curve B. In a very stiff testing arrangement it is possible to observe continued crack extension with dropping load as illustrated by the intersection of R with curve C. However, in normal testing such a load drop is not observed, and onset of rapid fracture appears to coincide with maximum load. The tangency point should occur at larger values of R (and G) with increase of specimen size, and a trend of K_c with specimen size remains because of this in typical measurements, as illustrated by Fig. 7.9. This trend could be eliminated more or less successfully, depending upon plastic-flow properties, by choosing a larger plastic-zone correction factor. However, it seems unwise to eliminate a trend due to one cause by overcorrecting for a second and different effect. In

any case, the effect of this trend upon results is small compared with the differences generally looked for in fracture testing.

To review crack-toughness testing, the important elements are as follows: The crack-edge stress field has a characteristic pattern. By limiting attention to cracks pulled directly open by tensile forces, the major influence of the stress field can be given a one-parameter representation. It is convenient to study crack extension in laboratory tests in terms of this parameter, which can be expressed alternatively as the crack-extension force G or as the stress intensity factor

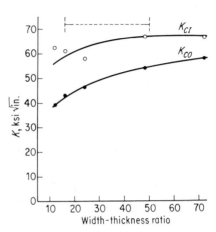

Fig. 7.9 Width effect in 0.125-in. 7075-T6 aluminum centrally notched sheets in tension.

K. A natural selection for standard measurement of crack toughness is the K value K_c for onset of rapid fracture. Any specimen shape might conceptually be used for this measurement, granting that a stress analysis appropriate for K value calculation was applicable and bearing in mind also the moderate dimensional size effect illustrated in Fig. 7.9. In the same terms these laboratory K_c values can be used for a service component containing a crack. In this way the measurement and analysis procedures establish a relationship between stress level, crack size, and crack toughness applicable to real structures.

Fracture-mode Transition. Consider next the influence upon crack toughness of elastic constraint. Shown in Fig. 7.10 are measurements of K_c for 7075-T6 aluminum plotted against the reciprocal sheet thickness $1/B$. For plates $\frac{3}{8}$ in. or larger in thickness the values of K_c were measured with a notch-bend testing procedure. A still higher degree of elastic constraint can be obtained with circumferentially notched bars. Several values from tests of this nature are shown on the ordinate axis.

Assume, for the moment, that the plastic-zone size can be estimated as just twice the plasticity correction factor, or as $\dfrac{1}{\pi}\left(\dfrac{K_c}{\sigma_{YS}}\right)^2$. In these terms the dashed line in Fig. 7.10 corresponds to a plastic-zone size equal to three-fourths of the sheet thickness. Beyond a plastic-zone size which is ten times the sheet thickness, the measured K_c values

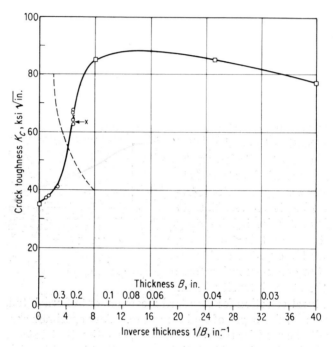

Fig. 7.10 K_c versus reciprocal plate thickness $1/B$ for 7075-T6 aluminum.

begin to decrease. The decrease with thickness is understandable, but it is not of primary interest here. The region in which the fracture changes from flat tensile to oblique shear with rapidly increasing toughness is the region close to the intersection of the dashed line with the curve through the measurements. Notice that a $\frac{1}{4}$-in. thickness falls below the dashed line while the $\frac{3}{16}$- and $\frac{1}{8}$-in. thicknesses are above.

Figure 7.11 shows the fracture appearances for these three thicknesses. When the plastic zone is less than twice the sheet thickness, the shear lips tend to develop independently.

Because of the importance in fracture-mode transition of the relative plastic-zone size, it is convenient to write

$$\beta_c = \frac{1}{B}\left(\frac{K_c}{\sigma_{YS}}\right)^2 \tag{7.28}$$

and

$$\beta_{Ic} = \frac{1}{B}\left(\frac{K_{Ic}}{\sigma_{YS}}\right)^2 \tag{7.29}$$

The plastic-zone size is roughly one-third of $B\beta_c$.

Figure 7.12 shows fracture appearance in terms of per cent shear for a large number of high-strength steels and several Ti alloys. The abscissa is β_c. Note that beyond a β_c value of 2π (or 6) the transition to oblique shear fracture is nearly complete. As will be explained presently, a rational basis exists for using the rule $\beta_c \geq 2\pi$ as a minimum toughness standard for high-strength metallic pressure vessels.

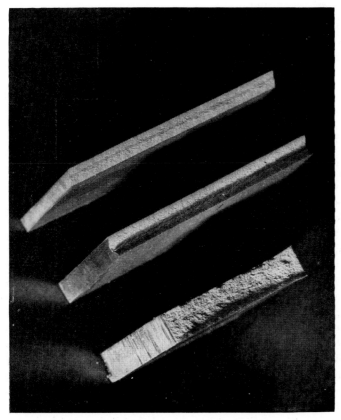

Fig. 7.11 Fracture appearance for $\frac{1}{4}$-, $\frac{3}{16}$-, and $\frac{1}{8}$-in. plates of 7075-T6 aluminum.

Reviewing briefly, we find it evident that fracture-mode transition can be regarded as a mechanical effect controlled by the relative plastic-zone size [12, 13]. Essentially, conditions of plane strain must exist at the leading edge of a flat tensile crack. This is readily provided in central regions of the plate by making the plate thickness large relative to the plastic-zone size. At the side free surfaces where thickness-direction stress relaxation must occur, there is always an oblique shear

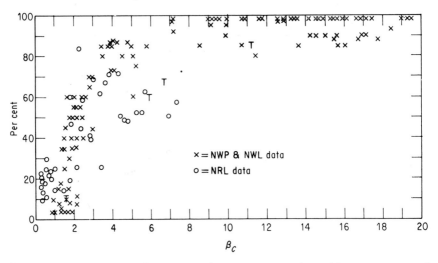

Fig. 7.12 Per cent shear lip as a function of β_c for a variety of heat treatments of various high-strength steels (x, o) and titanium alloys (T). Sheet thicknesses ranged from 0.07 to 0.22 in. and all tests were at room temperature.

border. The relative size of the shear border increases with degree of thickness-direction stress relaxation. When the plastic-zone size is several times the plate thickness, the transition to oblique shear is virtually complete. The abruptness of this change is assisted by the large increase in maximum shear stress induced by thickness-direction stress relaxation and the corresponding shift from plane-strain to plane-stress conditions. A plastic-zone size comparable to the plate thickness and mid-range conditions of fracture-mode transition are usually observed when β_c is in the range of 2 to 3 and β_{Ic} is close to unity.

Minimum Requirement for Tough Behavior. The topic considered next is a minimum-toughness criterion for pressure vessels built by using high-strength steel, aluminum, or titanium alloys [14]. Flaws in the form of through cracks are not expected. Although the pressure vessel may not be perfect, it is assumed that it does not leak. Examination of fracture failures reveals that these happenings always develop from the deepening and spreading of a part-through crack, as illustrated in Fig. 7.13. If inspection is good and such part-through cracks as exist do not have lengths greater than the plate thickness, then the development of a through crack of about twice the plate thickness in effective length must precede general crack propagation. In the initial stages of crack growth pictured here, elastic constraint prevents any plastic contraction parallel to the leading edge. This means a relatively low resistance to crack growth. In later stages shear lips form and the

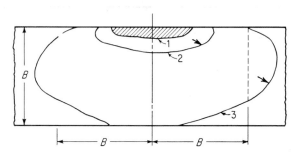

Fig. 7.13 Spreading of part-through crack.

governing toughness is the K_c value, measured as previously discussed. The equation for K^2 for a through crack of half length a is

$$K^2 = \frac{\pi\sigma^2 a}{1 - \frac{1}{2}(\sigma/\sigma_{YS})^2} \qquad (7.30)$$

Assuming that the K value is the critical value K_c, that $\sigma = \sigma_{YS}$, and that $a = B$, we find

$$K_c^2 = 2\pi\sigma_{YS}^2 B \qquad (7.31)$$

or

$$\beta_c = \frac{K_c^2}{B\sigma_{YS}^2} = 2\pi \qquad (7.32)$$

Thus when β_c is larger than 2π the resistance to rapid extension of the small through crack should effectively arrest its spread, and a stress larger than the yield stress should be required for crack propagation. On the other hand, when β_c is less than 2π, fast propagation begins from a small part-through starting crack and cannot be arrested by the later development of plastic yielding in the thickness direction.

Crack Toughness of Welds. Normally cracks, or flaws which develop into cracks, occur in the rolled and welded-type pressure vessels primarily in the welds or in the weld borders. The crack toughness of interest is therefore the weld or weld-border toughness. This can be measured by use of sheet tensile specimens as shown in Fig. 7.14. The slot with natural cracks at the ends is inserted along either the weld border or the weld center depending upon the measurement wanted   A. number of measurements of this type have been made by Dr. Romine at the Naval Weapons Laboratory near Washington and have been published in government reports [15] from that laboratory. K_c values were always less than those found when the starting crack was inserted in the specimen in the base metal away from the weld.   For steels this difference was small when the welding and heat treating were carefully done.

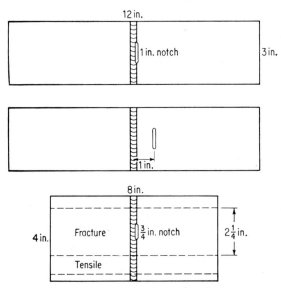

Fig. 7.14   Typical test specimens for measurement of weld-border and base-metal crack toughness.

For titanium alloys at a yield stress of 150,000 psi or more, a weld of satisfactory toughness is a more difficult problem.

Tests of this nature have been conducted both with flush-ground plate surfaces and with the extra thickness of the undressed weld present. For the latter type of specimen, any weakening influence of the weld-border notch must have been balanced by the strengthening or stiffening influence of the extra thickness because the supported maximum load values were essentially the same for a given crack length regardless of whether or not the weld had been flush-ground.   The primary advantage gained by flush grinding of welds in pressure vessels is a large increase in effectiveness and sensitivity for each of the various methods of nondestructive inspect on.

Influences of Repeated Loading and of Liquids.   We may as well note at this point that the reliability of a high-strength pressure vessel for use at near yield stress level is a difficult thing to establish with certainty. In addition to careful design and fabrication, the principal requirements for success in this endeavor are meticulous inspection assisted by smooth surfaces and a degree of crack toughness sufficient to resist the spread of any small cracks which are, nevertheless, overlooked. Hydrostatic testing provides a smaller degree of assurance than we might naïvely expect because the vessel may be weakened by the test procedure. Each loading cycle assists the spread of existing cracks and the development of others. A study of this subject is in progress at the University of Illinois, based upon observations of crack growth in a high-strength steel during tension-tension cycling. Based upon his data for M 255 steel, Corten suggested that if hydrotesting is used, the procedure should be a single loading cycle at a 10 per cent overload [16].

Assistance from water environment to crack growth during load cycling as well as to stress-rupture type of behavior has been observed in many high-strength steels [17–19]. For this reason moisture should be excluded from steel pressure bottles, especially those expected to hold a high pressure for a long time; an oil of high dielectric constant is preferable for hydrotesting. Unfortunately for the completeness of our knowledge about influences of load cycling and stress corrosion, these subjects have been studied in past years with specimens carefully prepared so that no cracks were initially present. Crack development, rather than crack extension, was the primary object of these studies; and the information gained applied to real structures only to the degree that some correlation exists between speed of crack development and speed of crack growth. The techniques of fracture mechanics apply nicely to these subjects, but most of the applying has yet to be done.

Opening-mode Crack Toughness. To assist fundamental studies of crack toughness, it is clear that measurements of crack toughness of the opening-mode or plane-strain type are needed. If we grant that crack-toughness evaluation as now conceived must be done with relatively large starting cracks, the influence of plate thickness can at least be eliminated. The simplest measurement procedure for this purpose employs a circumferentially notched round bar in tension. The usual convention of a notch depth which makes the net section area half the gross section area is a convenient choice; and a notch root radius of 0.0006 in., which a careful machinist can produce, is sharp enough for most metals. As in the case of sheet tensile tests, it is preferable to precrack to a small depth with fatigue. To ensure applicability of elastic-theory stress analysis, the net section stress at fracture should not be larger than 1.35 times the uniaxial tensile yield stress. The calculation of results uses the equations

$$x(1 - \tfrac{1}{2}x^2)^2 = 0.233 \frac{\sigma_N}{\sigma_{YS}} \tag{7.33}$$

$$K_{Ic} = x\sigma_{YS}\sqrt{\pi D} \tag{7.34}$$

Starting crack instability develops in these tests so close to the initial edge of the notch that there is no need for ink staining to measure slow crack growth. Thus the only measurement made is maximum load, and the test is convenient for use over a wide temperature range.

Table 7.1 Typical K_{Ic} and G_{Ic} Values at Room Temperature ($\sim$250°C)

Material	K_{Ic}, ksi $\sqrt{\text{in.}}$	G_{Ic}, lb/in.
Lantern slide glass (2% RH)	0.26	0.08
Lantern slide glass (moist)	0.19	0.04
Polymethylmethacrylate (cast plates)	1.3	4
Polyesters (plates)	.7	1
7075-T6 aluminum	37	115
2024-T3 aluminum	59	300
SAE 4330 steel, 450°F temper (Frankford Arsenal gun-steel modification)	53	85
SAE 4340 steel, 800°F temper	55	92

Table 7.1 gives values of K_{Ic} and G_{Ic} for several materials at room temperature. Not all of these were obtained by the round-notched-bar procedure which was recommended above. This is also the case with the measurements shown in Fig. 7.15. The rotor steels used had a yield strength of nearly 100,000 psi. Some of the data came from General Electric Company tests [20] using 6-in.-thick centrally notched disks tested by spinning them faster and faster until fracture occurred. At Westinghouse, Wessel [21] made crack-notch tensile tests of a similar material in a range from room temperature to −380°F. These results, added to the General Electric Company data, suggest that plane-strain crack toughness is a smoothly increasing function of temperature through the entire range from −380 to +400°F. Although there is a change in crystallinity in the appearance of the fracture facets, this change also is gradual. As yet there is no evidence for any metal that the plane-strain fracture toughness undergoes an abrupt upward trend at a special point in the temperature scale.

However, if the specimen dimensions and geometry permit stress relaxation parallel to the leading edge of the crack, a large and relatively abrupt increase in the mixed-mode G_c value may be expected to occur.

The total increase in G_c due to this specimen dimension influence is roughly a factor of 10.

Path from Surface Energy to Macroscopic Toughness. Consider next the relation of macroscopic crack toughness to the basic structure of solids. The original idea of the Griffith theory was to assume

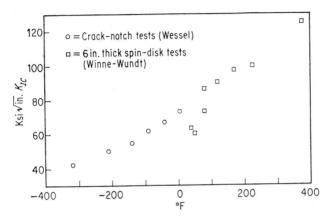

Fig. 7.15 K_{Ic} values from crack-notch tensile tests by Wessel on specimens from a rotor-steel forging are shown in the range -320 through $0°F$. K_{Ic} values calculated from centrally notched spin disk tests reported by Winne and Wundt for a similar rotor forging are shown in the range of 0 to 400°F.

G_{Ic} equal to twice the surface energy. Gilman [22] has suggested 2,400 ergs/cm² would be a fair estimate of solid-state surface energy for ferrite.

Table 7.2 shows G_{Ic} estimates in units of 10^5 ergs/cm². The entry for a guess based upon twice the solid-state surface energy is about 0.05.

Table 7.2†

Solid-state surface energy of ferrite	Increase for dislocations energy	Opening-mode crack strength of steels	Shear-mode crack strength of steels
0.05	2.5–10	100–400	~4,000

† Units of 10^5 ergs/cm² ($= \frac{5}{9}$ lb/in.).

On the right we place a value range which includes the G_{Ic} room-temperature values for a number of tough steels. The lower value is for tough representatives of the high-strength-steel class. Friedel [23] has discussed energy requirements for a cleavage crack moving through a forest of dislocations. Since the crack-stress field creates the dislocations, their formation energy must be included. In addition, dislocations introduce minute jogs or level differences in the fracture surface. Friedel estimated these energy requirements at fifty to two hundred times the surface energy. Multiplying 0.05 by 50 and by 200, we obtain the range 2.5 to 10 in units of 10^5 ergs/cm^2. Granting that this is somewhat speculative, we note that there still remains a substantial difference from actual measurements of G_{Ic}. In addition to lattice slip there must

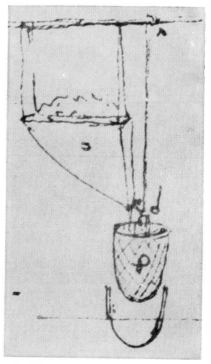

Fig. 7.16   Sketch by Leonardo da Vinci of his apparatus for testing iron wire.

be another mechanism for introduction of crack toughness. If we compare the G_{Ic} for dry glass and for polymethylmethacrylate in Table 7.1, it will be seen that the dry-glass G_{Ic} is smaller by a factor of 50. Observationally, the methylmethacrylate fracture surface shows parabola markings, evidence of noncoplanar advance fracture initiations. On the other hand, parabola markings are not seen on glass fracture surfaces and the measured crack toughness of glass is within a factor of 10 equal to twice the surface energy. The toughening influence of noncoplanar advance origins should exceed a factor of 50 in materials tougher than Plexiglas.

From this viewpoint, the toughening mechanisms for ductile metals can be considered to consist of (1) lattice slip, (2) noncoplanar fracture origins, and (3) section yielding to introduce fracture-mode transition. It is this route that must be followed if calculations of the fracture strength of real materials from fundamental considerations are to become possible. Plastics do not possess the lattice-slip mechanism, and G_{Ic} measurements for such materials are correspondingly small.

Flaw-probability Aspect of Filament-wound Chambers

Leonardo da Vinci once made a study of the strength of a supply of iron wire [24]. Figure 7.16 is the drawing of his apparatus that appeared

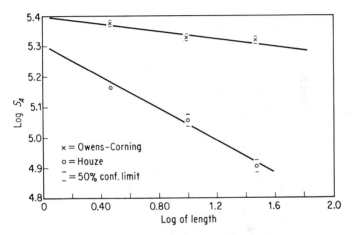

Fig. 7.17 Logarithm of average tensile strength (in pounds per square inch) as a function of logarithm of specimen length (in centimeters) for carefully protected glass fibers (x) and fibers damaged by rough handling (o).

in his notebook. He concluded that short lengths were stronger than long ones. Considering the quality of wire in that era, a flaw-probability type of size effect large enough to explain his conclusion no doubt existed. Figure 7.17 shows the results of measurements of specimen-length effect of the da Vinci type done 400 years later at the U.S. Naval Research Laboratory with single fibers of glass [25]. Two supplies of glass were used. In the case of the fibers used for the upper curve, precautions had been taken to prevent damage in handling. For the lower curve, the fibers came in a loose skein and contained numerous flaws. It seems a long reach from da Vinci to rocket chambers. However, those who are attempting the fiber-winding type of chamber construction are concerned with the length effect indicated here. If the handling of the fibers during winding introduces flaws (current procedures do little to prevent this type of damage), then there is a potentially large strength loss.

But much of the intrinsic fiber strength can be recaptured if the bonding between fibers introduces sufficient load transfer so that the effective strength corresponds to very short fiber lengths. If one goes to extremes in this direction, the chamber is weakened because the composite material is too brittle. If the fiber bonding is relatively weak, the chamber is weakened because the strength of the longer effective average fiber length is then too small. Difficulties in maintaining a satisfactory balance removed from either of these extremes would be greatly assisted if the techniques of manufacture, coating, and winding of fibers prevented introduction of flaws into the individual filaments.

Fracture mechanics is of such recent origin that areas of applicability remain which are, potentially, much more important than those that have received initial attention. Two obvious examples at present are (1) crack extension by fatigue and (2) fracture of adhesive joints. Efforts to improve the safety of aircraft from structural fracture failure have resulted in some work on the first topic. The second topic may receive sufficient stimulus for development from problems related to filament-wound rocket chambers.

REFERENCES

1. Wells, A. A., and D. Post: The Dynamic Stress Distribution Surrounding a Running Crack: A Photoelastic Analysis, *Proc. Soc. Exp. Stress Anal.*, vol. 16, p. 69, 1958.
2. Neuber, H.: "Theory of Notch Stresses," Springer-Verlag OHG, Berlin, 1937; trans. no. 74, David Taylor Model Basin, Washington, 1945.
3. Muskhelishvili, N. I.: "Some Basic Problems of the Mathematical Theory of Elasticity," Erven P. Noordhoff, NV, Groningen, Netherlands, 1953.
4. Green, A. E., and W. Zerna: "Theoretical Elasticity," Oxford University Press, Fair Lawn, N.J., 1954.
5. Sneddon, I. N.: The Distribution of Stress in the Neighborhood of a Crack in an Elastic Solid, *Proc. Roy. Soc. (London)*, vol. 187, p. 229, 1946.
6. Westergaard, H. M.: Bearing Pressures and Cracks, *Trans. ASME*, vol. 61, p. A-49, 1939.
7. Griffith, A. A.: The Theory of Rupture, *Proc. Intern. Congr. Appl. Mech.*, p. 55, 1924.
8. Irwin, G. R.: Analysis of Stress and Strains Near the End of a Crack Traversing a Plate, *J. Appl. Mech.*, vol. 24, no. 3, p. 361, 1957.
9. Irwin, G. R.: "Encyclopedia of Physics," vol. VI, Springer-Verlag OHG, Heidelberg, 1958.
10. Inglis, C. E.: Stresses in a Plate Due to the Presence of Cracks and Sharp Corners, *Trans. Inst. Naval Arch. (London)*, vol. 55, p. 519, 1913.
11. *ASTM Bull.*, January and February, 1960.
12. Irwin, G. R.: Fracture Mode Transition for a Crack Traversing a Plate, *J. Basic Eng.*, vol. 82, series D, no. 2, p. 417, 1960.

13. Irwin, G. R.: Size and Shape Effects on Fracture of Solids, ASTM Annual Meeting, June, 1960.

14. Irwin, G. R., and J. A. Kies: Fracture Theory As Applied to High Strength Steel Pressure Vessels, Golden Gate Conference, ASM, February, 1960.

15. Romine, H.: Fracture Roughness Test on Welded Titanium Alloys, *Naval Research Laboratory, NRL Tech. Memo* 148, December, 1960.

16. Corten, H. T.: Slow Crack Extension in High Strength Steels, presented at Seventh Sagamore Ordnance Research Conference, Raquette Lake, N.Y., August, 1960.

17. Shank, M. E., C. E. Spaeth, V. W. Cooke, and J. E. Coyne: Solid-fuel Rocket Chambers for Operation at 240,000 psi and Above, *Metal Progr.*, vol. 76, no. 5, November, 1959; vol. 76, no. 6, December, 1959.

18. Irwin, G. R.: Unpublished note for ASTM Committee Meeting, July, 1960.

19. Steigerwald, E. A.: Delayed Failure of High-strength Steel in Liquid Environments, *Materials Research and Development, Thompson Ramo-Wooldridge, Inc., Tech. Mem.* TM 1574 CM, Cleveland, Ohio, July 1, 1960.

20. Winne, D. H., and B. M. Wundt: Application of the Griffith-Irwin Theory of Crack Propagation to the Bursting Behavior of Disks Including Analytical Experiment for Studies, *Trans. ASME*, vol. 80, p. 1643, 1958.

21. Wessel, E. T.: The Influence of Preexisting Sharp Cracks on Brittle Fracture of a Forging Steel, ASM Meeting, Chicago, November, 1959.

22. Gilman, J. J.: Cleavage, Ductility, and Tenacity in Crystals, in B. L. Auerbach et al., "Fracture," John Wiley & Sons, Inc., New York, 1959.

23. Friedel, J.: Propagation of Cracks and Work Hardening, in B. L. Auerbach et al., "Fracture," John Wiley & Sons, Inc., New York, 1959.

24. Timoshenko, S. P.: "History of Strength of Materials," McGraw-Hill Book Company, Inc., New York, 1953.

25. Kies, J. A.: The Strength of Glass, *Naval Research Laboratory Rept.* 5098, 1958.

26. Irwin, G. R.: Fracturing of Metals, Am. Soc. Metals Seminar, Cleveland, Ohio, 1948.

27. Orowan, E.: "Fatigue and Fracture of Metals," M.I.T. Symposium, 1950; John Wiley & Sons, Inc., New York, 1950.

8
Temperature Control of Spacecraft

R. P. LIPKIS

HEAD, SPACE VEHICLE TRANSFER SECTION
SPACE TECHNOLOGY LABORATORIES
LOS ANGELES, CALIFORNIA

Before considering the problems encountered and the techniques employed in controlling the thermal environment of spacecraft, it is desirable to examine the goal of the temperature-control effort, namely, to determine how closely the pertinent temperatures must be held. Electronic devices, which generally comprise the bulk of the components of a typical spacecraft, can generally be made to operate satisfactorily over a wide range of temperatures, perhaps of the order of 150 to 200°F. At first sight, then, it would appear that the thermal requirements would normally be quite loose, and indeed the Vanguard and early Explorer satellites could tolerate quite a wide range in internal temperature. Present-day spacecraft, which might be called the second generation of spacecraft, generally have far more restrictive limits on the allowable internal temperatures. To see why this is so, it is necessary to consider the specific components and environmental factors in a typical spacecraft that tend to restrict the allowable temperature range. Some of the components that restrict the *lower* limit are discussed in the following sections.

Need for Temperature Control

Chemical Batteries. Sealed nickel-cadmium batteries, for example, are commonly used as the secondary storage in the spacecraft power-supply system, in part because of their outstanding recharge-cycle capabilities. These batteries suffer a significant loss of capacity at temperatures below 20 to 25°F. Other chemical batteries behave similarly, in some cases demanding an even higher minimum temperature.

The nickel-cadmium batteries cited above also lose capacity significantly when their temperature exceeds 80 to 90°F. Furthermore, since

230

the battery itself dissipates power, it is generally at some temperature, typically 5 to 15°F, above that of the surroundings. This may reduce the allowable upper spacecraft ambient temperature by that amount.

Liquid Propellants. One of the more commonly considered liquid fuels is hydrazine, used either as a monopropellant or as part of a bipropellant system. Hydrazine has a freezing point at about 34°F and, therefore, must be maintained above this level, not only in the fuel tank itself but in the fuel lines as well; these often extend to or beyond the outer shell of the spacecraft and, therefore, have a tendency to be at a lower temperature than the main spacecraft ambient temperature.

Solid Propellants. Many of the solid rockets that have been considered for various propulsion requirements in the spacecraft have been qualified operational only at so-called room-temperature conditions, i.e., above 40°F.

Transistors. Germanium transistors generally operate satisfactorily at temperatures up to 160°F and silicon transistors even higher, but these circuit elements are often located at or near the source of quite large power dissipations, so that if the thermal resistance between the transistors and, say, the external mounting plate of the component is large, the internal temperature gradient will likewise be large. This will impose a requirement for a relatively low mounting-plate temperature so that the allowable transistor operating temperature will not be exceeded.

General Electronic Reliability. The factor of perhaps greatest importance in limiting the upper end of the allowable temperature range is associated with overall electronic reliability. As a general rule, the mean time to failure of individual electronic elements decreases with increasing temperature; as a very crude guide, the mean time to failure is cut in half for each additional 20°F temperature increase. As the complexity of a spacecraft increases, the number of individual electronic elements increases; consequently, an ever-decreasing upper temperature limit is required to maintain a fixed overall reliability. For a typical complex satellite of today (1960–1961), with a lifetime requirement of a year or longer, an upper limit of the order of 80°F may be imposed by reliability considerations.

Other factors tend to narrow the allowable temperature range. It is often difficult to maintain instrument calibrations or keep circuits in tune over wide temperature ranges. Particularly, components such as gyros, very stable oscillators, photomultipliers, and vidicon tubes may require unusually close temperature control. It is often possible to solve some of the special requirements by tight local control without necessarily imposing a restricted requirement on the overall spacecraft temperature. However, some of the components tend to dominate the spacecraft (batteries, fuel tanks, etc.) so that special local control may be difficult to achieve.

No precise specification or definition has been made of the temperatures referred to above. For the present purposes, it is adequate to define the requirements in terms of mounting-plate temperatures or perhaps local mean radiant temperatures. In terms of this rather loose definition, typical allowable temperatures range from 30 to 40°F for the lower limit to perhaps 70 to 80°F for the upper limit.

Factors Involved in Temperature Control. The mean temperature of an object in space is determined by the energy balance on that object. Except for the last few moments before plunging into a planetary atmosphere, a spacecraft is generally in a vacuum far below that which will support conductive or convective heat transfer; and since mass transfer is generally negligible, the only significant exchange is by radiation. Consider for simplicity a satellite made of a material of infinite thermal conductivity so that it is at a uniform temperature throughout. If it is not in the vicinity of a planet and has no internal power, its energy balance at equilibrium is found by equating the absorbed solar energy with the infrared energy emitted from the spacecraft:

$$\alpha G A_i = \epsilon \sigma T^4 A_e$$
$$T^4 = \frac{\alpha}{\epsilon} \frac{G}{\sigma} \frac{A_i}{A_e} \tag{8.1}$$

where T = absolute temperature

α = absorptance of surface coating for zero air mass solar spectrum

ϵ = emittance of surface for blackbody infrared spectrum corresponding to temperature of spacecraft

G = solar flux at local radial distance of spacecraft from sun

σ = Stefan-Boltzmann constant

A_i = cross-sectional area intercepting solar energy

A_e = emitting surface area

As is well known for opaque materials, absorptance equals emittance at a given wavelength or integrated over the same spectral curve, but by custom α is here reserved for the solar wavelengths and ϵ for the infrared wavelengths, so that α in general does not equal ϵ. The fourth power of the temperature is seen in Eq. (8.1) to be proportional to the ratio α/ϵ, so that the ratio itself becomes a convenient material property of interest.

If internal power w is uniformly dissipated throughout our imaginary spacecraft, the energy balance then becomes

$$\alpha G A_i + w = \epsilon \sigma T^4 A_e$$
$$T^4 = \frac{\alpha}{\epsilon} \frac{G}{\sigma} \frac{A_i}{A_e} + \frac{w}{\epsilon \sigma A_e} \tag{8.2}$$

The effect of the internal power on the mean temperature depends on the ease with which that energy can reach the surface and be radiated away, which in the case of our infinite-conductivity spacecraft is a function of the emittance ϵ only. Thus we are concerned with the emittance separately as well as with the ratio α/ϵ. It has often been the case with the spacecraft launched to date that the second term on the right, the internal-power term, is small relative to the first term, so that the internal power has only a minor effect on the spacecraft mean temperature.

In the preceding discussion, it has been tacitly assumed that the spacecraft exterior was a continuous surface of a single material. This is generally not the case. For multiple-surface materials and with no internal power, the temperature is expressed by

$$T^4 = \frac{G}{\sigma} \frac{\alpha_1 A_{i1} + \alpha_2 A_{i2} + \alpha_3 A_{i3} + \cdots}{\epsilon_1 A_{e1} + \epsilon_2 A_{e2} + \epsilon_3 A_{e3} + \cdots} \tag{8.3}$$

where the numerical subscripts represent the n surface materials. If our idealized isothermal spacecraft has moved to the vicinity of a planet, the energy balance including the transient effect becomes

Absorbed solar energy + absorbed solar energy reflected from planet + absorbed planet-emitted energy + internally dissipated power + stored energy = infrared energy emitted by spacecraft

Symbolically,

$$\sum \alpha_j G A_{iSj} + \sum \alpha_j' E_R A_{iRj} + \sum \epsilon_j' E_E A_{iEj}$$
$$+ w + W c_p \frac{dT}{d\theta} = \sum \epsilon_j \sigma T_j^4 A_{ej} \tag{8.4}$$

where E_R = flux of solar energy reflected from planet
E_E = flux of planet-emitted energy at altitude of spacecraft
A_{iS} = area absorbing direct solar energy
A_{iR} = area absorbing reflected solar energy
A_{iE} = area absorbing planet's emitted energy
α' = absorptance for solar reflected energy
ϵ' = absorptance for planet's emitted energy
w = internally dissipated power
$W c_p$ = thermal capacity of shell
θ = time

The summation signs indicate that the appropriate terms are summed over the j isothermal surface areas. The model represented by Eq. (8.4) is still highly idealized. In an actual case, each small region of the surface radiates at a different temperature, there is generally a highly complex radiation and conduction interchange within the spacecraft, there may be several sources of internal power (each with different thermal resistances to the exterior), and the thermal capacity of each element of the surface and interior must be separately treated. A complete mathematical description of the satellite temperature distribution involves the coupled problem of the external radiation exchange and the internal conduction, radiation, and convective energy exchanges. Convection is generally of concern only with a pressurized spacecraft which has some forced convection source or an artificially induced gravity, as in a spinning spacecraft.

Factors That Cause Temperature Changes

Depending on the spacecraft configuration and the particular mission under consideration, most factors occurring in Eq. (8.4) can vary and can, in turn, cause a change in the mean temperature of the spacecraft. These changes are now considered.

Solar Flux. 1. Eclipses. To examine the eclipse environment for a given satellite mission it is necessary to consider briefly some of the various possible satellite orbits.

a. A satellite whose orbit lies in the ecliptic plane will obviously be eclipsed by the planet once each orbit throughout the lifetime of the spacecraft.

b. If the orbit lies in the equatorial plane, and is at a relatively low altitude, the satellite will be eclipsed each orbit. At a sufficiently great altitude, because of the 23° tilt of the earth's equatorial plane, the satellite will experience an eclipse once each orbit during two periods of the year and will experience no eclipses for the other two periods. This is the case for a satellite in the so-called 24-hr orbit of the earth, which is roughly at an altitude of 19,400 nautical miles above the surface and in which the satellite stays approximately above a single location on the surface of the earth.

c. The case of the polar orbit is similar to the high-altitude equatorial case in that the satellite is eclipsed once each revolution for two periods during the year and is in full sunlight for the other two periods. Each of the two eclipsing intervals starts out with an eclipse of momentary duration, gradually increasing to an eclipse of maximum duration (the length depending on the satellite velocity) and gradually decreasing the shorter eclipse durations.

One special orbit is a near-polar 85° azimuth orbit in which the nodes regress just so as to compensate for the approximately 1°/day shift in the direction toward the sun. In this orbit the satellite will be in full sun continuously throughout the year or, depending on the launch time during the day, will be eclipsed once each orbit throughout the year.

The duration of the eclipse depends on the altitude of the satellite and the ellipticity of the orbit. For example, in a highly elliptical orbit it is possible to have very long eclipses, of the order of many hours, if they occur at the apogee of the orbit. It is often possible to delay the occurrence of such an apogee eclipse for several years, depending upon the orbit characteristics, by suitable choice of launch time.

The thermal consequences of an eclipse can be conveniently thought of as two effects. One is the transient cooling during the eclipse. The extent of this, in a simplified model, depends on the thermal capacity of the satellite and the external radiation resistance as determined by the surface infrared emittance. In an actual satellite, the various components each have different thermal capacities and different thermal couplings to the exterior and will therefore experience different transient thermal behavior during the eclipse. The other effect is due to the reduction in the total solar input integrated around the orbit. For example, a satellite in a polar orbit will at one time during the year experience full sun, 442 Btu/(hr)(ft^2); and at another time of the year, in a low-altitude orbit, the total solar flux averaged around the orbit will be only slightly greater than one-half of the nominal value.

2. The ellipticity of the earth's orbit results in a ± 3.7 per cent fluctuation in the solar input throughout the year, so that, other factors remaining constant, a satellite will be about 9°F hotter in December than in June.

3. For interplanetary missions the solar flux can change radically depending on how far toward or away from the sun the spacecraft progresses. At the orbit of Venus, solar flux is about 1.9 times that at the earth; at Mars, it is about 0.43 times that at the earth; at Mercury, 6.7 times; at Jupiter, 0.037 times; and at Saturn it is about 0.01 times that of the earth. The consequence of these changes in solar flux in terms of mean temperature is large. For example, a spacecraft will experience roughly a 90°F rise in temperature as it moves from the earth to Venus orbit, assuming other factors constant.

Uncertainties in the Solar Flux. The preceding more or less predictable factors all tend to cause changes in the radiation environment of spacecraft and therefore changes in the spacecraft temperature, if no means for compensation are provided for. In addition, we must be concerned with uncertain factors which will not actually change the radiation environment of the spacecraft once it is in orbit but which do require that the thermal design of the spacecraft be capable of accommodating a wider range of environment because of these uncertainties. Some of the uncertain factors that relate to the solar flux are as follows:

1. The present best estimate of the solar flux at the earth's mean orbital distance from the sun is 442 Btu/(hr)(ft^2), with an uncertainty of ± 2 per cent.

2. Guidance errors can lead to uncertainty in the trajectory of a planetary earth satellite that can have a marked effect on the eclipse situation. This may be especially true for the apogee eclipse of a planetary satellite in a very highly elliptical orbit.

3. For interplanetary flights, the final velocity may be only slightly in excess of earth escape velocity, so that relatively small uncertainties in burnout velocity can result in a relatively large uncertainty in the mid-course or coasting velocity. This in turn leads to a large uncertainty in the radial distance to the sun and therefore in the solar flux as a function of time of flight. Such velocity uncertainties were of great significance to the temperature-control system in the Pioneer V interplanetary probe.

Planetary Emitted Flux. For the earth—and presumably for any other planet with an appreciable atmosphere—the infrared energy emitted by the planet is relatively independent of latitude and longitude and varies in a predictable manner with altitude. For the earth at low altitude the flux is about 68 Btu/(hr)(ft^2). In the absence of an atmosphere, as for example in the case of the moon, the emitted flux varies with angular position measured from the subsolar point because of the large temperature variations on the surface.

Two aspects of the earth-emitted flux result in uncertainties that must be accounted for in the thermal design of the spacecraft. One is the magnitude of the flux, which is known with much less precision than that of the solar flux. This is still truer of the moon, and for the other planets there is relatively poor knowledge of the planetary thermal-balance conditions and the emitted flux. The second factor arises from lack of adequate knowledge of the emission spectral characteristics. In the case of the earth, for example, it is known that the emitted flux comes primarily from the surrounding gaseous atmosphere whose spectral characteristics differ significantly from the blackbody spectrum corresponding to the earth's equilibrium temperature. Lack of knowledge of this spectral characteristic results in uncertainty in the effective absorptance of the spacecraft surface material for the earth-emitted energy.

Planetary Reflected Solar Energy. The same altitude dependence applies for the solar energy reflected from the earth or a nearby planet as for the infrared energy emitted by the planet. In addition, the reflected solar energy varies with the orbit-plane attitude with respect to the sun and with the instantaneous position of the planet in the orbit. For example, in a twilight polar orbit the reflected solar flux is approximately constant, whereas in a noon orbit in which the sun lies in the orbit plane the reflected flux varies from zero to a maximum of about 160 Btu/(hr)(ft^2) at the subsolar point.

The magnitude of this flux is approximately as uncertain as the earth-emitted flux and is known to vary with such factors as cloud coverage.

The absorptance of the surface materials for the planetary reflected solar energy is not precisely the same as for the direct solar flux because of changes in the spectral characteristics after reflection from the planet and its atmosphere. The extent of these changes and, in turn, the effective absorptance for this flux are not well known.

Thermal-radiation Properties. Knowledge of the thermal radiation properties of the spacecraft surfaces can be deficient in two respects. The first has to do with uncertainties in measurement of the properties in the laboratory; and the second is concerned with the changes in those properties due to handling and exposure to the air before launch, to possible heating during launch, and to exposure to the space environment in orbit. These factors are discussed further in the sections on Thermal-radiation Properties and Materials and on Optical Properties in the Space Environment.

Shape-factor Considerations. For a spin-stabilized spacecraft the spin axis is nominally fixed in inertial space, though various disturbing torques can decrease the spin rate and gradually shift the spin-axis attitude in space. Furthermore, the initial attitude of the spin axis may be uncertain because of possible angular tip-off at separation of the various stages of a multistage booster vehicle. For an attitude-controlled spacecraft or a spin-stabilized one not affected by the above-described uncertainties, the shape factors for the various incident radiation fluxes are predictable at least in a formal sense. However, shape irregularities and miscellaneous appendages such as interstage structure, solar-cell paddles, and various other projecting components all tend to make determination of the shape factors difficult and, to some extent, uncertain.

Internal Temperature Gradients. The preceding factors all result in either actual variations or uncertainties in the spacecraft mean temperature. For the present purpose mean temperature can be defined to be that temperature which the spacecraft would attain if zero internal thermal resistances are assumed. An actual spacecraft can support large temperature differences across it. For example, temperature differences exceeding 100°F were encountered in Explorer VI. A given component of this spacecraft located near one end of the thermal gradient will experience large changes in temperature as the sun orientation changes during the spacecraft lifetime.

Internal Power Fluctuations. As various components are turned on and off, or changed in power level, the locally dissipated energy causes local temperature changes, the amount depending on the power dissipated and the particular thermal circuitry of the spacecraft interior.

Summary. The possible range in a thermal environment for which a temperature-control system must be designed depends strongly on the particular mission and spacecraft configuration. The predictable factors just described may tend to compensate partially for one another and must be taken into account in their proper time-history sequence, and the uncertain factors must be accounted for in a statistically meaningful manner. Typical missions have been examined for actual spacecraft designs in which the predictable factors alone yield temperature variations of 70°F and more for an earth satellite in a low-altitude polar orbit. The corresponding figures for an interplanetary probe could be much larger, depending on the distance traveled radially to or from the sun. When, in addition, all the uncertain factors are included, it is clear that the possible range in temperature experienced by the spacecraft components can far exceed the limits generally desired, as discussed in the section on Need for Temperature Control, unless an active thermal-control system is employed to confine the temperatures to the desired range. A thorough review of the factors entering into the thermal balance and treatment of the uncertainties is given by Camack and Edwards [1].

Thermal-radiation Properties and Materials

Material Form Required. Surface treatment of the spacecraft's external structural materials may provide the needed thermal-radiation properties. However, for various reasons it is often desirable that the materials be in the form of thin lightweight coatings that can be applied to the exterior surface. The area of coverage is generally extensive, so anything but a thin coating might impose an undesirable weight penalty. Patterns of several materials are sometimes appropriate, and these are most readily obtained with separately applied coatings. There occasionally arises a need for last-minute changes in the coating pattern because of a change in the launch date (this, for example, was the case in the original lunar probes Pioneers I and II; for Pioneer II the coating pattern actually was changed when the launch was rescheduled from the first planned day to the following day). Certain combinations of materials involving the same parent materials sometimes require incompatible processes and can only be achieved by separately applied coatings, for example, by the combination of vacuum-deposited aluminum and anodized aluminum in adjacent areas.

Properties Required. For various spacecraft thermal applications, good use could be made of values of solar absorptance α and infrared emittance ϵ covering the entire range from zero to one. In particular, both high and low values of the ratio α/ϵ are especially useful for certain forms of active temperature-control systems. Materials which absorb over the entire thermal spectrum, that is, have high α and high ϵ, are of use. Similarly, materials which reflect well over the entire spectrum, that is, have low values of α and ϵ, are also useful, although the effect of this combination of properties can sometimes be achieved by insulation techniques. For certain applications solar absorptance is of no importance and only high infrared emittance is needed. This is of importance because with presently available materials a higher infrared emittance can be achieved if there is no simultaneous requirement on solar absorptance.

For temperature-control systems we are generally interested only in diffuse properties, such as diffuse reflectance; whereas specular reflectance may be of importance for optical systems, solar collectors, and other special applications. Certain features of some temperature-control systems do make use of specular reflectance. For temperature-control applications, the appropriate radiation properties are needed at approximately room temperature. There are other applications where the need is for properties at high or low temperatures. For example, high-temperature properties may be needed for solar collectors and for radiators, whereas relatively low-temperature properties are of interest for solar cells during eclipse periods, for components which operate most suitably at cryogenic temperatures (such as infrared sensors), and for boil-off determinations of cryogenic propellants.

Applicability of Existing Thermal-radiation-property Data. A great body of thermal-radiation-property data exists in the literature. While these data are useful as a guide to the kinds of properties obtainable with various types of materials, most of them are useless for purposes of design. There are a variety of reasons for this:

1. Many of the data reported are for radiation properties not directly applicable to the spacecraft thermal-control problem; or, what is worse, no indication of the type of radiation property is given. In general, the diffuse properties are required; however, most data reported are for specular properties. For emittance, hemispherical values are generally required; however, most data reported are for normal or near-normal angles. Absorptance data are often needed as a function of incident angle, but most data reported are for a single near-normal angle. Many emittance data reported are for a total measurement, which is often made at a relatively high temperature; for thermal-control purposes such data are therefore applicable to a somewhat incorrect spectral curve and to the wrong material temperature. Total solar absorptances are often measured directly with the solar energy as it exists at the laboratory; this spectrum is generally markedly different from the solar spectrum in space. While total data (that is, integrated over the spectrum of interest) are generally needed, spectral data, from which the total value can be obtained, are generally more flexible because they can be applied to a wide range of radiation conditions.

2. Measurement errors. While radiation-property measurement is a moderately old art, having been given its initial significant impetus

around the turn of the century, it has not yet reached the status of a well-established laboratory science. In fact, only in the past few years have the subtleties of the various types of radiation measurements and techniques been fully appreciated [2, 3]. Equipment and techniques to measure directly the appropriate properties are, in many cases, still lacking. Therefore, a cataloging of the measurement errors represented by existing data is primarily an indication of the complexities and subtleties of the measurements in the present state of development of the science rather than a criticism of the experimenter. Nevertheless, from the standpoint of the designer using the data, such errors represent serious shortcomings that must be fully recognized.

A variety of experimental and equipment difficulties and shortcomings exist. Lenses and mirrors that do not have spectrally flat optical characteristics are often present in the instrument optical path. Water vapor may be present in detrimental amounts; the reflecting surface in integrating spheres, often MgO, is sensitive to water vapor and may have to be renewed as frequently as needed. Magnesium oxide is partially transparent in the wavelengths for which it is used and must be applied in a relatively heavy coat to avoid erroneous data, a fact not always appreciated by the experimenter. Nonuniform wall temperatures in a heated cavity used for infrared reflectance yield erroneous data. Spectral measurements are difficult to obtain at wavelengths longer than about 50 μ, and much of the available equipment is limited to about 25 μ. This last point is significant in its effect on the property obtained for a low-temperature spectrum (for example, 18 per cent of the energy of a 50°F blackbody spectrum, as well as 36 per cent of a −100°F spectrum, is beyond 25 μ).

Aside from the classical inadequacy of material descriptions such as *green paint*, many of the reported data are for materials that are poorly defined in more subtle ways. The surface optical properties are usually sensitive to the details of a materials processing technique. For example, in anodizing aluminum there are many parameters of importance to the process, specification of all of them being essential for a complete material description. In vacuum deposition, rate of deposit, residual chamber pressure, and a variety of other factors all contribute to a complete material definition. Usually such information is lacking in a tabulated material description. The condition of the specimen's substrate may be of importance; for example, striation and roughness resulting from machining can affect the property measurement and therefore represent a significant factor in the material description. Because of such lack of proper material description, materials cannot generally be duplicated, and a large part of the reported data is thus rendered useless. In most cases the only solution to this situation is to measure the appropriate properties on one's own materials by using, of course, proper instrumentation and correct measurement techniques.

Once the spacecraft has been prepared with materials of the desired properties, there remains a practical problem of ensuring that the properties remain unchanged before the spacecraft reaches altitudes above the atmosphere. A certain amount of handling of the exterior surfaces may be unavoidable. Some of the more delicate coatings can be protected by plastic peel coats until a few days before the scheduled launch, but if any last-minute cleaning is necessary to remove fingerprints, grease, dirt, etc., there is always a danger that the cleaning process itself may affect delicate surface properties. During the launch interval the satellite and its materials are presumably protected from aerodynamic heating by a protective fairing, which is jettisoned after leaving the sensible atmosphere. Because of the weight penalty in carrying the fairing along longer than necessary, there is often a potential danger in jettisoning it too soon and therefore causing heating of the satellite surfaces to a level that may affect the optical properties of the surfaces.

Optical Properties in the Space Environment

Most of the factors of the space environment represent new and untried conditions for spacecraft materials. Whether these materials and, in particular, their sensitive surface optical properties remain stable in this environment is a question of importance for all spacecraft with long intended lifetimes. Among the factors of importance are (1) the vacuum of space, in which the pressure is such that sublimation and decomposition occur virtually unimpeded; (2) ultraviolet radiation, X radiation, and the harder radiation of the radiation belts; (3) single-particle radiation; and (4) micrometeorites. Certain of these factors may present no problems. For example, micrometeorites are generally believed to be of sufficiently low flux that they will have no significant effect from the standpoint of spacecraft thermal control [4]. On the other hand, the deleterious effect of some of the other factors can be readily demonstrated on particular materials. Sensitive materials can generally be avoided, but the prediction of the general behavior of even seemingly rugged materials in space is impeded by two factors. One is that many aspects of the environment are not well known, for example, the detailed structure of the solar ultraviolet spectrum and of the radiations in the trapped radiation belts. The second aspect is that many of these factors of the space environment are difficult or impossible to reproduce in the laboratory, even singly, let alone in combination where their effects may enhance one another. Ultimately material experiments must be performed in space, and in fact in many different types of environments to be found in the various regions of space. The designer does not always have the freedom to choose materials that are apparently rugged; certain optical properties are available, for example, only in delicate vacuum-deposited forms. It remains for experience and space experiments to determine whether fears of the space environment are well grounded or not. For the present, it would seem prudent both to avoid suspicious materials and to provide a temperature-control system with sufficient flexibility to allow for some change in material optical properties due to exposure in the space environment.

Temperature-control Systems

Passive Systems. A passive thermal-control system is defined here to be one employing fixed external coatings in which there is no active element, either mechanical or electrical. The great majority of spacecraft flown to date have had passive thermal-control systems. In the first- and second-generation satellites, the mission requirements in terms of orbit, lifetime, internal component complexity, etc., have generally been sufficiently simple from the thermal-environment standpoint to allow a passive system to be used successfully. Experience to date demonstrates that a passive design can achieve a spacecraft mean temperature in orbit within about 5 to 10°F of the designed mean temperature (this was the experience, for example, in the case of Explorer VI).

An interesting application of a passive design was that of Pioneer V, a spacecraft designed to reach the vicinity of the Venus orbit. In the course of its journey, it would experience approximately a doubling of the solar flux from that occurring at the earth's distance from the sun. Pioneer V was launched on March 11, 1960, and covered a distance of over 22 million statute miles from the earth, over a period of 31 months, before radio contact with it was lost. This spacecraft was spin-stabilized, that is, its spin axis was fixed in inertial space. In an approximate manner, the trajectory flown may be considered to be such that the sun moved halfway around the spin axis during the half orbit to Venus. That is, the sun look-angle increased from zero (looking straight down the spin axis at one end of the spacecraft) to 180° (looking at the opposite end of the spin axis and spacecraft). If the external coating is chosen to be appropriate for the solar flux at the earth's distance from the sun at the start of the flight (sun look-angle equal to zero) and is also chosen appropriately on the other half of the spacecraft for the Venus distance from the sun, then in a rough sense the temperature will be appropriate at both the earth and Venus. In actual fact, partly because of three-dimensional effects and partly because of other considerations, the orbit that was flown resulted in a sun look-angle of 35° at the start, decreasing down to about 15° at 20 days, increasing back to 35° in about 40 days, and increasing to 135° upon reaching the Venus orbit at approximately 105 days after

Fig. 8.1   Pioneer V interplanetary spacecraft.

launch.   An appropriate pattern was chosen using two materials, one
with an α of 0.92 and ϵ of 0.87 and the other with an α of 0.25 and an ϵ of
0.84.   A pattern was achieved which maintained a mean temperature
within the desired range over the entire trajectory, as well as at the end

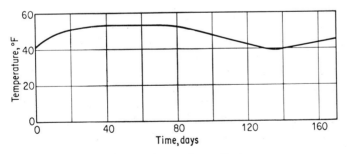

Fig. 8.2   Pioneer V mean internal temperature.

points of Earth and Venus.   The pattern is shown in Fig. 8.1 and the
mean temperature is indicated in Fig. 8.2.   During the $3\frac{1}{2}$ months of
transmitted data, the measured temperatures followed the predicted
curve within about 5 to 10°F.   This spacecraft is illustrative of the
rather intricate interrelatedness of the thermal-control system with the

trajectory and orbital conditions of flight which sometimes occur. The flight path that was finally selected was not the optimum one from purely trajectory considerations but rather was chosen to satisfy a thermal-control requirement that the sun look-angle increase from approximately zero to approximately 180°. It would be entirely possible, from trajectory considerations alone, for the sun look-angle to start at 90° at the earth, decrease to zero, and increase back to 90° at the Venus orbit. Clearly the coating pattern and therefore the effective α/ϵ of the spinning spacecraft at both the earth and Venus would be the same and would therefore not compensate for the increase in solar flux. The actual sun look-angle history noted above was about the limit of allowable deviation from the ideal 0 to 180° change.

Active Systems. A variety of mechanizations of active control may be envisioned.

1. The spacecraft can be made to be relatively cool by means of passive coatings, though still high enough to satisfy the majority of the components, with local thermostatically controlled electrical dissipation to warm those few components requiring a higher temperature. While this scheme is quite feasible, in practice the types of components that require the heating, such as liquid-fuel tanks and secondary storage batteries, may be so large that the "local" heating may involve a large fraction of the spacecraft and thus require a large power dissipation. Unless excess power is available, such a design may not be a practical one from the point of view of the overall system.

2. With a nonspherical shape, such as a relatively flat disk, the mean temperature can be increased or decreased by orienting the spacecraft so as to increase or decrease the surface area intercepting solar energy. This would normally not be a practical design in view of other conflicting requirements for the spacecraft attitude-control system.

3. A number of materials change optical properties as a function of temperature. For example, silicon monoxide and other materials like it have the self-controlling tendency to increase in emittance as their temperature increases, thus tending to limit the temperature rise, and vice versa. Various experimenters are currently examining such materials, but the materials unfortunately have a general characteristic that their emissivity is too weak a function of temperature to be advantageously employed in the manner indicated.

4. Some materials undergo reversible optical-property changes as a result of phase changes, Curie-point transitions, etc. For example, the so-called thermochromic materials reversibly change color, and therefore solar absorptance, as a sharp function of temperature. Unfortunately these materials may be in the form of gels, liquids, etc., generally with low vapor pressures and therefore unsuitable for the exterior surface. They

could be encapsulated in materials transparent in the solar wavelengths, but at the present at least they do not seem to offer enough advantages to overcome their obvious shortcomings for use in a temperature-control system.

5. Mechanical changes of radiation properties and areas are the systems presently given most consideration. Two general types of such systems are discussed below.

Fig. 8.3   Able 5 lunar satellite.

In a radiation-balance design the internally dissipated power is generally a small factor in the overall heat balance and therefore contributes only in a minor way to the mean temperature level, although the dissipated power may have important local effects. The energy relationship is then a balance, in the equilibrium state, between the absorbed incident radiant energy and the emitted radiant energy. Active control of the temperature may be effected by varying the exposed areas of two materials, one with a relatively high α/ϵ ratio and one with a relatively low α/ϵ ratio. This can be accomplished by a venetian-blind arrangement, by moving vanes, or in a variety of other ways.

The first spacecraft with such a temperature control-system were the

Atlas-Able 4 and Able 5 satellites, designed by Space Technology Laboratories, Inc., for NASA.   These were intended to be orbiting satellites of the moon, to be put into lunar orbit by means of monopropellant hydrazine engines aboard the spacecraft to reduce the approach velocity sufficiently to allow lunar capture.   Partly because of the hydrazine fuel and fairly severe environmental conditions, such as lunar-eclipse durations exceeding 2 hr, it was necessary to employ an active thermal-control system.   The spacecraft and its thermal-control system are pictured in Fig. 8.3.   The spacecraft was spin-stabilized with the possibility of any

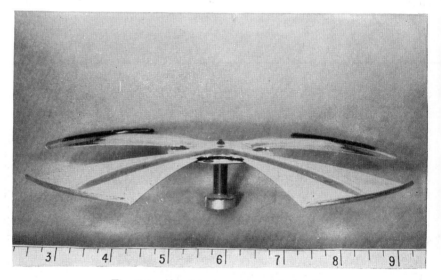

Fig. 8.4   Able 5 temperature-control unit.

sun orientation with respect to the spin axis during the spacecraft's lifetime.

The thermal design was briefly as follows.   Thermal energy exchange took place primarily at 50 circular areas well distributed over the external skin.   Each circle consisted of an alternating arrangement of two materials in the eight 45° sectors of the circle, one material with a high α/ϵ ratio and the other with a low α/ϵ ratio.   The circular areas were covered by a four-bladed mask shown in Fig. 8.4, which could completely cover one or the other of the two materials, or some fraction of each, at any intermediate position.   The mask was driven by a bimetallic spring at the inner end of the body, arranged so that the spring "saw" a portion of the spacecraft interior.   The plastic body of the unit was made of a poor thermal conductor so that the bimetallic spring was better coupled thermally to the spacecraft interior than it was to the skin of the spacecraft.

The mask was rotated the 45° of its travel by a 25°F change in temperature of the spring. With the spring at 50°F, the mask fully exposed the high α/ϵ material; and at 75°F, the low α/ϵ material was fully exposed. The activation thus provided self-powered closed-loop control of the interior temperature. The remainder of the spacecraft's skin, outside the control circles, was covered with a material of low α and low ϵ, so that the contribution to the overall energy balance from the uncontrolled area would be as small as possible. That area was vacuum-deposited aluminum, over a smooth plastic substrate, with an absorptance of 0.10 and an emittance of 0.05. The high α/ϵ material in the control areas was a form of titanium dioxide with an α of 0.65 and an ϵ of 0.13, and the low α/ϵ material was a particular form of anodized aluminum with an α of 0.20 and an ϵ of 0.80. A more complete description of this system is given in Ref. 5.

The system has the capability of compensating for fairly large changes in the external environment, such as an interplanetary mission to Venus; and furthermore it minimizes the decrease in temperature during long eclipses because the masks automatically decrease the effective emittance of the spacecraft during this time.

If a spacecraft is always oriented so that the sun irradiates only certain of its sides but not others, as may be the case in a fully attitude-controlled spacecraft or a spin-stabilized spacecraft with the spin axis normal to the ecliptic plane, then it is possible to insulate the solar-irradiated sides so that the solar input plays little or no part in the spacecraft energy balance. If, for simplicity, we consider the spacecraft far removed from a planet, then the energy balance is achieved between the internally dissipated power and the spacecraft-emitted energy. The unirradiated, uninsulated faces are covered with a surface of high emittance, and the emitted radiation is controlled by a set of louvers covering to the radiation surface. The emitting area is then a function of the louver position, which may be controlled by sensors measuring the radiation-plate temperature to which the spacecraft components are mounted. Even if the spacecraft is not oriented with respect to the sun as described, the system may still be employed if the radiation plate is covered with a material of sufficiently low α, and at the same time having a high ϵ, to minimize the solar input. It is required that the internally dissipated power be at least as great as the heat losses from the entire spacecraft when the louvers are fully closed. A very high order of insulation may be achieved for the spacecraft sides with multiple-layer reflective insulation, which, in the vacuum environment, achieves effective thermal conductivities of the order of 3×10^{-5} Btu/(hr)(ft²)(°F/ft).

The advantages of this design are that the spacecraft is insensitive to eclipses and other changes in the solar flux, as would occur on an interplanetary journey. The temperatures within the spacecraft are much more uniform than in the radiation-balance design since there is no large external input over any part of the surface, and the problem of sensitivity of optical properties of the space environment is greatly diminished. The primary property of interest is the high emittance on the radiating plate, but this is a property which tends to be stable in space environment in any case.

The two types of designs described herein, the radiation-balance design and the insulated design, are intended to be illustrative. In general, any spacecraft thermal design is at least partially a combination of the two, and there are many spacecraft designs in which both the external radiation balance and the insulated features are combined in a single spacecraft.

Spacecraft Internal Thermal Environment

The primary internal thermal problem is one of minimizing temperature gradients so that all points within the spacecraft will be at or near the mean temperature, as determined by spacecraft thermal-control system. The insulated thermal design discussed above eases this problem, but even here it may be necessary in the case of high-power-dissipating components to ensure that the components are well coupled thermally to the external radiating surfaces. In the radiation-balance thermal design discussed above it is clearly undesirable to couple the components well to those portions of the external surface which experience large temperature deviations from the mean temperature. In an unpressurized spacecraft of the radiation-balance type, minimizing the temperature gradients on the interior presents practical difficulties; providing good conduction paths is often costly in weight, and conduction interfaces between materials often introduce significant temperature differences, especially for interfaces in vacuum [6]. Interface thermal resistances can be reduced by use of retained greases and soft metal shims and by other techniques. There are occasions when it is desirable to isolate components thermally so that one is faced with the problem of increasing thermal contact resistances. There are a variety of techniques taken from vacuum technology to accomplish this, such as employing multiple interfaces or powder of hard oxide materials in an interface.

Silicon Solar Cells

The silicon photovoltaic converters which power today's long-life spacecraft have the characteristic that the minority-carrier lifetime is decreased as the temperature of the solar cell is increased. In terms of conversion efficiency, the temperature effect is to reduce the efficiency by about six-tenths of 1 per cent for each degree centigrade increase in temperature above a nominal standard. Unfortunately, the optical properties of a silicon solar cell are such as to cause relatively high temperatures at thermal equilibrium in space. This arises because silicon is partially transparent in the infrared and therefore has a low infrared emittance and, in consequence, a high value of α/ϵ. It becomes necessary therefore to coat the solar cells with a material of a high infrared emittance which is at the same time highly transparent in solar wavelengths from 0.4 to 1.1 μ, the region where the solar cell is electrically sensitive. Possible coatings are thin glass slips, silicon oxide vacuum-deposited on the cell, transparent plastic coatings, etc. To date, glass slips have been the primary means of raising the long-wavelength emissivity. When glass is used it must be cemented to the cell so that it is in intimate thermal contact with the cell, so as to avoid a greenhouse effect. The adhesives used to cement on the glass are generally sensitive to ultraviolet radiation and must be protected from it by means of selective ultraviolet cutoff interference filters to absorb or reflect the ultraviolet energy below 0.4 μ. If the filter is a reflecting type it further reduces the solar-cell temperature by rejecting a certain fraction of the unwanted solar energy. An additional small benefit can potentially be obtained by reflecting away the solar infrared energy above 1.1 μ rather than absorbing it in the glass and solar cell. Table 8.1 demonstrates the gain to be made by use of a typical glass–UV filter coating on solar cells at three positions in the solar system.

Table 8.1 Solar-cell Temperatures
(Normal to sun, nominal 10% cell, panel back $\epsilon = 0.9$)

Position	Temperature, °C		Efficiency, %		Relative power		
	Un-coated	Coated	Un-coated	Coated	Un-coated	Coated	Reference
Venus...........	130	96	4.7	6.4	0.90	1.22	1.91
Earth...........	66	35	8.0	9.5	0.80	0.95	1.0
Mars...........	2	−23	11.1	12.4	0.48	0.54	0.43

If solar cells are on the spacecraft body, they generally participate in the energy exchange with the body, to an appreciable extent. However, when the cells are on external panels, as is often the case, they essentially form an isolated thermal system, except for some radiation exchange with the spacecraft. In such case the temperature is determined by their complete thermal circuit, including radiation exchange at the back of the panel on which they are mounted as well as on their front surface.

Because solar cells, especially when mounted on external panels, have a very small thermal capacity per square foot of surface and for the reason stated above have high surface emittance, they tend to decrease in temperature very rapidly when the spacecraft is eclipsed from the sun. Depending on the eclipse duration and the remaining radiation environment (i.e., planetary radiation), the solar cells may drop to destructively low temperatures during the eclipse. Failures due to thermal stresses in the brittle assemblage of silicon solar cells, including glass, adhesives, and substructure, have been observed in temperatures beginning at about $-160°F$. This temperature can be reached by the solar cells in an eclipse of the order of 1 hr duration. Fortunately, progress is being made in reducing the temperature at which failure occurs. Assembled solar cells have been made to survive the temperature of liquid nitrogen, about $-320°F$, but there are missions and spacecraft configurations for which still lower temperatures are possible.

Other Thermal Problems

The range and difficulty of possible spacecraft thermal problems is limited only by the complexity of possible spacecraft configurations and components. Among some of the interesting thermal problems which have arisen or will arise are the following:

Mirrors for Solar-energy Collection. Spacecraft power systems such as the solar-thermionic type or solar-thermoelectric type require high temperatures for efficient power conversion, the former requiring $3000°F$ or higher and the latter $1500°F$ or higher at the collector focus of the mirror collection system. The figure of the mirror must be maintained very accurately in order to achieve such high temperatures, especially in the thermionic case. Thermal gradients across the mirror and transient changes of temperature due to eclipses or due to changing solar flux in an interplanetary mission can seriously affect the mirror shape and reduce the achievable temperature.

Telescopes. The mirrors in astronomical telescopes, and especially the dimensional stability between the critical mirrors and the sensor in the telescope, impose very severe limitations on possible temperature variations throughout the system, usually to the order of a small fraction of a degree. Generally massive construction, using materials with a high thermal conductivity per pound such as beryllium, is employed in the solution of this problem. It is essential to reduce the number of interfaces and the temperature drop across those which are unavoidable.

Manned Spacecraft. The presence of man in large spacecraft and space stations introduces requirements for air handling and air conditioning which may tend to ease the problem of reducing internal thermal gradients. In any case, such devices merely alter the temperature environment within the spacecraft by locally altering the distribution of temperature around the mean temperature. The mean temperature itself is still determined by the same kinds of energy-balance considerations that apply to small spacecraft as described above. The principles remain the same although the magnitude involved in area, volume, power levels, etc., will materially affect their practical solution.

It is apparent that spacecraft thermal control is a many-faceted problem which must be solved from a systems viewpoint rather than as a single subsystem. Thermal problems influence many aspects of the spacecraft structure, including shape, materials, location of components, use of panels for solar cells, etc. In addition, such diverse factors as vehicle launching time, trajectory and orbit considerations, and equipment operation schedules all have a strong interaction with the spacecraft thermal design.

REFERENCES

1. Camack, Walter G., and Donald K. Edwards: Effect of Surface Thermal Radiation Characteristics on the Temperature Problem in Satellites, in Clauss, F. J. (ed.): "Surface Effects on Spacecraft Materials," John Wiley & Sons, Inc., New York, 1960.
2. Bevans, J. T.: A Review of Thermal Radiation and Measuring Techniques, *Space Technology Laboratories* TN-60-0000-09096, June 24, 1960.
3. Dunkle, R. V.: Thermal Radiation Characteristics of Surfaces, paper presented at the ASME Annual Meeting, 1960. (To be published in *J. Heat Transfer*.)
4. Beard, David B.: Interplanetary Dust Distribution and Erosion Effects, in Clauss, F. J. (ed.): "Surface Effects on Spacecraft Materials," John Wiley & Sons, Inc., New York, 1960.
5. Acker, R. M., R. P. Lipkis, and J. E. Vehrencamp: Temperature Control System for the Atlas Able-4 Lunar Satellite, presented at the Aviation Conference, Dallas, Tex., June 5–9, 1960.
6. Fried, Erwin, and F. A. Costello: The Interface Thermal Contact Resistance Problem in Space Vehicles, presented at ARS Lifting Re-entry Vehicles Conference, Palm Springs, Calif., April 4–6, 1961.

9

Evaporation Effects on
Materials in Space

L. D. JAFFE
JOHN B. RITTENHOUSE
MATERIALS RESEARCH SECTION
JET PROPULSION LABORATORY
CALIFORNIA INSTITUTE OF TECHNOLOGY
PASADENA, CALIFORNIA

Sublimation of inorganic materials in the vacuum of space can be predicted accurately from knowledge of their vapor pressures and, for compounds, of their free energies. Among the elements, cadmium, zinc, and selenium are readily lost near room temperature, and magnesium at elevated temperatures. Selective loss at individual grains and at grain boundaries can produce some surface roughening. Evaporation rates of low-molecular-weight single-component oils can also be calculated from vapor pressures; most are rather high. Polymers lose weight in vacuum by decomposition; nylon, acrylics, polysulfides, and neoprene show high decomposition rates near room temperature. Many other polymers, including polyethylene and isoprene, are stable to high temperatures in vacuum. Engineering properties are, in general, little affected in vacuum unless appreciable loss of mass occurs.

The problem which perhaps first comes to mind in considering materials behavior in space is that of evaporation or sublimation into the space vacuum. The range of gas pressures encountered in space is indicated in Table 9.1. The pressure falls from about 10^3 mm Hg at the earth's surface to 10^{-6} mm at 200 km (125 miles) and to less than 10^{-12} mm beyond 6,500 km (4,000 miles) altitude. As 10^{-6} mm is a typical pressure for a good laboratory high-vacuum system, and 10^{-12} mm is about the best vacuum that has ever been achieved in the laboratory, these figures show that space is a very good vacuum indeed.

252

Table 9.1 Gas Pressures and Concentrations in Space†

Altitude	Pressure, mm Hg	Concentration, molecules, atoms, or ions/cm^3	Composition
Sea level.................	$760 \simeq 10^3$	2.5×10^{19}	78% N_2, 21% O_2, 1% A
30 km (100,000 ft)..........	$9 \simeq 10^1$	4×10^{17}	N_2, O_2, A
200 km (125 miles).........	10^{-6}	10^{10}	N_2, O, O_2, O^+
800 km (500 miles).........	10^{-9}	10^6	O, He, O^+, H
6,500 km (4,000 miles)......	10^{-13}	10^3	H^+, H, He^+
Above 22,000 km (14,000 miles).................	$<10^{-13}$	10^1–10^2	85% H^+, 15% He^{++}

† Based on Refs. 1 to 18.

Because there has been some confusion over the applicability of calculated rates of sublimation in vacuum, it may be worthwhile to review the basis upon which such calculations are made.

Loss of Inorganic Materials in Vacuum

The rate at which molecules leave a surface into vacuum was derived by Langmuir in 1913 [19]. Langmuir considered, essentially, a closed box made of the material of interest. The interior of the box contains no air, only vapor of the solid from which the walls are made (Fig. 9.1a). The temperature of the box is uniform and such that the vapor pressure

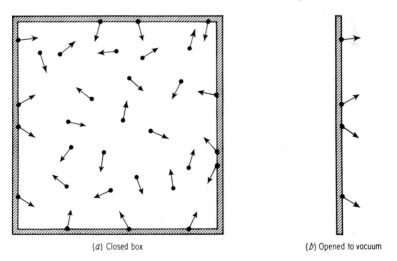

(a) Closed box   (b) Opened to vacuum

Fig. 9.1 Sublimation of solid into vacuum—schematic diagrams of motion of vapor molecules. (a) Closed box; (b) box opened to vacuum.

of the material is low; solid and vapor are in equilibrium. The number of gas molecules striking any area of the wall is then equal to the number leaving that area—otherwise the wall would thin or thicken, which would be inconsistent with the assumption of equilibrium. It has been shown experimentally [19–21] that reflection of vapor molecules from the surface can be neglected (that is, the accommodation coefficient is essentially unity); thus, the vapor molecules leaving the wall are those subliming from it. The rate of sublimation is therefore equal to the rate at which vapor molecules strike the wall.

The number striking the wall is given by the kinetic theory of gases as

$$u = \tfrac{1}{4}nv_m \tag{9.1}$$

where u = number of molecules striking wall per unit area per unit time
    n = number of molecules per unit volume of vapor
    v_m = mean velocity of molecules in vapor
To find n, the vapor may be considered to be an ideal gas, obeying the law

$$pV = NRT \tag{9.2}$$

or, for a unit volume,

$$p = NRT = nkT \tag{9.3}$$

so that

$$n = \frac{p}{kT} \tag{9.4}$$

where p = gas pressure
    V = volume
    N = number of moles
    R = gas constant
    T = absolute temperature
    k = Boltzmann's constant
To find v_m, note that the energy of a molecule per translational degree of freedom is

$$kT = \tfrac{1}{2}mv^2 \tag{9.5}$$

or

$$v = \sqrt{\frac{2kT}{m}} \tag{9.6}$$

where m = mass of gas molecule
    v = most probable molecular velocity
For a Boltzmann distribution, the average velocity is slightly different:

$$v_m = \sqrt{\frac{8}{\pi}\frac{kT}{m}} \tag{9.7}$$

Substituting from Eqs. (9.4) and (9.7) in Eq. (9.1) gives

$$u = \frac{1}{4} \frac{p}{kT} \sqrt{\frac{8}{\pi} \frac{kT}{m}} \frac{p}{\sqrt{2\pi mkT}} \tag{9.8}$$

The rate W at which mass reaches the wall is

$$W = um = p \sqrt{\frac{m}{2\pi kT}} \tag{9.9}$$

However,

$$m = \frac{M}{N_A} \tag{9.10}$$

where M = molecular weight
N_A = Avogadro's number

or

$$W = p \sqrt{\frac{M}{2\pi N_A kT}} \tag{9.11}$$

Inserting suitable values of the constants N_A and k gives

$$W = \frac{p}{17.14} \sqrt{\frac{M}{T}} \tag{9.12}$$

where W is in g/(cm²)(sec), p is in mm Hg, and T is in degrees Kelvin. Since this is the rate at which vapor molecules reach the wall, it is also the rate at which molecules sublime from the wall.

Now, let us open the box to a "perfect" vacuum, that is, a vacuum from which no molecules return (Fig. 9.1b). The rate at which the molecules leave the wall is unchanged. The Langmuir equation (9.12) thus gives the rate of sublimation of a solid into a perfect vacuum. It may be put in the form [22]

$$S = 1.85 \times 10^6 \frac{p}{\rho} \sqrt{\frac{M}{T}} \tag{9.13}$$

where S = rate of sublimation, cm/year
ρ = density of solid material, g/cm³

Equations (9.12) and (9.13) give the rate of sublimation when none of the molecules leaving the surface return to it. If the vacuum is poor, so that evaporating molecules can collide with air molecules and be scattered back to the surface, the net rate of loss will be lower, but it can never be higher. (Note that the sublimation rates W and S increase with temperature even though $\sqrt{T}$ is in the denominator, because the vapor pressure p increases rapidly with temperature.)

For most elements and inorganic compounds likely to be of interest, the vapor pressures and molecular weights are well known. Accordingly, it is not necessary to carry out experiments to determine rates of sublimation of such materials in vacuum; they can be calculated with confidence from Eq. (9.12) or (9.13). (As a matter of fact, many of the vapor-pressure data were obtained [21] from measurements of weight loss by using the Langmuir equation or a modification, the Knudsen equation.) Results for elemental metals and semiconductors are shown in Table 9.2, in terms of the temperature at which various amounts of thickness per year will be lost from a surface. For comparison, melting points are also given in the table.

Table 9.2 shows that appreciable loss of cadmium and zinc, which are commonly used as platings, will occur at temperatures likely to be encountered by these materials in spacecraft. Selenium, sometimes used in photocells, will likewise sublime. Magnesium, on the other hand, will not lose as much as 10^{-3} cm/year (0.0004 in./year) unless its temperature reaches about 170°C (340°F). This amount is too small to be of structural significance; it might be important if the magnesium were used as a thin film for, say, optical purposes. At about 240°C (470°F), 10^{-1} cm (0.040 in.) of magnesium will sublime per year; such a loss will usually be very significant structurally. Most other metals, such as aluminum, as well as the semiconductors germanium and silicon, will not lose significant thickness except at much higher temperatures. Many of these materials may, it is true, be expected to operate at high temperatures in spacecraft.

A metal as ordinarily used is not homogeneous but is composed of millions of microscopic crystals or grains. When the metal is exposed to vacuum at a temperature where sublimation occurs, the loss will not be even over the surface but, because of differences in crystal orientation, slightly faster on some grains than others. This selective loss is also directional, so that the exposed surfaces of individual grains do not remain parallel to the original position of the surface or to each other. Because metals, except for thin films or foils, are usually many grains thick, selective losses of this type will average out as they progress through the metal and will not lead to deep holes. The chief result of engineering interest will be a roughening of the surface on a microscopic scale.

A related effect is the accelerated sublimation which takes place at the boundaries between grains. Fears have been expressed that this will lead to development of holes extending completely through a metal wall. Formation of such holes will be prevented, however, by a balancing of surface-tension forces which arises as the boundary etches away. Thus,

Table 9.2 Sublimation of Metals and Semiconductors in High Vacuum[†]

| Element[‡] | Temperature at which sublimation rate is | | | | | | Melting point | |
| | 10^{-5} cm/ year (1,000 A/year) | | 10^{-3} cm/year (0.0004 in./year) | | 10^{-1} cm/year (0.040 in./year) | | | |
	°C	°F	°C	°F	°C	°F	°C	°F
Cd	40	100	80	170	120	250	320	610
Se	50	120	80	180	120	240	220	420
Zn	70	160	130	260	180	350	420	790
Mg	110	230	170	340	240	470	650	1200
Te	130	260	180	350	220	430	450	840
Li	150	300	210	410	280	530	180	360
Sb	210	410	270	520	300	570	630	1170
Bi	240	470	320	600	400	750	270	520
Pb	270	510	330	630	430	800	330	620
In	400	760	500	940	610	1130	160	310
Mn	450	840	540	1010	650	1200	1240	2270
Ag	480	890	590	1090	700	1300	960	1760
Sn	550	1020	660	1220	800	1480	230	450
Al	550	1020	680	1260	810	1490	660	1220
Be	620	1140	700	1300	840	1540	1280	2330
Cu	630	1160	760	1400	900	1650	1080	1980
Au	660	1220	800	1480	950	1750	1060	1940
Ge	660	1220	800	1480	950	1750	940	1720
Cr	750	1380	870	1600	1000	1840	1880	3410
Fe	770	1420	900	1650	1050	1920	1540	2800
Si	790	1450	920	1690	1080	1970	1410	2570
Ni	800	1480	940	1720	1090	2000	1450	2650
Pd	810	1490	940	1720	1100	2020	1550	2830
Co	820	1500	960	1760	1100	2020	1500	2720
Ti	920	1690	1070	1960	1250	2280	1670	3040
V	1020	1870	1180	2150	1350	2460	1900	3450
Rh	1140	2080	1330	2420	1540	2800	1970	3570
Pt	1160	2120	1340	2440	1560	2840	1770	3220
B	1230	2240	1420	2580	1640	2980	2030	3700
Zr	1280	2340	1500	2740	1740	3150	1850	3360
Ir	1300	2380	1500	2740	1740	3150	2450	4450
Mo	1380	2520	1630	2960	1900	3450	2610	4730
C§	1530	2780	1680	3050	1880	3400	3700	6700
Ta	1780	3250	2050	3700	2300	4200	3000	5400
Re	1820	3300	2050	3700	2300	4200	3200	5800
W	1880	3400	2150	3900	2500	4500	3400	6200

† Based on vapor-pressure data of Ref. 23.
‡ Gaseous molecules taken as monatomic, except Se, Te, Sb, Bi taken as diatomic.
§ C mean molecular weight taken as 24.

Fig 9.2 shows a two-dimensional section through a grain boundary which intersects the surface exposed to vacuum. The initially flat surface has developed a groove at the grain boundary. The groove angle θ at equilibrium is related to the grain-boundary tension γ_{gb} and the surface tension γ_s; balancing of forces (or, equivalently, minimizing energy) shows that

$$\cos \frac{\theta}{2} = \frac{\gamma_{gb}}{2\gamma_s} \tag{9.14}$$

Once this value of θ is reached, the groove cannot deepen relative to the

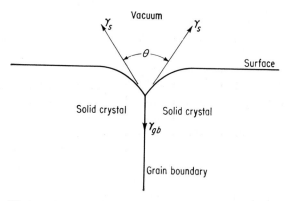

Fig. 9.2 Equilibrium shape of groove developed at grain boundary; section perpendicular to surface.

surface; this would require lowering θ and thus increasing the energy of the system by doing work against the surface tension γ_s. Only if

$$\gamma_{gb} > 2\gamma_s \tag{9.15}$$

so that no equilibrium θ can be reached, can the groove deepen indefinitely and separate the two grains. In three dimensions, a similar analysis [24–26] shows that development of a hole where three grains join at an edge can proceed only if

$$\gamma_{gb} > 1.7\gamma_s \tag{9.16}$$

Experimental measurements [27, 28] show, however, that

$$\gamma_{gb} > \gamma_s \tag{9.17}$$

Accordingly, inequalities (9.15) and (9.16) will not be satisfied, and an equilibrium angle and depth will be reached at which selective grain-boundary loss will cease. This depth will be only a fraction of the grain diameter. In ordinary polycrystalline material, the grain-boundary attack will therefore be shallow, and the practical result is likely to be, again, a microscopic roughening.

When alloys are used in the vacuum of space, some thought should be given to the possibility of loss of the more volatile constituents. Unless the temperature is high enough to permit diffusion of the volatile elements through the solid alloy, loss can occur only from a surface layer one or two atoms thick. Brass, which contains 30 to 40 per cent volatile zinc, is commonly used in laboratory vacuum systems at temperatures up to several hundred degrees with no difficulty from loss of zinc. To permit diffusion of atoms from inside the alloy to its surface, and so continue loss of the volatile element, the temperature must generally be high enough for the material to be in an elevated-temperature regime, in the sense that the material will creep significantly under load. This elevated temperature may be 120°C (250°F) for aluminum-base alloys, 550°C (1000°F) for steels, and several thousand degrees for tungsten-base alloys. Even at these temperatures, the maximum loss rate from the alloy will be less than that of the pure volatile metal in proportion to the composition of the alloy. For example, the commercial aluminum-base alloy 7075 contains 5.5 weight per cent zinc, equivalent to 2.3 atomic per cent. Table 9.2 indicates an appreciable loss rate for pure zinc at 180°C (350°F), and the temperature may be high enough for diffusion from inside to surface to occur. Since only 2.3 atomic per cent zinc is present, the loss rate [g/(cm²)(year)] will not exceed about 2 per cent of the rate for pure zinc. In fact, measurements [29] show that the loss of zinc and cadmium from silver–zinc and silver–cadmium alloys is many orders of magnitude less than from pure zinc and pure cadmium, even at 650°C (1200°F).

For inorganic compounds, the problem is a bit more complex, because loss may occur by several mechanisms. First, molecules of the compound may be sublime. Vapor-pressure data for calculation of the weight loss by this mechanism can usually be found in the literature. If vapor pressures were measured at temperatures other than those of interest, approximate values could be obtained by extrapolation, using the relation

$$\log p = A - \frac{B}{T} \qquad (9.18)$$

where A and B are constants. (This relation is derived from thermodynamics [30].) Once the vapor pressure is known for the appropriate temperature, the loss rate can be calculated by Eq. (9.13). Loss rates for a few compounds, obtained in this way, are given in Table 9.3.

Another process which may take place in inorganic compounds is decomposition to the elements or to simpler compounds, some of which

Table 9.3 Sublimation of Some Inorganic Compounds in High Vacuum

Com-pound	Temperature at which sublimation rate is						Melting point	
	10^{-5} cm/year (1,000 A/year)		10^{-3} cm/year (0.0004 in./year)		10^{-1} cm/year (0.040 in./year)			
	°C	°F	°C	°F	°C	°F	°C	°F
CsI	120	240	160	320	240	460	620	1150
MgO	540	1000	730	1350	1090	2000	2800	5100
MoS₂†	730	1350	960	1760	1480	2700		
ZrO₂	1070	1950	1320	2400	1480	2700	2700	4900
BeO	1340	2450	1480	2700	1700	3100	2550	4600
ThO₂	1400	2550	1600	2900	1900	3500	3300	6000

† Temperatures given for MoS_2 are not for sublimation but for decomposition to S_2 (gas) and Mo (solid).

may be volatile. For example,

$$MoS_2(s) \rightarrow Mo(s) + S_2(g) \tag{9.19a}$$
$$K = p_{S_2} \tag{9.19b}$$
$$MgO(s) \rightarrow Mg(g) + \tfrac{1}{2}O_2(g) \tag{9.20a}$$
$$K = (p_{Mg})\,(p_{O_2})^{\frac{1}{2}} \tag{9.20b}$$
$$2CeO_2(s) \rightarrow Ce_2O_3(l) + \tfrac{1}{2}O_2(g) \tag{9.21a}$$
$$K = (p_{O_2})^{\frac{1}{2}} \tag{9.21b}$$

The rates of loss by such a reaction can be calculated from the equilibrium constant K, which is the product of the pressures (in atmospheres) of the gaseous products, each raised to a power equal to the coefficient of the corresponding term in the chemical equation [Eqs. (9.19b) to (9.21b)]. If K is known, the decomposition pressure is readily computed by this relation and can be substituted in Eq. (9.12) or (9.13) to give the loss rate; K values are usually obtained from tabulated values of the free energies for the compound and its decomposition products by the equation

$$\Delta F = -RT \ln K \tag{9.22}$$

where ΔF is the change in free energy in the reaction. As an example, Eq. (9.19) gives a weight loss by decomposition 10^6 times as great as that due to sublimation for MoS_2.

Inorganic compounds, especially ceramics, may also suffer loss of a volatile element in such reactions as

$$ThO_2(s) \rightarrow ThO_{1.95}(s) + aO_2(g) \tag{9.23}$$
$$UC(s) \rightarrow U_{0.8}C(s) + bU(g) \tag{9.24}$$

Here, $ThO_{1.95}$ and $U_{0.8}C$ are the same phases as ThO_2 and UC, respectively; a change of composition has occurred within the limits of phase stability.

A complex inorganic material of considerable engineering interest is glass. Borosilicate glass is the standard material of construction for laboratory ultrahigh-vacuum systems which withstand baking at 450°C (840°F). Accordingly, sublimation and decomposition of borosilicate glass should not be a problem, at least up to this temperature.

A special problem may arise, particularly with electronic equipment, if a material which is somewhat volatile or unstable is used in a partial enclosure that is exposed to space vacuum and in which considerable temperature differences exist. Metal may then sublime from warm areas and condense on cold insulating surfaces in the form of a thin film, which could cause a short circuit. Cadmium, zinc, and magnesium are most likely to cause this trouble. Similarly, a compound may sublime or decompose, and the products may redeposit as an insulating layer on a cooler surface intended to conduct electricity or heat, such as a relay contact. This could interfere with proper operation. The thickness deposited may be estimated by first calculating the amount sublimed or decomposed, using Eq. (9.13) or Table 9.2 or 9.3. Multiplying this amount by the ratio of overall warm area to overall cold area gives an upper limit to the thickness condensed (because some material will be lost into space). A metallic deposit will not be continuous and, hence, will not be conducting unless the deposit is thicker than the diameter of an atom (about 5 A). If the possible metal thickness is greater than this, the thickness estimate can be used to compute the minimum possible resistance of the film. For insulating deposits, the thickness estimate can be used similarly to compute the maximum possible breakdown voltage or film resistance.

Concern has occasionally been expressed that metals, in particular, will grow or deposit as long thin crystals ("whiskers") which may short-circuit electrical insulators or gaps. Since whisker growth of this sort generally occurs from a supersaturated vapor phase or in connection with oxidation, it seems much less likely in space than on Earth.

One way in which it should be possible to reduce sublimation is by surface coating. These coatings may be platings or paints of various sorts, or they may be *chemical-conversion* coatings. These conversion coatings are mostly oxides and phosphates, which are often more stable in vacuum than the metal they coat. Nonporous stable coatings should provide substantial protection to the underlying material, unless the temperature is so high that diffusion through the coating is appreciable. Porous coatings are likely to be undermined and detached by loss of underlying material through the pores. Even porous coatings may, however, be of some help when a very small amount of undesirable loss would otherwise occur, as when redeposition on cold electrical surfaces is a problem.

Loss of Organic Materials in Vacuum

Organic materials of relatively low molecular weight, which evaporate or sublime in vacuum without decomposition, will obey the Langmuir equation [(9.12) and (9.13)].   Many oils fall into this category.   Table 9.4 gives loss rates calculated from vapor-pressure data for some oils of low volatility, specifically, oils used in high-vacuum diffusion pumps.   The table indicates that 0.1 cm/year (0.04 in./year) of these oils will be lost by evaporation at or below 50°C (120°F).   Chain length (molecular weight) has a major effect on the vapor pressure and evaporation rate of oils; the evaporation rate decreases as the molecular weight increases

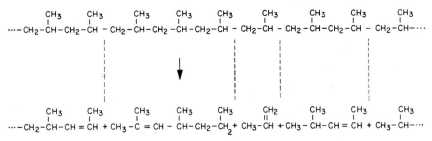

Fig. 9.3   Breakdown of high polymer in vacuum (schematic).

because of the accompanying sharp drop in vapor pressure.   Many commercial oils are mixtures of various molecular-weight compounds; some components may evaporate out of the mixture, while others remain. It is also worth noting that an oil which does not evaporate in vacuum is not necessarily a good lubricant in vacuum.

Most of the organic materials used in spacecraft are long-chain polymeric compounds which degrade in a vacuum, not by evaporation or sublimation but by breakdown of the compounds into smaller, more volatile fragments (Fig. 9.3).   The molecular weight of these fragments is not well established; neither is the equilibrium-decomposition pressure of most polymers.   Accordingly, the Langmuir equation is not generally useful for the organic materials of interest, and it is necessary to turn to direct experimental studies of the weight loss of polymers in vacuum.

A number of such studies have been made, which vary considerably in the care with which the work was performed and the pertinence of the tests to space conditions.   Good work has been done over the past dozen years by chemists interested in the kinetics of vacuum pyrolysis of high polymers; the contributions of Madorsky, Wall, Straus, and their

Table 9.4 Evaporation of Low-vapor-pressure Oils in High Vacuum†

Oil type	Commercial name	Presumed chemical name	Molecular weight	Temperature at which evaporation is					
				10⁻⁵ cm/year (1,000 A/year)		10⁻³ cm/year (0.0004 in./year)		10⁻¹ cm/year (0.040 in./year)	
				°C	°F	°C	°F	°C	°F
Hydrocarbon.........	Apiezon A	Alkane, 29 carbon	414	-55	-60	-30	-20	-5	20
	Apiezon B	Alkane, 33 carbon	460	-45	-50	-25	-10	5	40
Diester.............	Amoil	Di-n-butyl phthalate	278	-65	-90	-45	-50	-20	0
	Amoil S	Di-isoamyl phthalate	306	-65	-80	-40	-40	-15	0
	Octoil	Di-m-amyl sebacate	343	-45	-50	-25	-10	-5	40
	Octoil S	Di-2-ethylhexyl phthalate	390	-40	-40	-20	0	10	50
		Di-2-ethylhexyl sebacate	426	-30	-20	-5	20	20	70
Dimethyl silicone...	10-cs 200 Fluid	Permethyldodecasiloxane	900	-40	-40	-20	0	5	40
	50-cs 200 Fluid	Permethylhexadecasiloxane	1,200	0	30	20	70	50	120
Phenyl methyl silicone....	DC-704	Tetraphenyltetramethyltrisiloxane	490	-25	-10	0	30	30	90

† Based on vapor-pressure data in Refs. 21 and 31.

263

colleagues at National Bureau of Standards deserve particular mention [32–58]. In this work, the weight loss of small samples of pure well-defined polymers was measured as a function of both time and temperature in vacuums of 10^{-6} mm; the times ran from a few minutes to 50 hr. Information on vacuum exposure for times of a year or more is limited to a very few materials built into laboratory vacuum systems or into spacecraft, held at one temperature, and observed on a go–no-go basis only. Accordingly, it is worthwhile to attempt to obtain more information by extrapolating the short-time data to longer periods.   As the measured

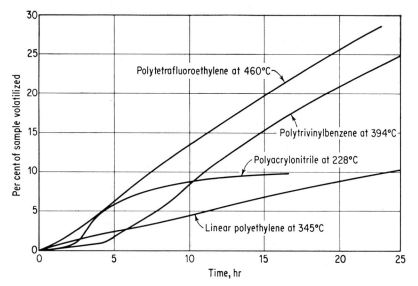

Fig. 9.4   Typical curves for weight loss of polymers in vacuum as a function of time. (*After Madorsky and Straus* [36, 44, 47].)

curves of weight loss versus time are usually nonlinear (Fig. 9.4), extrapolation of such curves is risky.   A better approach is to plot the time t for a given weight loss of interest versus the temperature.   Plots of measured $\log t$ versus $1/T$ are usually close to linear (Fig. 9.5), as would be expected from theory [30].   Although extrapolation of $\log t$ versus $1/T$ plots involves some risk, the risk is much smaller than for the nonlinear plots of weight loss versus time.   Those measurements, made as functions of both time and temperature, have been extrapolated in this way and are given in Table 9.5 as A-quality data.

Such measurements have not been made on all polymers of practical interest, however.   For a larger number, more limited data are available. In Table 9.5, qualities B and C denote measurements of weight loss versus temperature at one fixed time, B with high-purity well-defined polymers and C with commercial plastics or elastomers.   The quality D denotes measurement of weight loss or other properties at one elevated temperature only, while E denotes measurements of pressure change in a laboratory vacuum system at an elevated temperature.   These measurements were used only as a relative indication for interpolation of additional materials between the polymers for which A-quality measurements were found; in Table 9.5, temperatures assigned for the B through E measurements are also derived by interpolation.   Thus, Table 9.5 gives

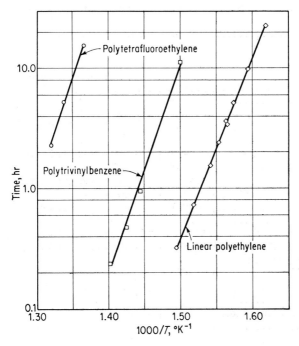

Fig. 9.5   Time-temperature relations for 10 per cent weight loss of polymer in vacuum. (*Data of Madorsky and Straus* [36, 42, 44, 47].)

an estimated order of merit for behavior of polymers in vacuum, together with temperatures for an estimated weight loss of 10 per cent per year. These temperatures are subject to considerable uncertainty; designers are urged to be conservative in using them.   A single temperature for a material in the table often means that only one determination was found in the literature.   It does not mean that the material is less variable than those for which a range of values is shown.

Inspection of Table 9.5 shows considerable scatter in temperature for most kinds of polymers.   One reason for this is that the designations refer to polymers made from whole classes of monomers; they could be

Table 9.5 Decomposition of Polymers in High Vacuum

Polymer	Temperature for 10% weight loss per year in vacuum		Quality of data	Literature references
	°C	°F		
Nylon...................	30–120	80–410	A	52, 53
Sulfide...................	40	100	C	59, 60
Cellulose nitrate...........	40	100	C	59
Cellulose, oxidized........	40	100	B	38
Methyl acrylate...........	40–150	100–300	A–C	35, 36, 50, 59
Ester....................	40–240	100–460	B–C	48, 59
Epoxy...................	40–240	100–460	B–C	48, 59
Urethane.................	70–150	150–300	C	59
Vinyl butyral.............	80	180	C	59
Vinyl chloride.............	90	190	A	54
Linseed oil...............	90	200	C	59
Neoprene (chloroprene).....	90	200	C	59
Alkyd...................	90–150	200–300	C–E	59, 61
Methyl methacrylate.......	100–200	220–390	A	35, 36, 50, 62, 63
Acrylonitrile..............	120	240	A	44, 62
Isobutylene-isoprene (butyl rubber).................	120	250	D	64
Styrene-butadiene..........	130	270	C	59
Styrene..................	130–220	270–420	A	34, 36, 41, 50, 63, 65, 66
Phenolic.................	130–270	270–510	B–D	46, 48, 59, 63
Butadiene-acrylonitrile (nitrile rubber)..........	150–230	300–450	B–D	51, 64
Vinyl alcohol.............	150	310	B	37
Vinyl acetate.............	160	320	A	67
Cellulose acetate butyrate...	170	340	C	59
Cellulose................	180	350	A	36, 38, 39
Carbonate...............	180	350	D	63
Methyl styrene............	180–220	350–420	A	32, 35, 36, 65
Cellulose acetate..........	190	370	A	38
Propylene................	190–240	370–470	A	36, 42, 68
Rubber, natural...........	190	380	B	50
Isoprene.................	190	380	B	49, 50
Melamine................	190	380	E	61
Silicone elastomer..........	200	400	D	64
Ethylene terephthalate (Mylar, Dacron).........	200	400	A	52
Isobutylene..............	200	400	B	36, 49, 50
Vinyl toluene.............	200	400	B	35, 36, 50
Styrene, cross-linked.......	230–250	440–490	A	45
Butadiene-styrene (GR-S=SBR)...........	240	460	B	49, 50, 51
Vinyl fluoride.............	240	460	B	40

Table 9.5   Decomposition of Polymers in High Vacuum (*Continued*)

Polymer	Temperature for 10% weight loss per year in vacuum		Quality of data	Literature references
	°C	°F		
Ethylene, low density.......	240–280	460–540	A	34, 36, 48, 49, 57, 65
Butadiene................	250	490	B	49, 50, 51
Vinylidene fluoride– hexafluoropropene........	250	490	A	69
Chlorotrifluoroethylene.....	250	490	A	36, 43, 69
Chlorotrifluoroethylene– vinylidene fluoride.......	260	500	A	69
Vinylidene fluoride........	270	510	A	40, 44, 69
Benzyl..................	280	540	B	36, 42
Xylylene................	280	540	B	36, 43
Ethylene, high density......	290	560	A	36, 42, 57
Trivinyl benzene..........	290	560	A	44
Tetrafluoroethylene........	380	710	A	33, 40, 47, 69, 70, 71
Methyl phenyl silicone resin.	>380	>710	B	48

subdivided further by the particular monomer or monomers used. The chain length (molecular weight), branching, and cross-linking of the polymer have some effect upon decomposition. Moreover, the data indicate that the rates of decomposition in vacuum are often greatly accelerated by small amounts of impurities and addition agents. In particular, the catalysts which are ordinarily used to induce polymerization of the monomer also, if left in the polymer, commonly catalyze decomposition of the latter. Many polymers can be made without catalysts, or the catalysts can be removed after polymerization, but this is difficult and not the usual commercial practice. Plasticizers and mold lubricants, used to help fabrication and to modify mechanical properties, are also highly detrimental to stability in vacuum. Certain degradation inhibitors (other than antioxidants) may increase vacuum stability. The particular formulation and curing procedure used may, therefore, have important effects upon vacuum stability. Accordingly, wide variations in behavior may be expected for any particular type of polymer. Trade names, too, mean little in this field; they serve to identify the manufacturer but often do not even define the type of polymer. Thus, the measurements are useful only as a general guide. For careful work, experiments are needed with particular formulations and curing procedures of interest.

The reader may wonder why the values in Table 9.5 are given in terms of per cent weight loss rather than as a loss of thickness per year. Since the process causing the loss is not one of evaporation or sublimation but of decomposition, it takes place not at the surface but throughout the volume of the piece. Moreover, measurements indicate that, at least in thicknesses up to 0.12 cm (0.050 in.) and times up to 48 hr [40, 62], the loss does not depend on the surface area but on the total volume or weight. Apparently, the decomposition itself, rather than diffusion of the decomposition products out of the solid, is the rate-limiting process. For sufficiently thick samples, diffusion will limit weight loss, and the per cent loss in a given time will fall somewhat [52, 70, 71]; however, the accompanying degradation in properties may not be retarded. The effect of time on the rate-controlling process has not been determined; at long times, degradation seems likely to be more important than diffusion.

It should be noted that Tables 9.2 to 9.5 do not imply that the materials are usable at the temperatures listed. These tables pertain only to rates of sublimation or decomposition in vacuum. Processes which occur in the same way in both air and vacuum, such as loss of strength with increasing temperature, may limit the usefulness of the material and are not discussed here. Polymers are commonly more stable at elevated temperatures in the absence of oxygen [72]. In many cases, the upper temperature limit for useful service in air is lower than that indicated in these tables and probably will be used to govern design for vacuum as well.

Coatings may be put over organic materials to reduce their net rate of breakdown in vacuum [59]. The coating prevents degradation products from leaving the underlying material and permits them to recombine to some extent. Either organic or inorganic coatings may be used.

If organic materials are used in partial enclosures containing temperature gradients and exposed to vacuum, there is a possibility that they, like inorganics, will evaporate or decompose to volatile products in the warmer areas and that the volatiles will redeposit on the cooler surfaces. If the cooler surfaces must conduct electricity or heat, this may lead to malfunction. In particular, oils and plasticizers (discussed in the section on Property Changes of Organic Materials) can redeposit on exposed relay contacts and prevent them from closing properly [73].

Property Changes of Inorganic Materials

There seems to be no good evidence of any important decrease in mechanical properties of inorganic materials in vacuum, as compared with their properties under the atmospheres in which they are ordinarily used, provided that the temperature is not so high that appreciable sublimation occurs. In fact, properties are usually better in vacuum because of freedom from corrosion [74]. An exception may occur under elevated-temperature conditions for a few materials, in which advantage is taken in air of internal oxidation to strengthen the material [75].

Similarly, the optical properties should not be affected if the temperature is low enough to avoid sublimation and change of composition. This last point may bear watching, both for alloys containing volatile elements and for ceramics to be used at high temperatures. Rather small losses of oxygen, and perhaps of nitrogen, which may occur in vacuum at high temperatures may be sufficient to change the emissivity of some ceramics appreciably. Also, some ceramics, particularly oxides, are hydrated; loss of water may occur in vacuum, with resulting emissivity changes. A possible case in which this may take place (on which no experimental work seems to have been done) is the hydrated aluminum oxide coating put on aluminum metal by the anodizing process. Related is the situation in which a metal readily forms a thin oxide coating on exposure to air, but the oxide is volatile or unstable in vacuum. Nickel would be an example; its emissivity may be different in space than in air.

Electrical properties, also, will be generally affected by vacuum only if sublimation or composition changes occur. Slight losses of oxygen, nitrogen, and water may affect resistivity and other properties of ceramics.

If uneven sublimation occurs, some properties may be more affected than if the sublimation is uniform. Thus, it is possible, though not confirmed, that the accelerated sublimation of grain-boundary material will introduce surface notches which lower resistance to crack propagation under conditions of rigid or repeated loading. Surface roughening resulting from grain-boundary sublimation and from differences in sublimation rates and direction in different grains of the microstructure can decrease optical reflectivity and increase optical emissivity and absorptivity [76]. This can be important both for conventional optical components and for the temperature-control surfaces which, by establishing the radiation balance, maintain spacecraft temperatures within prescribed limits.

Lubrication properties in vacuum are of interest for both inorganic and organic materials and are discussed elsewhere [73].

Property Changes of Organic Materials

It is possible, in principle, for internal chemical changes to occur in organic materials exposed to vacuum which would affect the properties of the material without appreciably changing the weight. There seems to be little good evidence, however, that detrimental property changes occur in practice without weight loss, except at temperatures at which detrimental changes also take place in air. When weight loss occurs, it may be accompanied by significant changes in mechanical, electrical, and optical properties, as well as in dimensions. Few quantitative data on these changes are available; if detailed information on a particular property of a particular material is required, it is usually necessary at present to test the property experimentally. In general, however, it may be said that weight losses of 1 or 2 per cent do not produce property changes of engineering importance but that weight losses of 10 per cent are accompanied by considerable changes in engineering properties [63, 64]. It is for this reason that 10 per cent weight loss per year was chosen as a criterion in Table 9.5.

An exception to the above general statement must be made for plastics and elastomers containing plasticizers which are volatile in vacuum [76]. In some cases, losses of less than 10 per cent of plasticizer from a plasticized polymer may be enough to embrittle the material significantly [77]. For this reason, again, plasticized materials, particularly those containing so-called "external" plasticizers, should generally be avoided for space applications.

Laboratory Simulation of Space Vacuum Conditions

When it is desired to simulate the vacuum of space for laboratory studies of sublimation and decomposition, conditions should be such that every molecule of the material which leaves a surface will stay away permanently. It is not necessary, or even advantageous, to have the air pressure in the system as low as in space. If the air pressure in the system is 10^{-5} mm Hg or lower, the mean free path of vapor molecules between collisions with each other and with air molecules will be several meters or more. Thus, collisions in the gas will rarely occur. Molecules of a material can then come back to the test surface only by condensing on the walls of the vacuum system and then resubliming. This can be prevented by keeping the walls cold compared with the specimen, so that the rate of sublimation from the walls is negligible.

For surface-property studies, on the other hand, when space conditions are simulated, air molecules should be prevented from reaching the contact surfaces and building up monomolecular and thicker layers of adsorbed atmospheric gases. This requires that the air pressure be considerably lower than is usual in laboratory vacuum systems. At 10^{-6} mm Hg, which is considered a good laboratory vacuum, molecules reach an exposed surface so fast that even if the surface is initially clean, a monomolecular adsorbed air layer will build up in less than 2 sec. At 10^{-9} mm Hg, however, it will take 25 min for an air monolayer to build up on a clean surface, which may be long enough to carry out the experiment [63]. This pressure is about at the limit of the present state of high-vacuum art under conditions in which the specimen of interest may be evolving gases and is commonly of a composition that cannot be baked out at high temperatures to clean it. Again, cold walls should be used to prevent return of evaporated material.

Because gas evolution plays an important part in the behavior of materials in vacuum, pumping systems which can cope with evolved gases are essential. Pumps which provide high pumping speed at appropriate pressures are therefore needed; ability to produce low ultimate pressure in a clean system is of little importance. Diffusion pumps should be provided with traps cooled by liquid nitrogen to prevent pump oil from diffusing or creeping back into the test chamber.

Conclusion

Metals and alloys are generally quite stable in the high vacuum of space at normal operating temperatures. Sublimation of cadmium and zinc may be of some concern, particularly where there is a possibility of the metal's plating out in an uncontrolled manner on a cold insulating surface. Sublimation of magnesium and its alloys becomes appreciable above 170°C (350°F). A slight roughening of polished optical surfaces of other metals may occur through selective sublimation.

Among the semiconductors, selenium, phosphides, and arsenides have high sublimation or decomposition rates in high vacuum at moderate temperatures. Most inorganic engineering insulators are unaffected by the vacuum of space except at high temperatures. Vapor-pressure and other thermodynamic data are usually available for inorganics of interest; and from these, loss rates can be calculated with good accuracy.

In selecting organic materials for use in space, it would be wise either to be conservative, choosing materials known to be safe, or to run tests on doubtful materials. Because of the complex composition of most oil and grease lubricants, simple estimates of their evaporation rates may not be reliable. Such polymers as nylon, acrylics, polysulfides, and neoprene show high decomposition rates in vacuum. On the other hand, some commonly used elastomers—vinylidene fluoride–hexafluoropropene, chlorotrifluoroethylene, butadiene-styrene, isoprene, and natural rubber—are rather stable in high vacuum. Similarly, such plastics as silicone resins, tetrafluoroethylene, polyethylene, polypropylene, and ethylene terephthalate exhibit good to excellent behavior in high vacuum. Polymers suitable for high-temperature service are generally best; the use of plasticizers should be avoided.

For both organics and inorganics, there seems to be little detrimental effect of vacuum on mechanical or electrical properties, except when appreciable loss of mass occurs.

REFERENCES

1. Brandt, J.: Interplanetary Hydrogen, private communication, Yerkes Observatory.
2. Chamberlain, J. W.: Interplanetary Gas. III. Hydrodynamic Model of the Corona. *Astrophys. J.*, vol. 133, pp. 675–687, 1961.
3. Gringauz, K. I., V. V. Bezrukikh, V. D. Ozerov, and R. E. Rybchinskii: Study of the Interplanetary Ionized Gas, High Energy Electrons and Solar Corpuscular Radiation Using Three-electrode Charged-particle Traps Installed on the Second Soviet Cosmic Rocket, *Dokl Akad. Nauk*, vol. 131, pp. 1301-1304, 1960. (English transl., *Phys. Express*, vol. 2, no. 10, pp. 29–31, July, 1960.)
4. Hines, C. O.: Symposium on the Exosphere and Upper F Region, *J. Geophys. Res.*, vol. 65, pp. 2563–2569, 1960.
5. Istomin, V. G.: Some Results of Measurements of the Mass Spectrum of Positive Ions by the 3rd Artificial Earth Satellite, *Proc.* 10*th Intern. Astronautical Congr.*, vol. 2, pp. 756–767, Springer-Verlag OHG, Vienna, 1960.
6. Johnson, F. S.: The Telluric Hydrogen Corona and Some of Its Consequences, in H. Kallmann Bijl. (ed.): "Space Research: Proceedings of the First International Space Science Symposium," North Holland Publishing Company, Amsterdam, 1960. pp. 736–745.
7. Kallmann Bijl, H. (ed.): "Space Research: Proceedings of the First International Space Science Symposium," North-Holland Publishing Company, Amsterdam, 1960.
8. Johnson, F. S.: Distribution of Hydrogen in the Telluric Hydrogen Corona, *Astrophys. J.*, vol. 133, pp. 701–705, 1961.
9. Johnson, F. S. and R. A. Fish: Telluric Hydrogen Corona, *Astrophys. J.*, vol. 131, pp. 502–515, 1960.
10. Kupperian, J. E., Jr., E. T. Byram, T. A. Chubb, and H. Friedman: Far Ultraviolet Radiation in the Night Sky, *J. Planet. Sci.*, vol. 1, pp. 3–6, 1959.
11. Minzner, R. A., K. S. W. Champion, and H. L. Pond: The ARDC Model Atmosphere 1959, Air Force Surveys in Geophysics No. 115, U.S. Air Force Cambridge Research Center, AFCRC-TR-59-267, Bedford, Mass., 1959.
12. Newall, Jr., H. E.: The Space Environment, *Science*, vol. 131, pp. 385–390, 1960.
13. Shklovsky, I.: The Earth's Corona, *Pravda*, May 25, 1960. (Astronautics Information transl. No. 13, Jet Propulsion Laboratory, California Institute of Technology, Pasadena, Calif., July 1, 1960.)
14. Shklovsky, I. S.: The Interplanetary Medium and Some Problems of the Physics of the Upper Atmosphere, *Astron. Zh. Akad. Nauk SSSR*, vol. 35, 1958; transl. *Soviet Astron. AJ*, vol. 2, pp. 516–527, 1958.
15. Shklovsky, I. S.: Hydrogen Emission in the Night Glow, *J. Planet. Space Sci.*, vol. 1, pp. 3–6, 1959.
16. Pope, J. H.: Estimate of Electron Densities in the Exosphere by Means of Nose Whistlers, *J. Geophys. Res.*, vol. 66, pp. 67–75, 1961.
17. The Universe Discloses Its Mysteries, *Pravda*, July 15, 1959; Astronautics

Information transl. no. 3, Jet Propulsion Laboratory, California Institute of Technology, Pasadena, Calif., July 31, 1959.

18. Weinberg, J. L.: Distribution of Electron Density inside the Earth's Orbit, *Astron. J.*, vol. 66, p. 57, 1961.

19. Langmuir, I.: Vapor Pressure of Metallic Tungsten, *Phys. Rev.*, vol. 2, pp. 329–342, 1913.

20. Verhoek, F. H., and A. L. Marshall: Vapor Pressures and Accommodation Coefficients of Four Non-volatile Compounds: Vapor Pressure of Tri-*m*-Cresyl Phosphate over Polyvinyl Chloride Plastics, *J. Am. Chem. Soc.*, vol. 61, pp. 2737–2742, 1939.

21. Dushman, S.: "Scientific Foundations of Vacuum Technique," pp. 18–24, 220–222, 253–254, John Wiley & Sons, Inc., New York, 1949.

22. Happe, R. A.: Materials in Space, *Jet Propulsion Laboratory, California Institute of Technology, Tech. Release* 34-143, Pasadena, Calif., 1960.

23. Honig, R. E.: Vapor Pressure Data for the More Common Elements, *RCA Rev.*, vol. 18, pp. 195–204, 1957.

24. Smith, C. S.: Grains, Phases, and Interfaces: An Interpretation of Microstructure, *Trans. AIME*, vol. 175, pp. 15–51, 1948.

25. Smith, C. S.: Interphase Interfaces, in Shockley, W., J. H. Hollomon, R. Maurer, and F. Seitz (eds.): "Imperfections in Nearly Perfect Crystals," pp. 377–401, John Wiley & Sons, Inc., New York, 1952.

26. Shockley, W., J. H. Hollomon, R. Maurer, and F. Seitz (eds.): "Imperfections in Nearly Perfect Crystals," John Wiley & Sons, Inc., New York, 1952.

27. Fisher, J. C., and C. G. Dunn: Surface and Interfacial Tensions of Single-phase Solids, in Shockley, W., J. H. Hollomon, R. Maurer, and F. Seitz (eds.): "Imperfections in Nearly Perfect Crystals," pp. 317–351, John Wiley & Sons, Inc., New York, 1952.

28. Aust, K. T., and B. Chalmers: Energies and Structure of Grain Boundaries, *Trans. ASM*, vol. 44A, pp. 153–178, 1952.

29. Santalov, F. A.: Influence of Additions of Low Melting Metals on the Rate of Expulsion of a Volatile Component from Solid Solutions and on the Structure of the Specimens, *Fiz. Metal i Metalloved.*, vol. 3, pp. 247–253, 1956.

30. Glasstone, S.: "Thermodynamics for Chemists," pp. 227–234, 291–292, D. Van Nostrand Company, Inc., Princeton, N.J., 1947.

31. Huntress, A. R., A. L. Smith, B. D. Power, and N. T. M. Dennis: "New Silicone Diffusion Fluid," Fourth National Symposium on Vacuum Technology, pp. 104–111, Pergamon Press, New York, 1958.

32. Brown, D. W., and L. A. Wall: Pyrolysis of Poly-*a*-Methylstyrene, *J. Phys. Chem.*, vol. 62, pp. 848–852, 1958.

33. Florin, R. E., L. A. Wall, D. W. Brown, L. A. Hymo, and J. D. Michaelsen: Factors Affecting the Thermal Stability of Polytetrafluoroethylene, *J. Res. Natl. Bur. Std.*, vol. 53, pp. 121–130, 1954.

34. Madorsky, S. L.: Rates of Thermal Degradation of Polystyrene and Polyethylene in a Vacuum, *J. Polymer Sci.*, vol. 8, p. 133, 1952; Polymer Degradation Mechanisms, *Natl. Bur. Std. Circ.* 525, pp. 221–238, 1953.

35. Madorsky, S. L.: Rates and Activation Energies of Thermal Degradation of

Styrene and Acrylate Polymers in a Vacuum, *J. Polymer Sci.*, vol. 11, pp. 491–506, 1953.

36. Madorsky, S. L.: Thermal Degradation of Polymers at Low Rates, *J. Res. Natl. Bur. Std.*, vol. 62, pp. 219–228, 1959.

37. Madorsky, S. L.: Unpublished work quoted in Achhammer, B. G., M. Tryon, and G. M. Kline: Chemical Structure and Stability Relationships in Polymers, *Kunststoffe Plastics*, vol. 49, pp. 600–608, 1959; *Ger. Plastics Dig.*, vol. 49, pp. 11–18, November, 1959; *Mod. Plastics*, vol. 37, no. 4, pp. 131–135, 139, 142, 144–145, 148, 216–217, 220, 222, 227, December, 1959.

38. Madorsky, S. L., V. E. Hart, and S. Strauss: Thermal Degradation of Cellulosic Materials, *J. Res. Natl. Bur. Std.*, vol. 60, pp. 343–349, 1958.

39. Madorsky, S. L., V. E. Hart, and S. Strauss: Pyrolysis of Cellulose in a Vacuum, *J. Res. Natl. Bur. Std.*, vol. 56, pp. 343–354, 1956.

40. Madorsky, S. L., V. E. Hart, S. Straus, and V. A. Sedlak: Thermal Degradation of Tetrafluoroethylene and Hydrofluoroethylene Polymers in a Vacuum, *J. Res. Natl. Bur. Std.*, vol. 51, pp. 327–333, 1953.

41. Madorsky, S. L., and S. Straus: High Vacuum Pyrolytic Fractionation of Polystyrene, *Ind. Eng. Chem.*, vol. 40, pp. 848–852, 1948; *J. Res. Natl. Bur. Std.*, vol. 40, p. 417, 1948.

42. Madorsky, S. L., and S. Straus: Thermal Degradation of Polymers as a Function of Molecular Structure, *J. Res. Natl. Bur. Std.*, vol. 53, pp. 361–370, 1954.

43. Madorsky, S. L., and S. Straus: Thermal Degradation of Polychlorotrifluoroethylene, Poly-*a*, *β*, *β*-Trifluorostyrene, and Poly-*p*-Xylylene in a Vacuum, *J. Res. Natl. Bur. Std.*, vol. 55, pp. 223–230, 1955.

44. Madorsky, S. L., and S. Straus: Thermal Degradation of Polymers at High Temperatures, *J. Res. Natl. Bur. Std.*, vol. 63A, pp. 261–268, 1959.

45. Madorsky, S. L., and S. Straus: Thermal Degradation of Polymers at High Temperatures, National Bureau of Standards unpublished work, 1960.

46. Madorsky, S. L., and S. Straus: Thermal Degradation of Polymers at Temperatures up to 1200°, *U.S. Air Force Wright Air Development Center Tech. Rpt.* 59-64, part II, Dayton, Ohio, 1960.

47. Madorsky, S. L., and S. Straus: Thermal Degradation of Polytetrafluoroethylene as a First-order Reaction, *J. Res. Natl. Bur., Std.*, vol. 64A, pp. 513–514, 1960.

48. Madorsky, S. L., and S. Straus: Thermal Stability of High-temperature Carbon Chain Polymers, in unpublished U.S. Air Force Wright Air Development Division Technical Report, 1960.

49. Madorsky, S. L., S. Straus, D. Thompson, and L. Williamson: Pyrolysis of Polyisobutene (Vistanex), Polyisoprene, Polybutadiene, GR-S and Polyethylene in a High Vacuum, *J. Res. Natl. Bur. Std.*, vol. 42, pp. 499–514, 1949.

50. Straus, S., and S. L. Madorsky: Pyrolysis of Styrene, Acrylate, and Isoprene Polymers in a Vacuum, *J. Res. Natl. Bur. Std.*, vol. 50, pp. 165–176, 1953.

51. Straus, S., and S. L. Madorsky: Thermal Degradation of Polyacrylonitrile, Polybutadiene, and Copolymers of Butadiene with Acrylonitrile and Styrene, *J. Res. Natl. Bur. Std.*, vol. 61, pp. 77–81, 1958.

52. Straus, S., and L. A. Wall: Pyrolysis of Polyamides, *J. Res. Natl. Bur. Std.*, vol. 60, pp. 39–45, 1958.
53. Straus, S., and L. A. Wall: Influence of Impurities on the Pyrolysis of Polyamides, *J. Res. Natl. Bur. Std.*, vol. 63A, pp. 269–273, 1959.
54. Stromberg, R. R., S. Straus, and B. G. Achhammer: Thermal Degradation of Poly Vinyl Chloride, *J. Polymer Sci.*, vol. 35, pp. 355–368, 1959.
55. Wall, L. A. Polymer Decomposition: Thermodynamics, Mechanisms, and Energetics, part 1, *Soc. Plastics Engrs. J.*, vol. 16, pp. 810–814, August, 1960.
56. Wall, L. A.: Energetics of Polymer Decomposition, part II, *Soc. Plastics Engs. J.*, vol. 16, pp. 1031–1035, September, 1960.
57. Wall, L. A., S. L. Madorsky, D. W. Brown, S. Straus, and R. Simka: Depolymerization of Polymethylene and Polyethylene, *J. Am. Chem. Soc.*, vol. 76, pp. 3430–3437, 1954.
58. Wall, L. A., and S. Straus: Pyrolysis of Polyolefins, *J. Polymer Sci.*, vol. 44, pp. 313–323, 1960.
59. Matacek, G. F.: Vacuum Volatility of Organic Coatings, in F. J. Clauss (ed.): "Surface Effects on Spacecraft Materials," pp. 263–285, John Wiley & Sons, Inc., New York, 1960.
60. Clauss, F. J. (ed.): "Surface Effects on Spacecraft Materials," John Wiley & Sons, Inc., New York, 1960.
61. Santeler, D. J.: Outgassing Characteristics of Various Materials, *Trans. 5th Natl. Symp. on Vacuum Technol.*, 1958, pp. 1–8.
62. Grassie, N., and H. W. Melville: Thermal Degradation of Polyvinyl Compounds, *Proc. Roy. Soc. (London)*, vol. A199, pp. 1–55, 1949.
63. Vanderschmidt, G. F., and J. C. Simons, Jr.: Material Sublimation and Surface Effects in High Vacuum, in Clauss, F. J. (ed.): "Surface Effects on Spacecraft Materials," pp. 247–262, John Wiley & Sons, Inc., New York, 1960.
64. DeWitt, E. A., S. Podlaseck, and J. Suhorsky: Effect of Low Pressure at Elevated Temperatures on Space Vehicle Materials, *Martin Company Rept.* RM-29, Baltimore, 1959.
65. Jellinek, H. H. G.: Thermal Degradation of Polystyrene and Polyethylene, part III, *J. Polymer Sci.*, vol. 3, pp. 850–865, 1948; vol. 4, pp. 13–36, 1949.
66. Grassie, N., and W. W. Kerr: Thermal Depolymerization of Polystyrene. Part I—Reaction Mechanism, *Trans. Faraday Soc.*, vol. 53, pp. 234–239, 1957.
67. Grassie, N.: Thermal Degradation of Polyvinyl Acetate, *Trans. Faraday Soc.*, vol. 48, pp. 379–387, 1952; vol. 49, pp. 835–842, 1953.
68. Moiseev, V. D., M. B. Neiman, and A. I. Kryukova: Thermal Degradation of Polypropene, *Vysokomole kul. Soedin.*, vol. 1, pp. 1552–1557, 1959.
69. Wright, W. W.: Thermal Degradation of Fluorine-containing Polymers, Polyphenylene Oxides and Polyphenylenes, High Temperature Resistance and Thermal Degradation of Polymers," pp. 248–269, Society of Chemical Industry Monograph No. 13, London, 1961.
70. Siegle, J. C., and L. T. Muus: Pyrolysis of Polytetrafluoroethylene, presented to American Chemical Society, September, 1956. (Abstract No. 16, p. 8S, in Abstracts of Papers of 130th Meeting.)

71. Siegle, J. C., L. T. Muus, T. P. Lin, and H. A. Larsen: Molecular Structure of Perfluorocarbon Polymers. II. Pyrolysis of Polytetrafluoroethylene (submitted to *J. Am. Chem. Soc.*).
72. Druesdow, D., and C. F. Gibbs: Effect of Heat and Light on Polyvinyl Chloride, in Polymer Degradation Mechanisms, *Natl. Bur. Std. Circ.* 525, pp. 69–80, 1953.
73. Clauss, F. J.: Surface Effects on Materials in Near Space, *Aerospace Eng.*, vol. 19, no. 10, pp. 16–19, 56, 58–59, 62, October, 1960.
74. Atkins, J. H., R. L. Bisplinghoff, J. L. Ham, E. G. Jackson, and J. C. Simons, Jr.: Effects of Space Environment on Materials, National Reserve Corporation Report to U.S. Air Force Wright Air Development Division, *Tech. Rept.* 60-721, Dayton, 1960.
75. Achter, M. R.: Effects of High Vacuum on Mechanical Properties, in Clauss, F. J. (ed.): "Surface Effects on Spacecraft Materials," pp. 286–306, John Wiley & Sons, Inc., New York, 1960.
76. Lad, R. A.: Survey of Materials Problems Resulting from Low Pressure and Radiation Environment in Space, *NASA Tech. Note* D-477, 1960.
77. Riehl, W. A., W. C. Looney, and S. V. Caruso: Compatibility of Engineering Materials with Space Environment, U.S. Army Ballistic Missile Agency Final Report on Item 1, Part II, U.S. Dept. of Defense, ARPA order 92-59, Huntsville, Ala., 1960.

10
Lubrication

FRANCIS J. CLAUSS

RESEARCH SCIENTIST, LOCKHEED AIRCRAFT CORPORATION
MISSILES AND SPACE DIVISION
PALO ALTO, CALIFORNIA

One of the major material problem areas for advanced spacecraft systems is that of friction and wear of rubbing or sliding surfaces as encountered in the operation of gears, bearings, and electric contacts used in various spacecraft mechanisms. Lubrication is needed to reduce frictional drag and minimize the power required to drive the mechanisms. Excessive wear resulting from inadequate lubrication can be the limiting factor in the lifetime of the mechanisms, as well as that of the entire system. There are many special problems that complicate the lubrication problem such as, for example, the very high vacuum that exists in space.

The difficulties in providing lubrication for spacecraft mechanisms can be met in several ways. The effects of operation under vacuum conditions can be avoided, for example, by enclosing the moving parts within hermetically sealed containers. Where necessary, forced-feed systems can be used so that lubricant lost by evaporation in the vacuum of space is periodically replenished from a reservoir. These and other stratagems are often impractical, however, and at best have the disadvantage of increasing the weight, size, and complexity of the spacecraft systems. Their use should be restricted, therefore, to those cases where they are the only feasible means for providing lubrication.

A much better approach lies in the application of lubricants and self-lubricating materials that themselves provide a reliable and straightforward solution to the problems of space lubrication. Unfortunately, very little information exists on either the implications of the space environment for the lubrication problem or the behavior of lubricants and self-lubricating materials under space-environment conditions. Further, there is no organized compilation of the little information available in this area.

277

The purpose of this chapter is to discuss some of the problems that may be anticipated in providing satisfactory lubrication for spacecraft mechanisms and to summarize available information on the applicability of various lubricants and self-lubricating materials to solve such problems.

Environmental Conditions

Although this chapter is primarily concerned with the use of lubricants and self-lubricating materials for long periods under orbital conditions in space, there are other environmental conditions to which mechanisms are subjected. These too must be considered, or the spacecraft may never be successfully placed in orbit. Some of these conditions are imposed a second time on vehicles that reenter the earth's atmosphere. In order to ensure that parts operate reliably for the duration of the vehicle mission, therefore, all the environmental conditions must be considered. These include the following:

1. Ground activities: operation for test and checkout; handling; transportation; storage; and exposure to the elements
2. Short-time operation during launch, ascent, and reentry: acceleration and shock; vibration; temperature extremes; and contact with reactive fuels and oxidizers
3. Long-time operation in orbit: ultrahigh vacuum; temperature extremes; zero gravity; and radiation

Ground Activities. Assembled mechanisms used in spacecraft and missiles are repeatedly tested on the ground prior to actual launch during the checking out of various components and entire systems. As a result, parts that will operate for less than a minute during the launch and ascent phases can accumulate as much as several hundred hours of test operation prior to the time of launching. Lubricants selected for use with these parts under the vacuum conditions in space will normally have to operate for a considerable period under atmospheric conditions.

Necessary handling and transportation of delicate mechanisms involve an ever-present potential for damage from major shocks and vibration. Dropping a part on a concrete floor, for example, can be more injurious than the effects of actual launching. Handling and transportation by rail can cause shocks of as much as 30 g, and, without special handling and packaging, such damage as Brinell marks in ball and roller bearings can result.

Inadequate protection of parts during storage or while standing at launch sites can render them ineffective by allowing exposure to the elements with resulting corrosion, contamination, or changes in the lubricants. Elements and conditions that contribute to this hazard, and which are generally found at launching sites, include high-humidity atmospheres, mist, fog, water, salt, sand, and dust.

For gears and bearings materials should be either corrosion-resistant or protected by suitable films of oils, greases, or other coatings. Seals should be provided around joining surfaces or couplings to exclude minute particles of dirt. These precautions are particularly important for parts mounted on the exterior of a vehicle since they are most subject to weathering.

Short-time Operation during Launch, Ascent, and Reentry. Heavy shock and vibration loads that occur during the short-time periods of launch, ascent, and reentry can cause Brinell marks in ball and roller bearings. The rotors of most fractional-horsepower motors are light enough so that Brinelling does not appear to be a real problem with such parts. However, bearings which support heavy loads and which are stationary during launch and ascent are most susceptible to this type of damage. Two methods may be used to prevent Brinell marks from being caused by heavy loads. One is to rotate the shafts and bearings by having the mechanism in operation during the launch phase. The other provides for blocking the load so that it is not supported on the bearings during the launch phase and subsequently removing the blocks after the vehicle is in orbit.

Since high temperatures are generated by fuel burning and by aerodynamic heating, certain bearings (such as those used on control surfaces) and other parts must be designed to withstand high temperatures. At the other extreme, the use of cryogenic fluids for propulsion (e.g., liquid hydrogen, fluorine, and oxygen in conventional types of power plants and liquid helium in nuclear power plants) means that pumps, valves, and other moving parts will require the maintenance of lubrication at very low temperatures (e.g., below $100°K$). Since the fluids used for propulsion are very reactive and include the strongest oxidizers known, lubricants which might come into contact with such fluids must be extremely inert.

Long-time Operation in Orbit. Satellites that must operate in orbit for long periods are subjected to such special conditions as ultrahigh vacuum, temperature extremes, zero gravity, and radiation. Certain parts used in such satellites must operate in the hard vacuum of space, which is on the order of 10^{-9} mm Hg, more or less, depending upon the orbital altitude. These include bearings, gears, and sliding electric contacts on antennas, solar-cell assemblies, or other exposed gear. Rotating parts inside certain electronic tubes also must operate in vacuum. The special problems created by vacuum include higher evaporation rates of oils and greases, oil creepage along surfaces, and cold-welding of metals that are in contact with each other.

Although most payloads on satellites are maintained near room temperature, temperatures of several hundred degrees will be experienced around electric motors that operate continuously; such temperatures will markedly accelerate evaporation under vacuum conditions. Parts that are outside the skin of a satellite, such as bearings on solar-cell arrays, will experience wider orbital-temperature fluctuations than those inside, and their low temperatures may be about $-200°F$ when the satellite is passing the shadow side of the earth. Oils selected for such use must not freeze or become too viscous under such conditions, nor must they become to thin or volatile at high temperatures when directly exposed to the sun. For spacecraft and satellites with secondary propulsion systems, temperature extremes can include the high temperatures associated with combustion and the low temperatures associated with cryogenic fuels and oxidizers.

Zero gravity is an item on the credit side, since it means that, once in orbit, bearings need not support any structural loads. Bearing loads will be reduced to levels required by inertial loads associated with accelerating and decelerating mechanisms, the effects of unbalanced dynamic forces, and the centrifugal forces of balls against races in rotating ball bearings. The reduced bearing loads mean less wear. On the other hand, gravity-type feed systems for lubricants are obviously ineffective.

Radiation includes the penetrating Van Allen radiation and solar corpuscular radiation that exist in space, supplemented by nuclear radiation that would result from use of a reactor power source. Both the materials used for gears and bearings and any lubricants used with them must resist such radiation.

Purposes of Lubrication

Lubricants serve to maintain satisfactory equipment operation and part functioning in several ways. Some reasons for their use are to reduce wear, minimize frictional drag, carry away heat, prevent corrosion, and exclude dirt. Reduction of wear is the cost important objective in this list since wear limits part lifetime. Frictional drag increases the power required for operation (certainly at a premium in spacecraft) and generates heat that must be dissipated by radiation from the surface of the spacecraft. Frictional drag and wear are closely related although it does not follow that minimum friction is associated with minimum wear.

Carrying away the heat generated between moving surfaces, preventing corrosion of the components, and excluding dirt or foreign matter are other important functions that lubricants usually serve, although their importance is usually secondary to reducing wear or minimizing frictional drag. Preventing corrosion and excluding dirt are of no concern once a satellite has been established in orbit since conditions causing corrosion or contamination are then absent; however, they can be important considerations during storage and launching.

Although a lubricant can thus serve a number of purposes, the present chapter is concerned principally with the first two items in this list. And, perhaps at the risk of oversimplification, we can adopt as a working definition that lubrication consists in maintaining a film of low shear strength between moving surfaces.

Two general types of lubrication are used for spacecraft, namely, hydrodynamic lubrication and boundary lubrication.

Hydrodynamic Lubrication.   Hydrodynamic lubrication provides minimum friction, and this capability has been responsible for its extensive

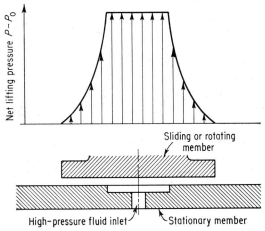

Fig. 10.1   Geometry and pressure distribution in an externally pressurized plain slider bearing.

use with bearings for guidance and control systems of missiles and spacecraft. Hydrodynamic lubrication is more a matter of mechanical design than material selection, and it is, therefore, discussed only briefly in the following paragraphs.

Hydrodynamic lubrication is a type of lubrication in which the rubbing surfaces are separated by a continuous and relatively thick film of a gas such as air or a liquid such as oil. The fluid carries the load or weight of the free member of the rubbing pair and separates it from the stationary member. It also provides a medium of very low shear strength or viscosity. The resistance to relative motion between surfaces provided with hydrodynamic lubrication is very low, owing to the viscosity of the fluid. The coefficients of friction are generally less than 0.001.

Hydrodynamic lubrication is accomplished by either external pressurization or self-action. Figure 10.1 illustrates the principle of an externally pressurized slider bearing. With this type, the fluid is supplied under pressure so that the free body can swim on a film of oil or gas which flows within the clearance spaces of the bearing. When the clearance is adjusted to maintain the minimum safe clearance between the surfaces, only very small amounts of fluid are needed. The load-bearing capacity depends upon the practical l'mits of fluid pressure and volume.

With the self-acting type of hydrodynamic lubrication (see Fig. 10.2), the part acts as its own pump to maintain the hydrodynamic film. The parts operate in a bath of the fluid which, for spacecraft applications, is contained in a leakproof container. The relative motion of the rubbing surfaces generates a film pressure within the clearance spaces and keeps

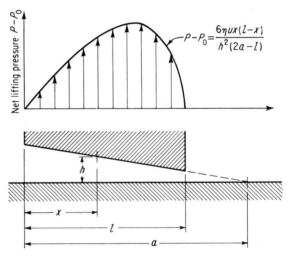

Fig. 10.2　Geometry and pressure distribution in a self-acting plain slider bearing.

the surfaces separated. It is necessary to incline one of the surfaces, as indicated in Fig. 10.2, in order to obtain a lifting component. The net lifting pressure at any point along the surface is given by the following equation:

$$P - P_0 = \frac{6\eta u x(l - x)}{h^2(2a - l)}$$

where P = pressure at point x

P_0 = ambient pressure

η = viscosity of fluid

u = velocity of relative motion

l = length of slider

h = film thickness at point x

a = length of base of triangle formed by the two surface contours

It should be noted that the lifting pressure increases linearly with the fluid viscosity and with the speed of relative motion between the two surfaces and that it varies inversely as the square of the film thickness. This means that the self-acting type requires close machining tolerances and high speeds for efficient operation. Since the viscosity of gases is low, self-acting gas bearings are limited to lighter loads than those which can be sustained by self-acting oil bearings.

With both the externally pressurized and self-acting types of hydrodynamic lubrication, a film of low shear strength is maintained between the moving surfaces.

Hydrodynamic lubrication, using either a gas or an oil as the working fluid, offers the following advantages:

1. Operation with very low friction. A friction coefficient as low as 0.000004 has reportedly been achieved with the externally pressurized oil bearing used to float the large telescope mirror at Mount Palomar. The very low friction in bearings is important in improving the accuracy of gyroscope applications.

2. Operation at very high speeds. As a consequence of their low friction, speeds of 400,000 to 500,000 rpm, or even higher, are possible with gas bearings.

3. Positional accuracy. Maximum positional accuracy can be obtained. Moreover, the accuracy does not alter with time because no wear takes place.

4. Long operating life. Since no wear takes place, the lifetime of hydrodynamic bearings appears unlimited.

5. Wide temperature range of operation (especially with gas films). Since gases are stable over wide temperature ranges, gas bearings can operate at either very high or very low temperatures.

6. Minimum vibration. The fluid film acts as a cushion to damp vibrations so that vibrations are not easily transmitted from one part to another.

7. Long storage life. There is less deterioration during storage for long periods than with other types of lubrication.

8. Resistance to shock and vibration. Bearings can withstand high accelerations and random vibrations. This is important during the launch and ascent phases as well as during the transportation of the vehicles to the launch site.

There are a few disadvantages in using hydrodynamic lubrication for spacecraft and missile systems. These are as follows:

1. Pressure maintenance. The externally pressurized type requires a pump or blower to maintain the supply of oil or gas under pressure. This requirement increases the weight, size, complexity, and power needs of the total system.

2. Load capacity. The self-acting type has a negligible load capacity at zero speed and has less load capacity than the externally pressurized type at high speeds.

3. Lubricant retention. This type of lubrication can be used only in components or parts that can be totally enclosed; otherwise, a large storage capacity would be needed to replenish fluid escaping into space.

Both self-acting gas bearings and externally pressurized oil bearings have been used and are planned for use on United States missiles and spacecraft. The first United States satellite, for example, was put into orbit by a guidance system that used gas bearings.

Boundary Lubrication. Full hydrodynamic lubrication cannot always be realized in practice. Most moving parts with fluid lubrication operate under conditions of boundary lubrication in which there is at least a partial breakage of the continuous film so that the surfaces of moving solids come into contact. This occurs when the speed or the fluid pressure between the surfaces becomes too low to support the bearing load, causing the hydrodynamic film to become so thin that its thickness is less than the height of the surface irregularities. Some of the asperities—the high points on even the smoothest surface—then begin to rub on one another; the coefficient of friction rises; and surface wear occurs.

An important first point in explaining the mechanism of friction and wear under boundary conditions of lubrication is that even the most highly polished surfaces are quite rough when viewed on a microscopic scale. Someone has described the actual situation very graphically by saying that placing even the smoothest polished surfaces together is rather like turning Switzerland upside down and placing it on Austria. This situation is illustrated in Fig. 10.3, which is a topographical map showing 90 miles of straight-line cross section through Switzerland and the Salzburg ranges of Austria. The profile in Fig. 10.3, at a scale of 2 million to 1, corresponds very exactly to the profile of a ground-steel surface with a finish of 8 μin. rms at a magnification of 2000X [1].

Early workers in this field have ascribed the friction of clean solid surfaces to the interlocking of the surface irregularities, and the frictional work to the energy dissipated in raising one set of surface roughnesses over the other. It was believed that the function of a lubricating film was to fill in the "valleys" and form smooth surfaces so that the hard bodies could not come into contact with one another, interlock, and thus cause friction.

The more modern theories of boundary lubrication interpret frictional resistance as the net result of the effects of two concurrent conditions, namely, the shearing of welded junctions formed between points of contact and the ploughing out of the softer material to an appreciable depth below the surface by the harder material's riding over it. For hard materials in contact with one another, analysis indicates that the ploughing term is relatively small and that friction is largely due to the shearing of the welded junctions.

Three important points in the adhesion theory of friction and wear, that is, the welded-junction theory, are as follows:

1. The area of true contact is only a small fraction of the apparent contact area.

2. High localized temperatures are generated at the points of contact by frictional heating.

3. The two surfaces interact with each other.

When clean metal surfaces are placed together, they touch only where the asperities or high spots meet, as indicated by the profile view in

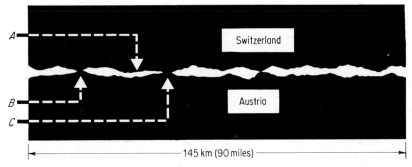

Fig. 10.3 Topographic profile corresponding to ground-steel surface. Portion of Switzerland inverted on Austria, showing 90-mile straight-line cross section through Swiss passes of Gothard, Splugen, and Poschiavo and the Salzburg ranges of Austria. *A*, Bernina range (elevation, 10,669 ft); *B*, Hochkoenig (9,840 ft); *C*, Dachstein (9,829 ft) [1].

Fig. 10.3, and the real area of contact is much smaller than the apparent area. The greater the force pressing the surfaces together, the more the asperities are crushed down and suffer plastic deformation. This action increases both the number and the size of the contacts involved in supporting the load, so that the area of real contact increases.

When solids slide over one another, extremely high surface temperatures are generated even under moderate conditions of load and speed. The high temperatures are confined to very thin surface layers at the contacting points and are of very brief duration. For example, for a constantan cylinder sliding on a steel surface under a load of 4.1 lb and a sliding speed of 120 ips, temperature flashes of 1000°C (1832°F) were measured that lasted for less than 10^{-4} sec (see p. 41 of Ref. 2).

Sliding between metal surfaces is not a continuous, smooth process but often proceeds in a series of intermittent jerks. The friction rises to a maximum during the "stick" and falls rapidly during the "slip," and there are corresponding changes in the area of contact and the surface temperature. Experiments indicate that, under the intense pressure acting at the summits of the surface irregularities, localized adhesion or welding between the metal surface takes place. The occurrence of this condition is undoubtedly aided by the frictional heating. The metallic junctions that are formed must be sheared if the surfaces are to slide past one another, and the force required to shear the junctions and permit sliding is proportional to the product of the shear strength of the junctions and the area of real contact.

Figure 10.4 illustrates, in simple form, the conditions that exist during boundary lubrication. The first example (Fig. 10.4a) represents a hard

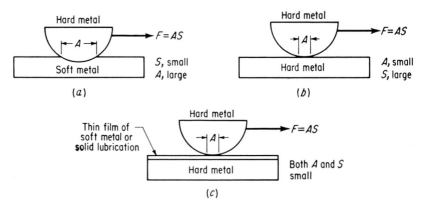

Fig. 10.4 Lubrication of solids by thin films.

body riding in contact with a soft one. The hard body presses into the soft one so that the area of real contact is large. Even though the strength of the junctions formed with the soft metal is low, the frictional force F, which equals the product of the shear strength S and the area A of the welded junctions, is relatively high. For the second case (Fig. 10.4b), indicating two hard bodies in contact with one another, the area of real contact is small, but the strength of the junctions formed is large so that again the frictional force is relatively high. The ideal situation is that shown in Fig. 10.4c. Here, a film of soft material with a low shear strength is placed between two hard bodies. The hard substrate supports the load and keeps the contact area small while the film of soft metal reduces the junction strength. These two factors thus combine their effects to reduce the frictional force.

Films of low shear strength can be provided by using laminar solids, such as molybdenum disulfide, which have low shear strength along certain crystallographic planes or by using soft metals such as silver, gold, and lead which have low shear strength in all directions.   Boundary lubrication by oils, greases, and liquid metals accomplishes the same purpose, but they are not tightly bonded to the surface.   Duplex bearing alloys, such as copper-lead, that contain hard and soft constituents in their metallurgical structure function by much the same principle; that is, the hard portions of the structure support the load and the lubricant is fed to the surface from the areas containing the soft constituent. Variation on this same idea is to rule or knurl a grid into the surface of a hard metal and then smear a soft metal into the indentations.   This permits combinations of hard and soft metals that cannot be melted and cast together and provides storage capacity for the soft constituent.

Effect of Surface Films and Their Removal in Vacuum.   It should be clear that the surface conditions of the mating parts are more important for boundary lubrication than for hydrodynamic lubrication. Physical and chemical interactions between the surface, the immediately adjacent layers of lubricant molecules, and the prevailing atmosphere have more effect on what happens at the solid contact points than do the bulk properties of the lubricant, such as its viscosity.

Adsorbed or chemisorbed gas films, such as oxides, are normally present on even the cleanest metal surfaces in the normal atmosphere.   These films prevent bare metal-to-metal contact and the formation of strong welded junctions so that the coefficient of friction is less than if bare metal-to-metal contact were obtained.

Parts that are exposed to the hard vacuum of outer space will operate at pressures on the order of 10^{-9} mm Hg (more or less, depending upon the altitude).   Surface films of adsorbed or chemisorbed gases that are removed by wear or by sublimation into space will not re-form, so the films present on surfaces in the normal earth atmosphere will vanish within some time after being put into orbit.   Under these conditions, gross seizure or cold-welding can occur between the surfaces when they are brought together under even very slight contact forces.   This phenomenon has been illustrated by laboratory experiments described on pages 145 to 149† of Ref. 2.

Figure 10.5 shows the equipment used in the first of these studies. The method consists essentially in propelling a metal cylinder C along a wire XY and photographically estimating its deceleration.   From the resulting data, the frictional force between the two surfaces can be calculated.

The cylinder is propelled by the spring S which is released by the electromagnet M.   The lower surface XY is degassed by passing a heating current through it, and the cylinder C is degassed by lifting it off the

_____
† These experiments were performed by Hughes and Young at Cambridge University [3, 4].

lower surface with the molybdenum rail support R and heating it by electron bombardment from the filament F. The entire apparatus, except for the electromagnet, is encased in a silica envelope O which is connected to the vacuum system.

Both metals are kept at a temperature just below that at which excessive evaporation occurs during the final stages of degassing. During the friction measurements, the pressure in the envelope was maintained below 10^{-6} mm Hg and, except when otherwise stated, the friction was measured immediately after the degassed surfaces had cooled to room temperature.

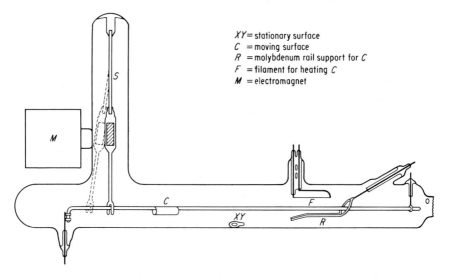

Fig. 10.5   Apparatus for measuring friction between outgassed metal surfaces.

Figure 10.6 presents the main results of the experiment using nickel on tungsten and copper on copper. Figures 10.6a and c show that the coefficient of friction was initially about 0.5 and that, after degassing in vacuum and cooling to room temperature, the coefficient increased by a factor of 10 or more. When the clean surfaces were allowed to stand at room temperature in a vacuum of 10^{-5} to 10^{-6} mm Hg, the coefficient of friction steadily decreased, presumably because of the gradual recontamination of the surfaces by residual gases in the apparatus. Figures 10.6b and d show that when a trace of oxygen was deliberately admitted, there was a sudden large reduction in friction, followed by a slower reduction that continued with time. On the other hand, admitting pure hydrogen or nitrogen had little effect on the friction of the clean surfaces.

Figure 10.7 shows another apparatus used in a second study [4]. The

upper surface A and the lower surface B are fashioned in the form of
hollow cylinders to facilitate heating by high-frequency induction.   The
upper surface is a moving specimen with a small curved protrusion to
provide localized contact.   The lower surface is fixed and has a flattened

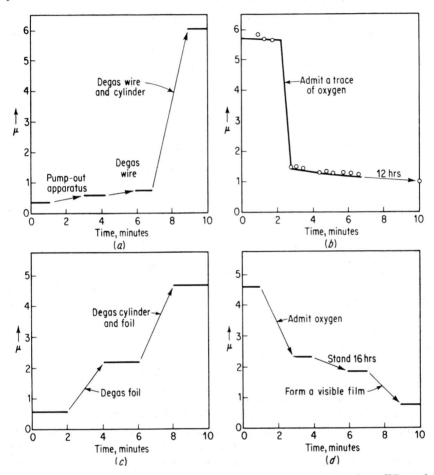

Fig. 10.6   Effects of surface films on coefficient of friction.   (a) and (c) Effect of
removing adsorbed film of oxygen and other contaminants from metal surfaces; (b)
and (d) effect of adding a trace of oxygen to clean outgassed metals.

face.   Surface A is connected by silica link C to a sealed bulb of soft iron
D.   The sealed bulb D is moved by electromagnet E and hence moves
surface A.   The frictional force on A is measured by the silica spring
device F, and the high-frequency induction coil G provides the necessary
heating.   The entire apparatus, except for the electromagnet, is encased
in a silica envelope H which is connected to the vacuum system.

The main difference between the apparatus shown in Fig. 10.7 and the one presented in Fig. 10.5 is that the upper surface A was dragged slowly over the lower surface B instead of being propelled along it. Also, the load was appreciably higher, on the order of 15 g, as compared with less than 1 g for the equipment shown in Fig. 10.5. Further, the region of contact between the surfaces was more clearly defined as it occurred between the small curved protrusion of surface A and the flat face of surface B. Degassing was accomplished by the high-frequency induction-heating coil, and a vacuum of about 10^{-6} mm Hg was employed.

"Clean" nickel surfaces prepared in air had coefficients of friction of about 1.4. The surfaces were then heated to 1000°C (1832°F) in vacuum to remove contaminant films. On cooling in vacuum to room temperature, the coefficient of friction of the degassed surfaces readily reached a value of 9. Admitting air or a trace of oxygen reduced the friction, but

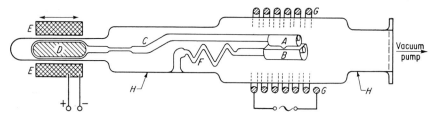

Fig. 10.7 Apparatus for measuring the friction between outgassed metal surfaces. A, moving upper surface with small curved protrusion; B, fixed lower surface with flattened face; C, connecting silica links; D, sealed soft-iron bulb; E, electromagnet; F, silica spring device; G, induction-heating coil; H, silica envelope.

hydrogen had no measurable effect. On surfaces that were even more thoroughly degassed, large-scale seizure occurred on contact. Separation of these surfaces was possible only by prying them apart, and the friction was too high to be measured.

In general, similar materials are more likely to weld together during rubbing than those that are dissimilar. In the case of metals, their tendency to weld to each other is strongly dependent upon their solid solubilities in one another.† Metallic couples that have negligible solid solubility at a given temperature generally have the best antiscoring properties at that temperature, whereas couples that have complete solubility in one another show the greatest increase in friction [6–8].

† Two metals tend to form solid-solution alloys with one another when the following conditions are satisfied: (1) The atoms of both metals are approximately the same size (extensive solubility is favored when the atomic diameters of both metals are within 15 per cent of each other); (2) both metals have the same crystal structure (e.g., both are face-centered cubic, as with copper and gold); (3) both metals have similar chemical reactivities (i.e., they are on the same side of the periodic table) so that they have a minimal tendency to interact and form intermediate phases [5].

Although mutual solubility appears a significant factor in the tendency of metals to cold-weld together, it is not a completely satisfactory criterion. Recent studies have attempted to develop a criterion for cold-welding on the basis of the relative values of the work of adhesion and the strength of the weaker component. Since accurate values of the work of adhesion are not usually available, however, such theories have not been rigorously tested and have limited the usefulness of such a hypothesis.

For application to the lubrication problems of spacecraft mechanisms, the following conclusions regarding the effect of surface films and their removal in vacuum are significant:

1. Where metal parts operate in contact with one another, tenacious surface films that are not stripped off in vacuum and that offer some lubrication for the moving parts to which they are applied should be used.

2. Running metals in direct contact with each other should be avoided, particularly if the contacting metals are mutually soluble in one another.

3. Where possible, materials that come in contact with each other should be dissimilar, e.g., a metal surface with a plastic or a ceramic surface.

These conclusions can often be applied without much difficulty. As rubbing speeds increase and as greater requirements are placed on lifetime and reliability, however, the selection of the proper lubricants as self-lubricating materials becomes more important and more difficult. Such selection requires knowledge of the advantages and disadvantages of the various lubricants and self-lubricating materials available for use in spacecraft mechanisms. The following sections of this chapter present specific information on such materials and lubricants as a means of achieving such an objective.

Oils and Greases

General Considerations. Oils and greases provide the significant advantages of lower torque and greater availability as compared with other types of lubricant. However, the special conditions existing in space affect the suitability of oils and greases for parts in spacecraft mechanisms. These factors must be considered in addition to the standards normally applied to their selection for use under earthside conditions. The major considerations involved are as follows:

1. Loss of lubricating fluids by entrainment, evaporation, and creepage

2. Frictional polymerization catalyzed by clean metal surface and frictional heating

3. Effect of absence of oxygen and other gases on the formation of lubricating films

4. Radiation stability

Continued loss of oil from an oil-lubricated surface means that the surface must eventually operate dry and that wear rates and the tendency for wear and cold-welding will increase. In the case of greases, the loss of oil from the soap bases causes the greases to thicken and eventually converts them to hard residues which do not lubricate and which can, in fact, jam such parts as ball bearings. The loss of lubricating fluids therefore sets an upper limit to the lifetimes of moving parts unless provision is made for feeding additional lubricant from an oil or grease reservoir.

Three mechanisms by which lubricating fluids can be lost warrant consideration. Although it is difficult to assign quantitative values for the rates at which the fluids will be lost under actual space conditions, some general comments may be helpful in designing for the use of oils and greases in spacecraft.

For an assembly that is open to the atmosphere, oil can be lost in the form of macroscopic droplets entrained in an escaping gas stream during the time that the pressure within the assembly is dropping (e.g., during the ascent phase or the initial period in orbit). This loss would be especially severe if the pressure dropped suddenly and caused a stream of escaping gas to move rapidly past a lubricated part. For a system that is totally enclosed and well sealed, there would be no oil loss from the entire system and entrainment would not present a problem. For assemblies in which a shaft emerges from an enclosed housing into space, the use of a seal about the shaft minimizes entrainment losses by reducing the rate of pressure drop and the rate of exit of the gas stream.

Rotating seals also minimize oil loss by evaporation. Even in a totally enclosed system, however, oil can evaporate from a lubricated part (especially if it is hot) and condense on the walls of the container or on other surfaces. Evaporation is more rapid into vacuum, of course, than into atmospheric air.

Liquids wet surfaces and spread over them much more thoroughly in vacuum than in air so that lubricating oils can be expected to flow through seal clearances and over adjoining surfaces (e.g., oil will flow out of double-shielded ball bearings and over shafts). One result of this creepage is to increase the total area from which evaporation of oils can occur and, therefore, the overall rate of evaporation. Although data are not available, oil loss by creepage through double-shielded ball bearings appears to be greater than by the loss through evaporation alone. Coating shafts and other surfaces with a nonwetting material should be helpful in minimizing oil creepage.

Lubricant failures are sometimes accompanied by the formation of a very heavy varnish or residue on rubbing or sliding areas. This formation is due to the polymerization of the lubricant and is promoted by frictional heating and by the bare-metal surfaces exposed by frictional wear. (It has been known for some time that clean, oxygen-free metal surfaces can act as catalytic agents for some organic reactions.)

Abrasive particles from finishing operations in part fabrication are not completely removed by conventional cleaning techniques and have been found in ball bearings. These particles abrade the metal surfaces during operation and expose oxygen-free surfaces, which promote polymerization of the lubricant. For gyro bearings, the resulting increase in bearing torque, although small, is sufficient to cause the gyro to fail to perform properly [9].

Normally, oxygen-free surfaces react quickly with oxygen from the atmosphere to re-form surface oxides. In vacuum, however, the recontamination of exposed bare-metal surfaces cannot occur, and the clean surfaces can therefore continue to promote polymerization of a lubricant.

Organic vapors can also undergo frictional polymerization. Organic vapors from molded phenolic relay structures on telephone switching relays have been found to polymerize and thus form amorphous nonconducting deposits about contact areas, resulting in open circuits [10]. Sliding surfaces of the platinum-group metals (i.e., palladium, platinum, etc.) as well as molybdenum, tantalum, chromium, and gold have also produced solid products by frictional polymerization of benzene vapor and a wide range of organic compounds. Polymer formation has been observed with as little as 4 ppm of benzene vapor. Metals that did not result in frictional polymerization include silver, nickel, iron, vanadium, tungsten, and zinc.

Although a small amount of frictional polymerization of lubricating oils can increase the oil viscosity and bearing drag sufficiently to be catastrophic in the case of gyro bearings, this condition would not limit the operation of bearings on motors and other mechanisms where torque is less critical. Based on the limited information now available, it does not appear that frictional polymerization would limit the use of oils and greases as lubricants in space. The effect of frictional polymerization, if a problem at all, would be most serious in causing open circuits about precious-metal contacts. This result would be more likely to occur if the surrounding structures were made of materials which contain volatile plasticizers and which are enclosed so that the organic vapors cannot escape.

Effective boundary lubrication depends upon the formation of films attached to the surface(s) being lubricated. Thus, experiments with fatty acids show that lubrication is not achieved by the fatty acid itself but by the metallic soap formed as a result of the chemical reaction between the metal and the fatty acid. This reaction proceeds by means of the metal oxide that is formed on the metal and is favored by the presence of water vapor. In the absence of oxygen (and water), the metallic soaps do not form and the fatty acids are ineffective lubricants (see pages 200 to 214 of Ref. 2).

In practice, a number of oils and greases that are effective lubricants in vacuum (i.e., in the absence of oxygen and other gases) can be selected for use in spacecraft systems.

The general changes in lubricants caused by excessive radiation include the following:

1. Viscosity. In oils, the viscosity initially decreases, followed by an increase, with such fluids eventually becoming rubbery or solid. In greases, some thickeners degrade rapidly, causing a very marked drop in consistency to a thin and soupy character. Eventually, polymerization of the grease-base fluid overrides the thinning effect, and the grease becomes thicker, harder, and ultimately solid.

2. Volatility. In both oils and greases, volatility generally increases; foaming tendencies increase; the flash point drops; and gases are released, owing to the formation of low-molecular degradation products.

3. Acidity and corrosiveness. These characteristics increase for both oils and greases.

4. Oxidation resistance. A decrease in oxidation stability occurs in both oils and greases.

5. Heat conductivity. A decrease occurs in both types of lubricant.

6. Coking. The tendency toward coking increases in both oils and greases; however, occasional decreases have been noted.

Most oils and greases are stable to 10^8 or 10^9 r of radiation dosage. Except for applications involving exposure to nuclear-propulsion sources, oils and greases appear sufficiently radiation-resistant even for satellites that have to operate for a year in orbits that subject them to Van Allen radiation. This estimate is based on our present knowledge of the radiation in space and of the radiation stability of oils and greases [11–15]; it will probably have to be revised as more information is obtained.

Operating Tests on Oils and Greases in Vacuum. Several series of tests have been conducted during the past few years on the life of ball bearings lubricated with various oils and greases and operated in vacuum. These tests are most informative in indicating the potential value of various oils and greases for use in spacecraft mechanisms under vacuum conditions. Because the problem of bearing wear and lubrication is most acute at high speeds, these tests have been conducted at speeds from 4,000 to 12,000 rpm, which are typical of the speeds at which many servomotors operate in satellite systems.†

† Because of the need for minimum weight and size and maximum efficiency in spacecraft systems, mechanisms that must operate at relatively low speeds are driven

Ball Bearings. For small, high-speed applications, ball bearings are generally the most suitable type of antifriction bearing. The ball bearings used in the experiments summarized in this section were of the R3 and R2 sizes (i.e., $\frac{3}{16}$- and $\frac{1}{8}$-in. shaft diameters, respectively), and had the following other characteristics:

All the bearings tested with oils and greases were of the deep-groove type, in which the grooves or raceways in the inner and outer races in which the balls move are deep enough so that the bearings can support axial loads as well as radial loads. All the bearings were double-shielded which reduced the rate of evaporation during operation and protected the bearings against contamination from foreign particles.

The retainers (also called separators or cages) were of either the ribbon type of pressed steel or the machined type of Synthane. Crown-type retainers, which are lighter in weight and operate with less torque than the ribbon-type retainers, were not satisfactory at the high speeds of these tests. Synthane is a laminated phenolic material that is light in weight and has several per cent porosity, so that it can be vacuum-impregnated with the oil under study. During operation, oil is released from the pores of the Synthane retainers and provides a lubricating film on the ball surfaces.

For small precision bearings, up to about $\frac{1}{2}$ in. in shaft diameter or a little over 1 in. in outside diameter, the standard materials are SAE 52100 and 51100 high-carbon chrome steel and 440C stainless steel, both of which were tested. The chrome steels have better fatigue life than the stainless steel, whereas stainless steel has the advantage of better protection against corrosion, which is important not only in the actual operation of the bearings but also in their fabrication. A hardness of about 62 to 64 on the Rockwell C scale is desirable for balls and races, since this hardness offers the best compromise between intolerable brittleness on the one hand and a loss of desirable torque and load-carrying characteristics through softness on the other hand. The chrome steels should not be used in continuous operation above 350°F, whereas the stainless steel remains dimensionally stable up to about 900°F, although there is some softening at lower temperatures. For use at higher temperatures, tool steels can be used.

Test Results. The results from three series of tests on ball bearings at

---

by small, high-speed motors and gear trains. Using a 400-cps power supply, the synchronous speed of induction motors varies with the number of poles as follows: 24,000 rpm for two poles; 12,000 rpm for four poles; 8,000 rpm for six poles; 4,000 rpm for 12 poles. Reducing the speed by increasing the number of poles becomes impractical beyond a certain point because of the increased weight and size of the motors and lowered efficiency that results. Reducing the speed by reducing the power frequency below 400 cps entails similar difficulties for spacecraft systems.

speeds of approximately 4,000, 8,000, and 12,000 rpm are summarized in Tables 10.1 to 10.3 and are discussed in the following paragraphs.

Silicone greases and oils were the most satisfactory lubricants tested by the Advanced Technology Laboratories Division of American Standard. Results are reported in Ref. 16 and summarized in Table 10.1. The vacuum in which the bearings were operated was approximately 1×10^{-6} mm Hg, motor speed was 11,500 rpm, and the temperature was 325°F, as measured on the motor case.

When results for different lubricants are compared, the lack of duplicate tests should be recognized; a short life might have been due to a poor

Table 10.1 Life of Ball Bearings Run in Vacuum with Various Lubricants [16]

Test no.	Lubricant	Type	Lifetime (hr:min)	Reason for test termination
16	Versilube F-50..	Silicone fluid	15:50	Excessive torque caused by severe bearing wear
15	Aeroshell Fluid 12	Diester fluid	27:10	Severe wear; retainer collapsed and jammed balls
23	MoS₂ in DC-703 silicone fluid	Solid in diffusion pump fluid	27:50	Severe wear; retainer deformed and jammed balls
20	P. R. Cosmolubric No. 58-2407	Experimental solid	29:25	Severe wear; retainer deformed and jammed balls
32	Apiezon-T applied in a solvent vehicle	High-vacuum grease	29:50	Excessive torque caused by severe wear of rear bearing; grease apparently applied too thinly
24	Aeroshell Fluid 12	Diester fluid	46:20	Excessive torque caused by severe bearing wear
18	Anderol L-795..	Grease	70:10	Severe wear; retainer broke and jammed balls
22	DBL-140-E....	Fluid	77:00	Severe wear; retainer deformed and jammed balls
17	Versilube G-300	Silicone grease	170:00	Excessive torque caused by hardened grease residue
30	Versilube F-50..	Silicone fluid	170:20	Excessive torque caused by severe bearing wear
31	Versilube G-300	Silicone grease	236:00	Excessive torque caused by hardening of the grease
19	DC-33 (medium)	Silicone grease	239:25	Excessive torque caused by hardening of the grease
34	Versilube G-300	Silicone grease	286:25	Excessive torque caused by hardening of the grease
33	Versilube F-50..	Silicone fluid	353:50	Excessive torque caused by severe bearing wear
27	Apiezon-T.....	High-vacuum grease	424:50	Excessive torque caused by powdery residue from the grease

Table 10.2 Life of Ball Bearings Run in Vacuum with Various Lubricants [17]

Lubricant	Type	Operating time, hr	Cause of failure
Group 1:			
HT-103..................	Petroleum oil	1,000	
HT-102..................	Petroleum oil	1,000	
Versilube G-300...........	Silicone grease	900	Electrical
ETR-B...................	Silicone grease	1,000	
Versilube F-50............	Silicone oil	1,000	
Group 2:			
L-760....................	Complex ester grease	1,000	
L-825....................	Diester oil	1,000	
L-827....................	Complex ester oil	1,000	
23-25....................	Complex ester oil	1,000	
23-25, outgassed..........	Complex ester oil	1,000	
DC F-60.................	Silicone oil	910	Electrical
X-522...................	Organo-silicone oil	670	Electrical
186-X...................	Petroleum grease	400	Mechanical
Group 3:			
DC-510..................	Silicone oil	400	Lubricant
L-762...................	Complex ester grease	230	Lubricant
DC-44..................	Silicone grease	220	Lubricant

bearing or lack of run-in rather than to a poor lubricant. On the other hand, the long lives obtained with the silicone greases and fluids indicates that such lubricants are satisfactory under the test conditions for periods of 200 hr or more.

Data for Versilube F-50 silicone fluid (Test 30) and G-300 silicone grease (Test 17) indicated similar lifetimes for these materials. The tests also provided the following information quoted from Ref. 16:

For the fluid, the failure was of a wearout type, the alternate welding and shearing of the rubbing surfaces destroying the surface finish of the internal parts of the bearings to such a degree that radial clearances were destroyed and the bearing required an excessive amount of torque in order to turn even slowly. For the silicone grease, failure was not caused by wearout. The metal surfaces remained in good shape, but the hardened residue from the grease prevented free movement of the bearing parts.

The long life obtained with Apiezon T high-vacuum grease is also noteworthy.

Results of endurance tests conducted by the Airborne Instruments Laboratory of Cutler-Hammer Corporation are summarized in Table 10.2. In these tests, the two bearings on each of 16 motors were lubricated with one of the selected oils and greases and then operated continuously† at 4,000 rpm for the duration of the test (1,000 hr) or until prior failure. The mounting bases for the motors were kept at a constant temperature of 75°C (167°F) and the vacuum at approximately 2×10^{-5} mm Hg. The bearings were double-shielded, R2 size (0.125-in. diameter bore), of 440C stainless steel, and had paper-based phenolic retainer rings. The oils and greases tested were selected on the basis of evaporation rates in preliminary tests on 38 commercial oils and 17 greases. In the case of oils, the bearings were vacuum-impregnated with between 15 and 20 mg of oil. In the case of greases, the bearings were first impregnated with a compatible oil in order to prevent the retainer from drying out the grease, and approximately 15 mg of grease was then added. Most of the motors operated for the full 1,000-hr life test. Only three failed because of inadequate lubrication.

Bearings in group 1 (see Table 10.2) still retained a large amount of lubrication at the end of 1,000 hr and showed no wear on the balls or on the retainer ring. The lubrication appeared adequate for possibly another 500 to 1,000 hr of operation. In group 2, the bearings were still operating at the end of 1,000 hr, but the races and balls showed slight scuffing. The condition of the lubricant indicated the possibility of only a slight amount of additional life. Bearings in group 3 failed in less than 1,000 hr and showed complete absence of any oil film. Substantial quantities of hard, abrasive material formed in these bearings, and the retainers were badly discolored, worn, and slightly charred because of excessive heat.

In these tests, Versilube F-50 silicone oil and G-300 silicone grease ranked in the top group, along with two high-temperature petroleum oils and another silicone grease.

Table 10.3 summarizes the running times accumulated to date in the tests being conducted in the author's group at the Lockheed Missiles and Space Division. In these tests, the oil or grease has been evaluated with R3-size ball bearings ($\frac{3}{16}$ in. inside diameter $\times$ $\frac{1}{2}$ in. outside diameter). The bearings were installed on small induction motors that were mounted inside vacuum chambers for testing. Both bearings on any one motor received the same lubricant. The radial load on each set of bearings was that provided by the weight of the motor rotor. It was 5.65 oz, divided between the two bearings. The motors were of the a-c induction type and rated at 0.01 hp. Their normal operating characteristics were as follows: 115 volts, 0.3 amp, 400-cps power input, and 8,000-rpm synchronous speed. The bearing housings were opened up to expose the bearings more readily to the vacuum.

In the absence of convection cooling, the stator windings overheated

† The tests were run continuously during the work week. The vacuum was broken and the motors stopped during weekends.

when the motors were operated above 100 volts in vacuum. This caused excessive outgassing and breakdown of the varnish insulation which, in turn, short-circuited the stator windings. For operation in vacuum, therefore, the motor voltage was reduced to a range of 70 to 90 volts in order to minimize the heat generated in the stator windings.

Temperatures were measured with iron-constantan thermocouples attached to the bearing housings. Temperatures as high as 104°C (220°F) were reached in the early parts of some tests while the motors were operated at near 115 volts. Operation at this voltage was accompanied by excessive stator temperatures and insulation breakdown; hence, subsequent operation was conducted at a reduced voltage to keep the temperatures of the bearing housings below 82°C (180°F).

The current drawn by the motors was generally in the range from 0.1 to 0.2 amp. Motor speed was 7,850 to 8,000 rpm and was measured with a Strobotac unit. The motor current was monitored by a milli-ammeter placed in the circuit of each motor, and an increase in bearing torque was reflected by an increase in current. When a motor stalled because of bearing failure, the current increased by a factor of 2 or more, causing a fuse in the circuit to blow and thus automatically cutting off power to the motor and its associated timer.

After a set of motors was operated for several hours in air to ensure satisfactory performance, the vacuum chamber was settled in place and the system evacuated. For tests with oils and greases, the vacuum systems employed oil-diffusion pumps and liquid-nitrogen traps. The vacuum was maintained between 1×10^{-6} and 3×10^{-8} mm Hg. The power to each motor was cut off periodically, and the time required for coasting from 8,000 rpm to full stop was measured. This coast time was determined in order to obtain an indication of the running torque of the bearings.

A series of tests is also being conducted in air to obtain data for a comparison with the results obtained in vacuum.

Of the oils and greases tested at Lockheed to date, the longest run has been achieved with ball bearings lubricated with Versilube F-50 silicone oil; these operated for 4,574 hr (i.e., a little over 6 months) before failure. Most of this operation was continuous at 8,000 rpm in vacuum between 1×10^{-6} mm Hg and 4×10^{-7} mm Hg. Even after 4,000 hr of operation, the coast time for these bearings was 9 min, 55 sec, thus indicating a very low torque and good operation.

Versilube F-50 silicone oil which had been molecularly distilled to remove the 50 per cent more volatile fraction was tried in the expectation that the *less* volatile fraction might lubricate in vacuum for a longer period. In the tests on bearings with steel ribbon-type retainers, one bearing failed after 1,856 hr; its replacement failed after only 409 hr.

Table 10.3 Life of Ball Bearings Lubricated with Oils and Greases and Operated in Vacuum [18]

Lubricant	Bearing type†	Initial weight of lubricant Bearing no.	Initial weight of lubricant mg	Temperature of bearing housing, °C (°F)	Pressure, mm Hg	Coast time (min; sec)	Lifetime results
Versilube F-50 silicone oil	2	1	26.1	54–99 (130–210)	1×10^{-6} to 4×10^{-7}	10:20, after 3,180 hr	4,574 hr to failure
		2	32.6			9:55, after 4,000 hr	
						4:13, after 4,299 hr	
	4	1	28.3	76–88 (169–190)	8×10^{-6} to 3×10^{-8}	2:54, after 108 hr	916 hr, still running
		2	20.6			3:10, after 460 hr	
						3:14, after 916 hr	
Versilube F-50 silicone oil, molecularly distilled to remove 50 % more volatile fraction	2	1	29.9	52–96 (125–205)	1×10^{-6} to 8×10^{-7}	....	2,265 hr, still good (brg. No.1) when test discontinued
		2	28.6				1,856 hr to failure (brg. No. 2)
		3	52.9				409 hr to failure (brg. No. 3)
	3	1	61.7	71–93 (160–200)	1×10^{-7} to 3×10^{-8}	1:56, after 760 hr	2,817 hr, still running
		2	62.0			9:14, after 1,580 hr	
						8:23, after 2,008 hr	
						10:15, after 2,362 hr	
						10:04, after 2,817 hr	
	3	1	54.4	39–57 (102–135)	1 atm	0:49, after 1,565 hr	3,843 hr, still running
		2	52.9			2:27, after 3,051 hr	
						3:26, after 3,387 hr	
						3:49, after 3,843 hr	
Oronite 8200 silicate ester oil	1	1	25.4	51–102(123–215)	1×10^{-6} to 4×10^{-7}	2:27, after 3,235 hr	4,244 hr to failure; bearings dry
		2	23.1			6:45, after 4,052 hr	
	3	1	18.4	67–81 (152–178)	8×10^{-5} to 4×10^{-7}	2:24, after 19 hr	672 hr, still running
		2	11.9			7:06, after 362 hr	
						8:25, after 672 hr	
Oronite 8515 silicate ester oil	1	1	28.0	49–74 (120–165)	4×10^{-5} to 2×10^{-6}	....	359 hr to failure, bearings dry and full of wear debris
		2	26.8				
OS-124 polyphenyl ether oil	3	1	72.4	66–99 (150–210)	1×10^{-7} to 6×10^{-8}	1:34, after 1,336 hr	2,476 hr to failure; complete loss of lubricant
		2	69.0			4:31, after 2,152 hr	
						1:38, after 2,344 hr	
	3	1	62.6	43–60 (110–140)	1 atm	0:34, after 1,600 hr	3,877 hr, still running
		2	59.8			0:35, after 2,418 hr	
						0:34, after 3,085 hr	
						0:31, after 3,877 hr	
						0:30, after 3,421 hr	

300

Diphenylbis-*n*-dodecylsilane oil	3	1	40.7	60–96(140–205)	1×10^{-7} to 6×10^{-8}	2:10, after 885 hr	1,367 hr to failure; complete loss of lubricant
		2	46.1			1:05, after 1,367 hr	
	3	1	31.0	39–60(102–140)	1 atm	1:42, after 1,600 hr	3,877 hr, still running
		2	33.0			1:34, after 2,418 hr	
						1:34, after 3,085 hr	
						1:34, after 3,877 hr	
Apiezon-K high-vacuum oil	3	1	49.5	66–99(150–210)	1×10^{-7} to 3×10^{-8}	0:16, after 1,313 hr	3,353 hr, still running
		2	58.2			0:18, after 2,131 hr	
						0:20, after 2,544 hr	
						0:18, after 3,353 hr	
	3	1	49.2	41–62(106–143)	1 atm	0:08, after 1,600 hr	3,878 hr, still running
		2	51.7			0:08, after 2,418 hr	
						0:10, after 3,086 hr	
						0:26, after 3,422 hr	
						0:22, after 3,878 hr	
Type SF-1017 silicone oil, molecularly distilled to remove 35% more volatile fraction	2	1	42.5	66–88(151–190)	3×10^{-5} to 1×10^{-6}	0:32, at start	458 hr, failed
		2	30.2			1:44, after 338 hr	
						2:16, after 377 hr	
	4	1	35.4	70–82(158–180)	8×10^{-6} to 3×10^{-8}	0:50, after 108 hr	916 hr, still running
		2	40.7			0:45, after 460 hr	
						0:43, after 916 hr	
Type SF-96 silicone oil, molecularly distilled to remove 93% more volatile fraction	4	1	32.3	77–88(170–190)	8×10^{-6} to 9×10^{-8}	0:30, after 108 hr	345 hr, failed
		2	37.9			5:39, after 269 hr	
Cellulube 90 tri-aryl phosphate oil	2	1	42.7	82–88(180–190)	3×10^{-5} to 1×10^{-6}	1:47, at start	164 hr to failure; complete loss of lubricant
		2	29.1				
Cellulube 220 tri-aryl phosphate oil	4	1	25.4	73–78(163–173)	8×10^{-6} to 9×10^{-8}	3:43, after 108 hr	336 hr to failure
		2	34.2			1:55, after 267 hr	
DC Type 704 silicone vacuum pump oil	4	1	24.8	82–89(180–193)	8×10^{-6} to 3×10^{-8}	10:05, after 107 hr	917 hr, still running
		2	24.8			9:02, after 461 hr	
						7:01, after 917 hr	
MolyKote M-55 MoS_2 colloidal dispersion in oil	2	1	32.6	68–82(154–180)	9×10^{-5} to 4×10^{-7}	1:47, after 19 hr	672 hr, still running
		2	34.5			2:32, after 362 hr	
						2:49, after 672 hr	
Versilube G-300 silicone grease	1	1	91.4	67–104(152–220)	1×10^{-6} to 4×10^{-7}	1:53, after 2,233 hr	4,363 hr, still running
		2	100.6			2:05, after 3,050 hr	
						1:57, after 3,651 hr	
						1:49, after 3,892 hr	
						2:00, after 4,363 hr	

† Type of bearing: 1—440C stainless steel, ribbon retainers, double-shielded; 2—52100 chrome steel, ribbon retainers, double-shielded; 3—440C stainless steel, Synthane retainers, double-shielded; 4—52100 chrome steel, Synthane retainers, double-shielded.

Results on bearings with Synthane retainers have been more encouraging. To date, running time in vacuum of 2,817 hr has been accumulated without failure.

Bearings lubricated with Apiezon K vacuum oil (not noted as a particularly good lubricant but possessing the virtue of an extremely low vapor pressure—about 10^{-9} or 10^{-10} mm Hg at room temperature) are still running in vacuum after 3,353 hr. The Apiezon K oil gives a coast time of about 20 sec and is much too viscous for use on cold parts because of the excessively high torque.

Several of the oils being tested at Lockheed are high-temperature lubricants, developed for Air Force use in turbojets. The reason for Lockheed's interest in these oils lies in their potential for use in vacuum. If they have low enough vapor pressures for use at the high temperatures for which they were designed, they should have still lower vapor pressures at lower temperatures and be useful in operation for long periods under vacuum conditions. One of these oils, Oronite 8200, gave a lifetime of 4,244 hr before failure and a coast time of 6 min, 45 sec after 4,052 hr of operation.

Of the other oils being tested, many have operated successfully for over 3,000 hr under the test conditions whereas others have failed in less than 1,000 hr. Only a small number of tests have been conducted to date on any one oil, and additional tests are necessary before reliable statistics can be established.

The only grease tested to date is Versilube G-300, which is the Versilube F-50 silicone oil in a lithium-base soap. These bearings are still running after 4,363 hr at 8,000 rpm. Their coast time has increased slightly with operation and was 2 min 8 sec at the last reading.

Laminar Solids

General Considerations. Laminar solids have crystal structures in which the atoms are closely packed together on widely spaced planes. The interatomic forces holding such a structure together are accordingly strong between neighboring atoms lying in the same plane but are weak between atoms lying in different planes. As a result, the planes can slide over one another with relative ease and without breaking down, thus enabling the solid to function as a lubricant.

Graphite is a laminar solid whose lubricating qualities in air are well known. However, it does not lubricate in vacuum and is therefore unsuited for many spacecraft applications. Of the many other laminar solids, molybdenum disulfide (MoS_2) appears the most suitable for use in space since, unlike graphite, it is an effective lubricant in vacuum. In addition, its coefficient of friction is about one-half that of graphite.

Being an inorganic compound, MoS_2 is quite resistant to space radiation and to radiation from nuclear power sources.

Properties of Molybdenum Disulfide. The crystal structure of MoS_2 is laminar, similar to that of graphite, and consists essentially of planes of molybdenum atoms alternating with planes of sulfur atoms in the sequence S:S:Mo:S:S:Mo . . . . The atomic arrangement in each MoS_2 layer is hexagonal, and the forces that hold the atoms together in each layer are stronger than those between adjacent layers of sulfur atoms. This permits the planes to slide readily over one another with low frictional resistance. These planes of easy sliding or slipping are also called cleavage planes.

The structure of MoS_2 has been likened to a stack of sliced bread in which the slices have been buttered on both sides; the bread slices represent the planes of molybdenum atoms and the butter represents the planes of sulfur atoms. The butter portrays the action of sulfur well since it sticks to the surface and yet slides easily.

Table 10.4 lists values for the coefficient of friction of MoS_2 measured under a variety of conditions. The first five values are representative for MoS_2 alone, uncontaminated by foreign material introduced by the method of application, and range from 0.04 to 0.1. For comparison, the range of values for graphite is about 0.1 to 0.2, which indicates that the friction coefficient of a thin film of MoS_2 on a metal surface is only about one-half of that for a graphite film. On the other hand, boundary lubrication with oil reduces the friction coefficient for steel on steel to an order of magnitude or more less than that obtained with MoS_2.

Unlike graphite, MoS_2 is an effective lubricant in vacuum. Research indicates that sulfur is released at the interfaces during sliding and performs the same function for MoS_2 as water vapor does for graphite [19]. Graphite does not lubricate in vacuum because the vacuum strips away the adsorbed water vapor that is an essential element of the material's mechanism of lubrication. The loss of this vapor results in the graphite's being ground away into carbon dust.

Forms in Which Molybdenum Disulfide Is Used. Four forms in which molybdenum disulfide can be used as a lubricant are as follows:

1. Burnished films. Molybdenum disulfide can be simply rubbed onto a metal surface or burnished on it. It clings to metal surfaces better than graphite; probably there is some chemical bonding between the sulfur atoms of the molybdenum disulfide and the metal atoms of the surface on which it is rubbed. In addition to using the dry powder, one can prepare molybdenum disulfide films by spraying or brushing a dispersion of the powders in a volatile liquid onto the surface and allowing the liquid to evaporate.

Table 10.4 Experimental Measurements of the Coefficient of Friction for MoS_2

Method of applying MoS_2	Test no.	Experimental conditions	Coefficient of friction	Reference no.
Rubbing or burnishing onto metal surface	1	MoS_2 pellets rubbing on MoS_2 film on stainless steel; speed, 310 cm/sec; load, 395 g; tests run in vacuum	0.06–0.10	19
	2	MoS_2 film rubbed on SAE 1020 steel; speed, 40 fpm; load, 900 g; (friction coefficient of untreated SAE 1020 steel under same conditions, 0.55)	0.05–0.095	20
	3	MoS_2 film rubbed on steel (friction coefficient of untreated steel, about 0.8)	0.05	21
Rubbing or burnishing onto chemically treated surface	4	MoS_2 filled in the porous structure of the phosphate surface layer on steel	0.04–0.1	22
Chemical formation	5	MoS_2 formed chemically *in situ* in sintered molybdenum; steel slider and 4-kg load, (friction coefficient range of untreated sintered molybdenum under same conditions, 0.4 to 0.55)	0.06–0.10	23
Bonding with organic binders	6	MoS_2 film bonded with corn syrup to SAE 1020 steel; speed, about 50 fpm; load, about 100 g (friction coefficient of untreated SAE 1020 steel under same conditions, 0.54)	0.19	24
	7	MoS_2 film bonded with corn syrup to SAE 1020 steel; speed, 400 fpm; load, 900 g; (friction coefficient of untreated SAE 1020 steel under same conditions, 0.55)	0.20	20
Impregnated in plastic†	8	Low per cent of MoS_2 in molded Perspex; steel slider and 4-kg load (friction coefficient of untreated Perspex under same conditions, 0.45)	0.10–0.15	25
	9	One per cent of MoS_2 in ebonite (a thermosetting plastic) spread as a thin film on a metal surface and baked; copper slider and 4-kg load (friction coefficient of untreated ebonite under same conditions, 0.4)	0.25	25
Porous metals impregnated with MoS_2	10	MoS_2 in sintered copper; steel slider and 4-kg load (friction coefficient range of untreated sintered copper alone under same conditions, 0.3 to 1.2)	0.13–0.2	21
	11	Cylinders of 10% MoS_2, 85% Ag, and 5% Cu (hot-pressed) with hemispherical ends against rotating steel disk; speed, up to 8,000 fpm, load, up to 1,017 g (friction coefficient of untreated cylinder of 95% Ag–5% Cu under same conditions, 0.26 to 0.29)	0.21	26
	12	50% MoS_2–50% bronze-tin (Sinite D-10, manufactured by Booker–Cooper, Inc.; sliding speed, about 40 fpm (friction coefficient of untreated hardened steel under same conditions, > 0.35)	0.10	27

† In both these series of tests, the small amount of MoS_2 had no significant effect on the mechanical properties of the plastics; its main effect was to lower the friction.

2. Bonded films. For maximum wear life, molybdenum disulfide films are bonded to the surface. A variety of binders, both organic and inorganic, serve this purpose. Epoxy, silicone, and phenolic adhesives are used most often, but water glass (or sodium silicate) has also proved very effective.

3. Impregnated compacts. Many plastics and powder metallurgy compacts can be impregnated with molybdenum disulfide particles for gears, bearings, cams, and similar applications. With such composites, the sliding process continues to feed a thin film of molybdenum disulfide to the surfaces so that the friction remains low even after prolonged rubbing.

4. Oil and grease additives. Fine particles of molybdenum disulfide, with dimensions on the order of a few microns, have been added to oils and greases to improve their lubricating qualities.

Operating Tests on Bonded Molybdenum Disulfide Films in Vacuum. A number of commercial bonded molybdenum disulfide films have been evaluated under vacuum conditions in the research program being conducted at Lockheed. Table 10.5 lists results obtained from tests conducted in an identical manner to the procedure for evaluating oils and greases, as described earlier. Results are also listed for a series of start-stop-reverse tests. In these tests, the motors were operated continuously for 52 min at 8,000 rpm in one direction, then allowed to coast to stop and to remain idle during the succeeding period of 8 min. The motors were then operated for another 52 min at 8,000 rpm in the opposite direction and again allowed to coast to stop and to remain idle during an 8-min period. The sequence was then repeated with operation of the motors in the original direction.

Preliminary runs had indicated that crown-type retainers were unsatisfactory, so all subsequent tests with MoS_2 films were conducted with ball bearings mounted in ribbon-type retainers of pressed steel. The MoS_2 films were applied to the races and retainers before assembly, and the coated parts were subsequently assembled with uncoated balls. Bearings were of the open (unshielded) type.

Bearings with MoS_2 films are initially very rough and have high torques. It is necessary first to run in these bearings by operating them very slowly and blowing out the particles of coating that flake off, then operating them somewhat faster and again blowing out any loosened debris. This procedure is repeated several times until a constant, low torque value is obtained and the bearings run smoothly.

The longest life obtained to date with an MoS_2 film has been with a film bonded with sodium silicate (Everlube No. 811). One pair of ball bearings coated with this film ran as long as 2,213 hr in vacuum at 8,000 rpm before failure. Two other pairs of ball bearings with this film, but

Table 105. Life of Ball Bearings† Lubricated with Bonded
Molybdenum Disulfide [18]

Lubricant	Temp. of bearing housing, °C (°F)	Pressure, mm Hg	Coast time, min: sec	Lifetime results
Everlube No. 811, sodium silicate–bonded (grit-blasted before coating)‡§	43–82 (110–180)	5×10^{-6} to 9×10^{-8}		174 hr, bearing no. 1 failed; 238 hr, bearing no. 2 failed; one bearing still operating satisfactorily at 884 hr
Everlube No. 811, sodium silicate–bonded (grit-blasted before coating)	64–82 (148–180); 93 (200) at failure	8×10^{-6} to 9×10^{-8}	1:07, at start 6:17, after 771 hr 3:51, after 1,588 hr 5:56, after 2,021 hr 4:31, after 2,181 hr 0:02, at failure	2,213 hr, failed; motor noisy and speed reduced to 7,000 rpm at time of failure
	60–85 (140–185)	5×10^{-6} to 5×10^{-7}	6:53, after 82 hr 5:18, after 223 hr 2:41, after 391 hr	Start-stop-reverse test Elapsed time: 391 hr Power off: 52 hr Still running
Everlube No. 811, sodium silicate–bonded (special surface pretreatment No. 1)	64 to 82 (148–180); 104 (220) at failure of bearing no. 1	8×10^{-6} to 8×10^{-7}	5:14, at start 3:39, after 753 hr 4:24, after 1,569 hr	1.862 hr, bearing no. 1 failed; bearing no. 2 still operating satisfactorily
Everlube No. 811, sodium silicate–bonded (special surface pretreatment No. 2)	59–71 (138–160) 92 (198) at failure	8×10^{-6} to 8×10^{-7}	4:14, at start 6:50, after 656 hr 5:04, after 1,472 hr	1,796 hr, failed
Poxylube No. 75, epoxy-bonded (grit-blasted before coating)‡	32–71 (90–160)	5×10^{-6} to 9×10^{-8}	. . . .	308 hr, bearing no. 1 failed; 467 hr, bearing no. 2 failed
Poxylube No. 75, epoxy-bonded (Group A)	60–79 (140–175)	5×10^{-6} to 5×10^{-7}	7:24, after 82 hr 5:50, after 222 hr 5:50, after 393 hr	Start-stop-reverse test Elapsed time: 393 hr Power off: 52 hr Still running
Poxylube No. 75, epoxy-bonded (surface treatment before coating; Group B)	57–78 (135–173)	5×10^{-6} to 5×10^{-7}	1:03, after 57 hr 0:56, after 181 hr 0:14, at failure	Start-stop-reverse test Elapsed time: 305 hr Power off: 41 hr Failed—motor noisy and rough at time of failure; would not restart
Microseal, bonded with colloidal silica‡	32–35 (90–95) 60–82 (140–180)	1 atm 7×10^{-6} to 2×10^{-7}		7.8 hr, bearing no. 1 failed 670 hr, bearing no. 2 failed
Microseal, bonded with colloidal silica	Room temp. to 38 (100)	1 atm to 2×10^{-6}		Start-stop-reverse test Elapsed time: 11 hr Power off: 1 hr Failed—motor noisy at time of failure; would not restart

† In all tests, bearings were of 440C stainless steel, had ribbon retainers of pressed steel, and were open (unshielded). MoS_2 films were bonded to the retainers and races but not to the balls.
‡ Minimum run-in before testing (operated briefly and loose debris blown out several times before testing). All other bearings were initially cleansed of loose debris, then run in for 30 min to 1 hr at 4 rpm. They were then recleaned, run in for 3 to 5 min at 8,000 rpm, and recleaned before testing.
§ No precure before final curing.

with special surface pretreatments, ran for 1,796 and 1,862 hr, respectively, before failure.   Coast times for these bearings were relatively long, indicating low running torque.   Use of a precure at 94°C (200°F) prior to final curing at 205°C (400°F) appears beneficial; the initial low-temperature cure allows water to be driven off more slowly and provides a more adherent film.

A similar bearing with an MoS_2 film bonded with colloidal silica (Microseal) ran 667.4 hr at 7,900 rpm before failure.   The 667.4 hr of operating time included 39 hr in air and 628 hr in a vacuum of 10^{-6} mm Hg or better.   Reproducibility with this type of film was particularly poor; a second bearing similarly treated failed in 7.8 hr.

Bearings with MoS_2 films bonded with an epoxy resin (Poxylube No. 75) ran for as long as 467.3 hr at 7,900 rpm before failure.   Of the total time, 12.4 hr was in air and the remainder in vacuum.

Although bearing lifetimes obtained in the Lockheed studies with bonded MoS_2 films are less than those obtained with oils and greases, the MoS_2 films have several other virtues that should be considered.   Since they are nonvolatile, their lifetimes are not likely to be markedly sensitive to increases in temperature, whereas oils and greases can be expected to volatilize at significantly greater rates with increasing temperature.† Also, the MoS_2 films are not likely to become viscous when used at low temperatures.   If radiation becomes an important consideration, MoS_2 films (especially those bonded with an inorganic binder like sodium silicate) may be particularly suitable since they are very resistant to radiation.

Soft Metals

General Considerations.   Soft metals with low shear strength, such as silver and gold, can be used as thin films over hard substrates to provide lubrication and prevent cold-welding [28, 29].   The theory behind their use is similar to that described for lubrication with molybdenum disulfide films; that is, a hard substrate keeps the area of real contact between the mating parts small, and films of low shear strength keep the strength of welded junctions small.   Together, these phenomena act to reduce friction and wear.

The lubricating film of soft metal can be formed in several ways.   The film itself can be initially deposited on the hard substrate by vacuum deposition, chemical plating, mechanical burnishing, or other techniques; or the soft metal can be initially infiltrated into a hard, porous substrate.   From this substrate, it is fed to the surface over which it is smeared to form the lubricating film.   Another technique is to use silver-infiltrated

† A temperature increase of about 28°C (50°F), for example, can double or quadruple the vapor pressure of many oils.

bodies. Porous bodies infiltrated with silver offer the advantage of providing a reservoir from which additional silver can be fed to the surface to renew surface films as they are worn away. The porous body can be made of a nonmetallic material to minimize its tendency to weld to a mating metallic surface.

Metals can be selected that have excellent stability in vacuum and under radiation. The conductivity of metal films can be an advantage where it is necessary to conduct an electric current through the parts.

Thin Films of Soft Metals. The thin metallic lubricants considered here and in the following section are those present as continuous films that adhere to the substrate metal. The underlying principle rests in the utilization of a thin, adherent film of material with low shear strength that lies between two hard surfaces.

Obtaining good adhesion between the metal-film lubricant and the metal substrate is the major problem in securing long wear life. Unfortunately, this involves an area of considerable disagreement since techniques that have worked for one group of investigators have been unsuccessful when used by others. Careful cleaning to remove greases, oxide films, and other contaminants is agreed to be an important first step. Following this step, various techniques that have been used to deposit the metal film include vacuum deposition, electrolytic plating, simple immersion plating, and mechanical burnishing.

The coefficient of friction is generally a minimum at film thicknesses on the order of 10^{-5} in. Thicker films of the soft metals result in larger areas of real contact and thereby increase the coefficient of friction at a gradual rate. Thinner films cause an abrupt increase in the coefficient of friction, apparently because they do not prevent the substrate from interacting with the mating part and thus forming stronger junctions. There is also some indication that thinner films can give low coefficients of friction if the surfaces are highly polished [28].

Extreme care must be taken to avoid disrupting the films by mishandling when the coated parts are assembled. Separable, angular-contact ball bearings are used with coated balls because the balls can be easily assembled into the bearings without disturbing the films. This type of bearing requires careful assembly with axial preloading into the bearing housing or mounting. Split races have also been used to facilitate assembly.

Silver films are compatible with lubricating oils if the oil is essentially free of sulfur, which reacts to form silver sulfide. The films are too thin to afford protection to the metal substrates. If the films are used on SAE 52100 steel, or other types of steel that require some protection against rusting in air, oils can be used to protect the base metal during the period that the parts are stored on earth, provided that sulfur-free oil is used. (The subsequent evaporation of the oil in space should not present a problem, since by the time the part is space-borne, the need for corrosion protection is past, and the necessary lubrication is provided by the silver coating.)

Experience with Thin Metallic Film Lubrication in Vacuum. Machlett Laboratories [30] has used silver films for a number of years on the balls of ball bearings for rotating-anode X-ray tubes. The bearings are heated by conduction from the X-ray target to temperatures estimated at 300 to 400°C (572 to 752°F). The vacuum in the tubes is on the order of 10^{-8} mm Hg, and the speed of rotation is between 3,300 and 3,600 rpm. Under these conditions, ball bearings with balls coated with thin silver films by a proprietary process have minimum lifetimes of 1,000 hr and have attained lifetimes of 10,000 hr or more. At the same speed, but at room temperature, the bearing lifetimes are said to be indefinite, that is, longer than 10,000 hr. One of the two bearings on the rotating-anode assembly has a split inner race; the other has a flat outer race which permits axial expansion and contraction. The balls and races are of Circle C tool steel, which does not soften at the operating temperatures.

Machlett Laboratories has a new tube under development that rotates at 10,000 rpm. Full complements of silver-plated balls of tool steel and races of tool steel are used with this tube. The bearings are separable, angular-contact types and are spring-loaded axially. Lifetimes achieved in vacuum are reportedly in excess of 2,500 hr [30].

Many of the tubes supplied by Machlett Laboratories are used intermittently over a period of years (e.g., X-ray tubes in dentists' offices and in hospitals). During this entire time, of course, the vacuum inside the tube is maintained. It is worth noting, therefore, that the silver films protect the bearings from cold-welding in vacuum during the long idle periods as well as provide low friction and wear at reasonably high rotational speeds during operation of the tube.

Plastics

General Considerations. Plastics have been found very useful in many applications involving friction and wear. Such applications include gears, bearings, cams, rollers, and similar parts requiring lubrication. Nylon, for example, has long been used to provide quiet-running gears that require little lubrication, and Teflon has been used for sleeve bearings that operate dry with little friction.

The form in which the plastic is used can be varied to meet specific needs, and many specialty grades and techniques are available that overcome some of the general disadvantages of plastics, thus allowing full use of their special properties. In many applications, plastics can be used in pure bulk form, as in the case of cast, molded, pressed and sintered, or machined articles. In other applications, bulk plastics incorporate various fillers that improve their frictional and mechanical properties. In still other uses, plastics are used in the form of thin films or as impregnants in porous solids.

For applications involving friction and wear, plastics offer, in general, advantages with regard to self-lubrication, cold-welding tendencies, vibration absorption, impact resistance, density, tolerances, machinability, contamination, corrosion, compatibility, and durability.

Either the plastic itself can be self-lubricating, as in the case of Teflon, or it can be made self-lubricating by adding fillers such as MoS_2. Such plastics can be used at temperatures below those at which oils and greases might become too viscous for effective lubrication. Porous plastic bodies can also be impregnated with oils to provide lubrication, as in ball-bearing retainers of Synthane (a porous paper-base phenolic composition). In other cases, a self-lubricating plastic like Teflon can be impregnated into a porous body to provide lubrication.

Plastics can be selected that have little tendency to "stick" or cold-weld to metals, even under ultrahigh vacuum. The antisticking characteristics of Teflon to metal, for example, are well known and, in fact, are a positive disadvantage at times when bonding of a film of Teflon to a metal is desired in order to form an inert film or take advantage of some of Teflon's other properties.

Plastics have a good capacity for absorbing vibration and therefore provide quiet running with minimum noise and vibration. This characteristic is well known in the case of gear trains of nylon.

Some of the plastics have very good impact strength. They can deform elastically to absorb shock and vibration so that, during the launch phase of missiles and other spacecraft, there is less danger of Brinelling with ball bearings using plastic balls than with those using steel balls. This characteristic has been used to advantage in several applications of ball bearings for armored-vehicle turrets. Montalbano [31] reports on the successful replacement of steel balls in the main bearing assembly of the United States Army T-92 light tank with 1-in.-diameter plastic balls. This bearing is 90 in. in diameter, supports the weight of the main turret and gun cupolas, and absorbs gun recoil and acceleration forces during high-speed travel over rough terrain. Another application of plastic bearings reported by Montalbano was their use in the gun mount of an LVT-5 landing vehicle. These bearings were 10 in. in diameter and carried a full complement of balls. Load-carrying plastic balls of 0.406 in. diameter alternated with spacer or idler balls of 0.394 in. diameter. These bearings survived recoil and other heavy loads without appreciable signs of wear or Brinelling.

Plastics have lower densities than most metals, so plastic parts can be lighter in weight. The densities of plastics are as low as $\frac{1}{6}$ or $\frac{1}{7}$ that of steel or about half that of magnesium.

Tolerances are less critical for plastics than for steel in such parts as balls, bearing races, and gear teeth. Plastics deform more readily to meet the needs of poorer tolerances and of less accurate mounting and alignment.

Plastics have good machinability and can be molded to close tolerances. They also have good dimensional stability. There are, however, some notable exceptions, namely, where moisture absorption occurs, as in the case of molded nylon.

Contamination by dust and wear debris is less of a problem with plastics than with metals. The plastics themselves are abrasion-resistant, and they allow contaminants to be embedded into them, thus preventing scoring of the mating part. This property makes sealing against contamination less critical with plastic components than with those fabricated from metal.

Plastics are free from corrosion, such as that which might be caused by humidity, fog, mist, or other moisture prevailing in the atmosphere at launching sites.

Plastics are compatible with oils, greases, and many chemicals, so such materials can be added for lubrication or to protect other parts against corrosion without harming the plastic components with which they come into contact.

Plastics have low wear rates and outlast metals in many applications.

Plastics suffer certain disadvantages for applications involving friction and wear when compared with metals. It would be improper to generalize too widely here, since disadvantages are not always common from one plastic to the next. Also, as previously stated, many specialty grades and techniques are available that overcome some of the disadvantages. With these reservations, the general disadvantages of plastics under conditions of friction and wear include poor thermal conductivity, high thermal expansion, poor thermal resistance, low operating speeds, low structural strength, and inferior radiation stability.

The thermal conductivity of plastics is much lower than that of metals. Consequently, they are less able to dissipate frictional heating generated at rubbing interfaces, so plastic parts run hotter than similar parts made of steel. For use at high speeds, it may therefore be necessary to use the plastic in the form of a thin film over a metal substrate so that the metal can conduct the frictional heat away more efficiently. Other techniques for accomplishing the same purpose include the use of metal fibers as fillers and of metal backing screens.

Plastics have high rates of thermal expansion. Their coefficients of thermal expansion are ten times or more that of steel.

Plastics cannot be used at as high temperatures as can steels. They soften with heat and generally should not be used above 93 to 149°C (200 to 300°F). Teflon, the most heat-resistant of the plastics, melts at 327°C (620°F) and cannot be used at temperatures approaching this level.

As a consequence of the three foregoing limitations, the use of plastics is restricted to lower speeds than those at which steels can be used.

Plastics are weaker than steels so that the load-carrying capacity of plastic gears and bearings is less than for the same size part in steel. Since plastics are strong enough for the lightly loaded applications common to spacecraft systems, however, this is not a major objection to their use under the proper conditions.

The radiation stability of plastics is poorer than for metals. Teflon, in particular, has very poor radiation stability, and nylon is not much better. However, published information on radiation stability can be misleading, unless the basis on which radiation stability has been judged is clearly established. In general, radiation-stability data are reported in terms of the dose that reduces the mechanical strength by 10 or 25 per cent of the initial strength of the pure plastic. For gears and bearings, therefore, where the use of plastics in the pure, unfilled form does not appear desirable, better results may be obtained by applying the plastic as a thin film over a metal substrate or by using a fiber-reinforced plastic to provide greater strength. Teflon represents a case in point. Even when subjected to enough gamma radiation to cause marked deterioration in its mechanical properties, Teflon retains its antifriction characteristics. Under these conditions of radiation, Teflon might best be used as a thin film over a metal substrate or in other forms that provide some strengthening.

Teflon. Teflon is the registered trademark of the Du Pont Company for its fluorocarbon resins. These resins have very good antifriction properties, inertness to many chemicals and solvents, stability at high temperatures, toughness and flexibility at low temperatures, and excellent dielectric properties.

Two forms of Teflon are available. Teflon TFE (polytetrafluoroethylene) is the original Teflon resin and has been used by industry since 1941. Teflon FEP (fluorinated ethylene-propylene) was introduced in 1958 and is more easily extruded and injection-molded. In comparison with Teflon FEP, the TFE form is harder, has a lower coefficient of friction, and is generally more wear-resistant. It can resist heat distortion at higher temperatures than Teflon FEP and can, in general, be used at higher temperatures. In view of generally greater suitability of Teflon TFE, the following discussion is confined to this form.

Teflon retains useful mechanical properties at temperatures from −260 to +260°C (−450 to +500°F). Compared with nylon, Teflon is somewhat soft and has a relatively low tensile strength. Because Teflon is a soft although tough material, hard, foreign particles that may be introduced into gears and bearings will embed into the plastic, thus minimizing the possibility of scoring the mating part. This plastic is subject to cold flow and, following the initial strain that occurs on application of a load, it continues to deform with time, although at a decreasing rate. Teflon is inert to most chemicals and solvents but can be attacked by molten alkali metals and fluorine at elevated temperatures and pressures. Water has no effect on Teflon.

The coefficient of friction of Teflon is lower than that of graphite, MoS_2, or any other known solid. A value of 0.04 is usually quoted for the coefficient of friction of Teflon against steel, but a value as low as 0.016 has been reported. The coefficient of friction of Teflon varies with the conditions; the static coefficient of friction is lower than the dynamic value, and the lowest values are obtained at high loads and low sliding velocities.

The use of unmodified Teflon in bulk form for bearings, gears, and similar applications is limited by excessive cold flow under load, which is accelerated by frictional heating of the rubbing surfaces and by poor thermal conductivity and the inability to dissipate heat efficiently. To overcome these disadvantages and yet permit making use of the antifriction characteristics of Teflon, the following modifications are useful:

1. Reinforced Teflon bodies
2. Porous compacts impregnated with Teflon
3. Teflon dispersions applied as films

Incorporating fillers in Teflon improves its mechanical strength and wear properties while retaining its antifriction properties and many of its chemical and electrical qualities. The most commonly used fillers are glass fibers and graphite; fibers of ceramic (aluminum silicate) and fillers such as molybdenum disulfide, coke fluor, and zirconia have also been used. The main purpose in making these additions is to improve the Teflon resistance to cold flow and its high-temperature deformation under load. At the same time, wear rates are reduced by factors on the order of several thousand, as indicated by the data in Table 10.6. Other benefits include lower mold shrinkage and cracking tendency, lower thermal expansion, and better thermal conductivity.

Compositions are available which are essentially porous-metal compacts impregnated with Teflon and which provide a film of Teflon at the sliding surface. One of their obvious advantages is that the metal body provides a hard substrate with good thermal conductivity for dissipating frictional heat.

Table 10.7 presents data demonstrating that impregnating sintered copper with Teflon gives a very low coefficient of friction and that this

Table 10.6 Wear Rates for Sleeve Bearings of Molded Teflon TFE Resins
with Various Fillers [32, 33]

Material	Wear rate, mg/hr	Test conditions
Unfilled Teflon................	200	Bearings: 1 in. long × 0.75 in. ID
Teflon and 25% graphite.........	0.7	Shaft: 410 stainless steel
Teflon and 22% glass............	0.2	Load: 42 lb or 56 psi
Teflon and 25% copper..........	1.2	Speed: 60 fpm
Teflon and 25% graphite.........	0.7	Bearings: 1 in. long × 0.75 in. ID
Teflon and 22% glass............	0.4	Shaft: 410 stainless steel
		Speed: 215 fpm
Unfilled Teflon................	0.74	Bearings: 0.50 in. long × 0.25 in. ID
Teflon and 15–25% graphite......	0.0015	Shaft: 303 stainless steel
		Clearance: 0.002 in.
Teflon and 15–25% glass.........	0.0015	Load: 250 lb or 2,000 psi
Teflon and 4–8% copper.........	0.032	Speed: 150 rpm or 9.83 fpm
Molybdenum disulfide...........	0.38	

coefficient is maintained up to high temperatures. At a temperature of
300°C (572°F), where decomposition of the plastic occurred, the friction
began to rise. When the metal was allowed to cool, however, the coefficient of friction again decreased to 0.05. The treated metal showed little
sign of surface damage whereas the untreated copper displayed marked
adhesion, surface damage, and wear. Since the thin plastic film can be
fed onto the surface by sliding, it was not worn away; in fact, repeated
sliding led to a reduction in the friction.

Table 10.7 Coefficient of Friction for Copper [34]

Material	Coefficient of friction for unlubricated sliding against steel					
	Temperature					After cooling to 30°C (86°F)
	15°C (59°F)	100°C (212°F)	200°C (392°F)	250°C (482°F)	300°C (572°F)	
Sintered copper, impreg- nated with Teflon to a depth of about 1 mm...	0.05	0.05	0.05	0.05	~0.12	0.05
Sintered copper, untreated	0.24	0.24	~0.7	~0.8	~1.2	~1
Solid copper............	1.3	~1.3	~1	~1	~1	~1

Sintered bronze impregnated with Teflon is said to have much better wear characteristics than ordinary oil-impregnated bronze [35]. Such materials are commercially available.

Dispersions of Teflon are now available for application as films on metals, plastics, and other materials. The aqueous dispersions introduced by Du Pont about 1950 require curing and sintering at about 385°C (725°F). More recently, dispersions have been marketed that cure at temperatures down to room temperature. Teflon films deposited on hard substrates usually have lower coefficients of friction than solid Teflon because of cold flow in the solid. Thin Teflon films permit higher speeds of operation without increase in friction and have good durability [36].

Nylon. Nylon is the generic term for a family of polyamide resins developed by the Du Pont Company. All these resins are related, but not identical, in chemical composition. By definition, a nylon is any long-chain synthetic polymeric amide which has recurring amide groups as an integral part of the main polymer chain and which is capable of being formed into a filament in which the structural elements are oriented in the direction of the axis.

Zytel is the registered trademark for Du Pont nylon resins. Zytel is supplied in the form of molding powders and converted into such forms as molded products, wire coatings, rods, and other extruded shapes. A number of different molding powders made from Zytel are produced commercially by Du Pont. Zytel 101 is the grade that is used most commonly in molded gears and bearings.

Nylon is a thermoplastic material. Unlike most thermoplastic materials, however, it has some degree of crystallinity, so it possesses a relatively sharp melting point, depending upon the particular grade. Nylon does not soften gradually as it is heated, but remains rigid although with decreasing stiffness as the melting point is approached.

Most applications of Zytel 101 should not involve temperatures over 177°C (350°F). Where the moldings are subjected to heavy loads, maximum temperatures should not be above 121°C (250°F).

The properties of nylon vary with moisture content. Nylon in the as-molded or extruded conditions has a moisture content of about 0.2 per cent; exposure to a normal atmosphere of 50 per cent relative humidity results in an increase in the moisture content to about 2.5 per cent and an increase in linear dimensions of approximately 0.006 in./in. [37].

A number of specialty nylons have been developed for specific end uses. Among these are filled nylons for wear and abrasion applications and sintered nylons for maximum dimensional stability and wear resistance.

Molybdenum disulfide is used as a filler in nylon Types 6, 66, and 610, primarily to improve wear, abrasion resistance, and frictional characteristics. Flexural strength, modulus, and heat resistance are also improved.

Graphite, aluminum stearate, and other fillers are used in some applications. As a dry-bearing material, filled nylon can generally be used at 50 per cent higher PV† ratings than unfilled nylon 66. An additional benefit is the reduced coefficient of thermal expansion (about one-half that of unfilled nylon), which provides better dimensional control and more accurate molding tolerances. Primary uses for filled nylon are in bearing or sliding parts such as aircraft-fuel-pump bearings, oven-door slides, sleeve bushings, wear pads, and thrust washers. The improved heat resistance also offers some advantages in certain electrical insulating applications.

Nylon powders can be precipitated from solution and subsequently pressed and sintered by a process somewhat similar to powder metallurgy. Sintered nylon was originally conceived as a practical means for reducing the dimensional instabilities found in injection-molded polyamides. Because of its higher crystallinity as compared with injection-molded nylon, sintered nylon has superior frictional and wear qualities and higher compressive strength although its tensile strength, elongation, and impact strength are lower. Various additives and fillers, including MoS_2, are easily blended with the fine nylon powders to give special properties.

Sintered nylon parts are made by cold-molding at high pressures (in excess of 20,000 psi) and then heating or sintering. For satisfactory bonding, the powder must be prepared by chemical precipitation; powder produced by mechanically grinding molding pellets does not give satisfactory strength when cold-pressed and sintered. Precipitation from high-temperature solution gives a powder that has a relatively high percentage of crystallinity, usually about 80 per cent. On the other hand, injection-molded nylon articles often have a highly amorphous skin resulting from quick cooling of the molten material against a cold die surface and normally have an average crystallinity of about 43 per cent. Although this skin condition does no harm in many applications, it appears detrimental where minimum wear and best load-carrying capacity as a bearing material are required.

The precipitated nylon powders required for cold-pressing and sintering are sold under the trademark of Nylasint. Two unfilled powders available commercially are as follows:

1. Nylasint Type 66, which has the higher rigidity, modulus of elasticity, and melting point
2. Nylasint Type 64, in which finer powders are used and which has higher impact strength and greater deformability

---

† Where P is the load in pounds per square inch and V is the sliding velocity in feet per minute.

Both compositions are available with MoS_2 additive (Nylasint Type MS and Nylasint Type M4), which further improves their frictional performance in some applications. Compositions containing various percentages of either graphite or zirconium silicate are also available [39–42].

Sintered nylon parts can be impregnated with oil. "Microporous" Nylasint can absorb and maintain up to 25 per cent of fluids by weight and provides a coefficient of friction of 0.01. Accelerated wear tests, summarized in Table 10.8, show the superiority of sintered nylon over injection-molded nylon in reference to friction and wear. These data were obtained at The Franklin Institute Laboratories on thrust rings of oil-sintered nylon and injection-molded nylon which were rotated against hardened tool steel (63 to 65 on the Rockwell C scale, 1.5-μin. finish) at various speeds and loads.

Ceramics and Cermets

General Considerations. The ceramics and cermets are essentially hard, brittle materials, such as sapphire, glass, cemented carbides, fully dense oxides, and Pyroceram. The idea behind their use for gears, bearings, and similar applications in vacuum is that there will be a minimum tendency for cold-welding of these materials to the steel or other metal parts with which they are in contact.

Experience to date indicates that the use of ceramics and cermets is limited to slow speeds and light loads. Shock loading to protect them against impact and vibration during the launch and ascent phases may be necessary for spacecraft applications.

Sapphire. Sapphire is a very hard crystalline solid (rating about 9 on the Mohs scale) with exceptional friction and wear properties. Synthetic crystals are available in various forms, including balls, rods, and parts of jewel bearings.

The frictional behavior of sapphire depends somewhat on the plane of the crystal on which rubbing occurs, but the effect is small and the friction is always low. For sapphire sliding on itself, the coefficient of friction is about 0.2, and the wear damage cannot be seen except by refined methods, such as electron microscopy. For sapphire against steel in air, the coefficient is 0.12 to 0.15; the low value is due to the lubricating action of the protective oxide film on steel. In a jewel bearing, the ferric oxide formed at the tip of a steel pivot acts as an abrasive, increases the wear of the sapphire cup, and leads to an increase in the friction. This increase results, presumably, from the clogging action of the detritus (see pages 162 and 163 of Ref. 2).

Experience with the use of sapphire in the tuners of klystron tubes

Table 10.8 Comparative Wear and Friction Data from Accelerated Tests of Sintered and Injection-molded Nylon†

Material	Type of lubrication	Load, psi	Surface speed, fpm	Coefficient of friction	Total wear,‡ mils	Pressure-velocity product (PV)§	Power consumption (FV)¶	Running time, hr
Nylasint 66	Sintered in Gulf Crest 55 (no other lubrication)	135	240	0.12 (smooth, no change)	1.5	32,400	3,890	48
Nylasint 66	Sintered in Gulf Crest 55 (no other lubrication)	195	240	0.10 (smooth, no change)	1.5	46,800	4,680	34
Nylasint 66	Sintered in Gulf Crest 55 (no other lubrication)	195	370	0.09 (smooth, no change)	1.5	72,200	6,500	24
Nylasint 64M	Sintered in Gulf Crest 55 (no other lubrication)	195	240	0.10 (smooth, no change)	1.5	46,800	4,680	24
Nylon 101 injection-molded	Two drops Gulf Crest 55	195	240	0.11 (smooth, no change)	2.7	46,800	5,150	21
Nylon 101, injection-molded	Two drops Gulf Crest 55	195	370	0.11–0.32 (very rough and variable)	0.6	72,200	8,000–23,000	Failed, 0.5
Nylon 101, injection-molded	None	29	240	0.26–1.18 (steady increase, rough during latter part of test)	1.6	6,900	1,800–8,200	Failed, 0.5
Nylon 101, injection-molded	None	52	240	0.19–0.67 (steady increase, very rough)	20.0	12,500	8,370	Failed, 3 min

† Courtesy Modern Plastics Magazine, New York [39].
‡ Wear based upon 24-hr test unless otherwise noted; values including deformation of samples.
§ PV = load in pounds per square inch times velocity in feet per minute.
¶ FV = frictional force in pounds per square inch times velocity in feet per minute.

indicates that cold-welding does not occur between sapphire and copper or stainless steel in a vacuum of 2×10^{-7} mm Hg for periods in excess of 3 years [43]. In this application, cylinders of clear sapphire are used in slow sliding contact with copper or AISI 304 austenitic stainless steel and under a load of several pounds. The tubes are baked out for 3 days at 450°C (842°F) and reach a vacuum of 2×10^{-7} mm Hg. When the klystron tubes are used for jamming operations, the above materials in the tuner slide back and forth over one another; in other uses, the tuner is usually set at a given position, and little further movement is necessary. Evidence of cold-welding between the moving parts has not been found, even in tubes which have been in service for periods on the order of 3 years.

The main disadvantage of using sapphire in spacecraft applications is that it is brittle and shatters under heavy loads. For example, in Lockheed tests of small ball bearings with sapphire balls and crown-type retainers, installed in an antenna positioning switch and converter assembly, the bearings failed during normal operation and when subjected to shock and vibration conditions. In the first test, the four ball bearings of the stepper-motor assembly were replaced with bearings with sapphire balls and subjected to shock and vibration. One of the bearings in the timer section failed, owing to shattering of the balls; the other three bearings survived. In the second test, an extra pair of ball bearings was added in the timer section; all bearings were new and had sapphire balls. None of the bearings failed under shock and vibration. The unit was then recleaned, assembled with six ball bearings with sapphire balls, and subjected to normal operation without shock or vibration. After only four steps, the balls in five of the six bearings had shattered, apparently because of the heavy thrust load of 20 lb acting on the bearings.

Tungsten and Titanium Carbides. Tungsten and titanium carbides, as available commercially, consist of a sintered body of very fine particles of the hard carbides bonded by a metal such as cobalt or nickel. Such materials are very hard and wear-resistant. Their use in cutting tools is well known. The coefficient of friction for typical tungsten carbides sliding on tungsten carbide is about 0.2; on steel, it is about 0.45 to 0.6 (see page 168 of Ref. 2). In tests conducted in air [44], carbide cermets suffered less rolling wear than sintered alumina (100 per cent theoretical density) and other ceramics and cermets, but wore considerably more than SAE 52100 steel.

Ball bearings with balls of tungsten carbide are more resistant to shock and vibration than bearings with sapphire balls. Tests at Lockheed indicate that tungsten-carbide balls are sufficiently resistant to shattering under shock and vibration loads comparable to those that occur during the launch and ascent phases of spacecraft operation and while supporting relatively light loads. However, the use of tungsten-carbide ball bearings dry is limited to low speeds or short lifetimes.

Conclusions

Mechanisms intended for use in present and future satellite systems and spacecraft must provide long-time operational reliability under a variety of earthside and space environmental and operational conditions. Lubricants and self-lubricating materials capable of lubricating such mechanisms satisfactorily are essential to the achievement of such reliability.

Environmental conditions to which lubricants and self-lubricating materials may be exposed include those attendant to ground activities; to short-time operation during launch, ascent, and reentry; and to long-time operation on orbit. During ground operations, the lubricants and materials must survive the effects of test and checkout, handling and transportation, and exposure to the elements. Under launch, ascent, and reentry conditions, they must function satisfactorily to resist the effects of heavy shock and vibration loads and high and low temperature extremes. When the spacecraft is in orbit, they must provide satisfactory lubrication despite the effects of ultrahigh vacuum, temperature extremes, zero gravity, and radiation.

Ultrahigh vacuum is the orbital environmental factor presenting the most serious obstacle to the provision of suitable lubrication. Although it is possible to protect parts and mechanisms from vacuum conditions by using hermetically sealed units, this and other stratagems are often impractical and involve the disadvantages of increasing the weight, size, and complexity of the spacecraft systems. It is believed that these disadvantages can be overcome through the use of lubricants and self-lubricating materials which themselves provide adequate lubrication under conditions of ultrahigh vacuum, as well as under the other environmental factors to which spacecraft mechanisms are exposed.

Lubricants such as oils and greases have the advantages of providing lower torques and of being more readily available than most other types of lubricant. Before they are used in specific applications on spacecraft, however, the following factors should be considered (in addition to considerations normally governing their selection for use on earth):

1. Loss of lubricating fluids by entrainment, evaporation, and creepage
2. Frictional polymerization catalyzed by clean metal surfaces
3. Effect of absence of oxygen and other gases on the formation of lubricating films
4. Radiation stability

In laboratory tests that have been conducted to date, double-shielded ball bearings lubricated with suitable oils and greases have successfully operated in vacuum of about 10^{-6} mm Hg, or better, for the following lifetimes:

1. At 4,000 rpm, 75°C (167°F) motor base temperature, 1,000 hr without failure.

2. At 8,000 rpm and approximately 79°C (175°F) bearing housing temperature, 4,574 hr before failure.

3. At 11,500 rpm and 121°C (250°F) motor casing temperature, 453 hr before failure.

Silicone oils and greases are among the most successful lubricants of those tested to date. The tests indicate that they should be suitable for 6 months of continuous operation in space on small, double-shielded ball bearings in many spacecraft applications, provided that operating temperatures do not exceed approximately 79°C (175°F) and that speeds do not exceed 8,000 rpm.

Thin films of laminar solids, such as molybdenum disulfide (MoS_2), can provide low running torques, long wear lives, low evaporation rates, relative insensitivity to temperature, and excellent radiation stability. In tests conducted at Lockheed, MoS_2 films bonded with sodium silicate have provided adequate lubrication on small ball bearings operating at 8,000 rpm in vacuum of 10^{-6} mm Hg, or better, for lifetimes of as much as 2,213 hr.

Soft metals with low shear strength, such as silver and gold, can be used as thin films over hard substrates to provide lubrication and prevent cold-welding under vacuum conditions. Proprietary silver films have reportedly lubricated ball bearings in vacuum of 10^{-8} mm Hg and at temperatures up to 204°C (400°F) for as long as 10,000 hr at 3,300 to 3,600 rpm and 2,500 hr at 10,000 rpm. Extreme care must be taken in handling parts with the silver films so as not to disrupt the surfaces during assembly.

Plastics, such as Teflon and nylon, offer many advantages as self-lubricating parts for spacecraft mechanisms, among which is a minimum tendency to cold-weld to metals under vacuum conditions. Many specialty grades of various plastics are available, including reinforced forms, sintered forms, dispersions that can be applied as films, and porous compacts impregnated with plastics. These specialty grades provide the advantage of retaining the desirable properties of the plastics while eliminating their disadvantages.

Ceramics and cermets are essentially hard, brittle materials such as sapphire, glass, cemented carbides, fully dense oxides, and Pyroceram. As in the case of plastics, the ceramics and cermets have little tendency to cold-weld to metals under vacuum conditions. Experience to date indicates that their use is limited to slow speeds and light loads. Shock mounting to protect them against impact and vibration during the launch and ascent phases may be necessary for spacecraft applications.

REFERENCES

1. Sonntag, A.: The Effect of Lubricants on the 'Wear In' of New Machinery, *Lubrication Newsletter* No. 5, The Alpha-Molykote Corporation, September, 1958.
2. Bowden, F., P., and D. Tabor: "The Friction and Lubrication of Solids," Oxford University Press, Fair Lawn, N.J., 1954.
3. Bowden, F. P., and T. P. Hughes: The Friction of Clean Metals and the Influence of Adsorbed Gases: The Temperature Coefficient of Friction, *Proc. Roy. Soc. (London)*, vol. A172, p. 263, 1939.
4. Bowden, F. P., and J. E. Young: Friction and Adhesion of Clean Metals, *Nature*, vol. 164, p. 1089, 1949.
5. Barrett, C. S.: "Structure of Metals," 2d ed., McGraw-Hill Book Company, Inc., New York, 1952.
6. Ernst, H., and M. E. Merchant: Surface Friction of Clean Metals: A Basic Factor in the Metal Cutting Process, *Proc. Spec. Summer Conf. on Friction and Surface Finish*, Massachusetts Institute of Technology, Cambridge, June, 1940.
7. Roach, A. E., C. L. Goodzeit, and P. A. Totta: Score Resistance of Bearing Metals, *Nature*, vol. 172, p. 301, 1953.
8. Coffin, L. F., Jr.: A Study of the Sliding of Metals, with Particular Reference to Atmosphere, *Lubrication Eng.*, vol. 12, pp. 50–58, January–February, 1956.
9. Hay, D. A., and E. Rabinowicz; Interim Report on an Investigation of Spin Axis Instrument Bearings, Alloyd Research Corporation, Watertown, Mass. (Navy BuShips Contract NObs. 72364), May 31, 1959.
10. Hermance, H. W., and T. F. Egan: Organic Deposits on Precious Metal Contacts, *Bell System Tech. J.*, vol. 37, pp. 739–776, May, 1958.
11. Cosgrove, S. L.: The Effect of Nuclear Radiation on Lubricants and Hydraulic Fluids, *Battelle Memorial Institute, REIC Rept.* No. 4, Apr. 30, 1958; 1st add., Mar. 31, 1959; 2d add., Mar. 15, 1960.
12. Rice, W. L. R.: Effects of Gamma Radiation on Organic Fluids and Lubricants, *Nucleonics*, vol. 16, pp. 112–113, October, 1958.
13. Gisser, H.: How Nuclear Radiation Affects Petroleum and Synthetic Lubricants, *Mater. Design Eng.*, p. 152ff., February, 1960.
14. Fisher, D. J., J. F. Zack, Jr., and E. L. Warrick: Radiation Stability of Silicone Greases, *Lubrication Eng.*, vol. 15, pp. 407–409, October, 1959.
15. Rice, W. L. R., D. A. Kirk, and W. B. Cheney, Jr.: Radiation Resistance Fluids and Lubricants, *Nucleonics*, vol. 18, pp. 67–71, February, 1960.
16. Corridan, R. E.: Summary Report, Bearing and Lubrication Study, American Standard Corporation, Advanced Technology Laboratories Division, (ATL Job 4611 for LMSD), Mountain View, Calif., June 30, 1959.

17. Freundlich, M. M., and C. H. Hannan: Problems of Lubrication in Space, paper presented at Annual Meeting, Society of American Lubrication Engineers, Cincinnati, April, 1960.

18. Clauss, Francis J.: Lubricants and Self-lubricating Materials for Spacecraft Mechanisms, *Lockheed Missiles Space Division Rept.* 894812, Sunnyvale, Calif. Apr. 18, 1961.

19. Johnson, V. R., and G. W. Vaughn: Investigation of the Mechanism of MoS_2 Lubrication in Vacuum, *J. Appl. Phys.*, vol. 27, pp. 1173–1179, October, 1956.

20. Feng, I-Ming: Lubricating Properties of Molybdenum Disulfide, *Lubrication Eng.*, vol. 8, p. 285, December, 1952.

21. Bowden, F. P.: Frictional Properties of Porous Metals Containing Molybdenum Disulfide, *Research (London)*, vol. 3, pp. 383–384, August, 1950.

22. Milne, A. A.: Lubrication of Steel Surfaces with Molybdenum Disulfide, *Research (London)*, vol. 4, p. 93, 1951.

23. Bowden, F. P.: Frictional Properties of Porous Metals Containing Molybdenum Disulfide, *Research (London)*, vol. 3, pp. 383–384, August, 1950.

24. Johnson, R. L., D. Godfrey, and E. E. Bisson: Friction of Solid Films on Steel at High Sliding Velocities, *National Aeronautics and Space Administration*, NACA TN-1578, 1958.

25. Bowden, F. P., and K. V. Shooter: Frictional Behavior of Plastics Impregnated with Molybdenum Disulfide, *Research (London)*, vol. 3, pp. 384–385, August, 1950.

26. Johnson, R. L., M. A. Swikert, and E. E. Bisson: Friction and Wear of Hot-pressed Bearing Materials Containing Molybdenum Disulfide, *National Aeronautics and Space Administration*, NACA TN-2027, February, 1960.

27. Smith, Roy: Personal communication, Booker-Cooper, Inc., Dec. 8, 1959.

28. Bowden, F. P., and D. Tabor: The Lubrication by Thin Metallic Films and the Action of Bearing Metals, *J. Appl. Phys.*, vol. 14, pp. 141–151, March, 1943.

29. Atlee, Z. J., J. T. Silson, and J. C. Filmer: Lubrication in Vacuum by Vaporized Thin Metallic Films, *J. Appl. Phys.*, vol. 11, pp. 611–615, September, 1940.

30. Rogers, T. H.: Private communication, Machlett Laboratories.

31. Montalbano, Joseph E.: Plastic Ball and Roller Bearings, *Machine Design*, vol. 30, no. 16, pp. 96–99, Aug. 7, 1958.

32. White, H. S.: *Natl. Bur. Std. Rept.* 2882, October, 1953.

33. Engineering Facts about Teflon, *E. I. Du Pont de Nemours and Co., Inc., Bull.* 6, Wilmington, Del., 1958.

34. Bowden, F. P.: Frictional Properties of Porous Metal Impregnated with Plastic, *Research (London)*, vol. 3, pp. 147–148, March, 1950.

35. Love, P. P.: Comment on the Frictional Behavior of Porous Metals Impregnated with P.T.F.E., *Proc. Roy. Soc. (London)*, vol. 212A, p. 484, 1952.

36. FitzSimmons, V. G., and W. A. Zisman: Thin Films of Polytetrafluoroethylene Resin as Lubricants and Preservative Coatings for Metals, *Ind. Eng. Chem.*, vol. 50, pp. 781–784, May, 1958.

37. Du Pont Zytel Nylon Resins, E. I. Du Pont de Nemours and Co., Inc., Polychemicals Dept., Wilmington, Del.
38. Stott, L. L., and L. R. B. Hervey: Pressed and Sintered Nylon Powder Parts, *Mater. Methods*, vol. 40, p. 108, October, 1952.
39. Stott, L. L.: Sintered Nylon, *Mod. Plastics*, vol. 35, pp. 157–158, September, 1957.
40. Alexander, L. W.: Additives Put Muscle into Sintered Nylon Parts, *Prod. Eng.*, Sept. 15, 1958.
41. Moly-sulfide Fillers Reduce Wear in Plastics, *Mater. Methods*, January, 1957.
42. Nylasint Sintered Nylon Parts, Technical Data, Halex Corporation.
43. Symons: Private communication, Varian Associates, Palo Alto, Calif., July 20, 1961.
44. Investigation of the Possibility of Using Ceramics or Cermets for Unlubricated Ball Bearing Applications, ASTIA AD No. 220798-L, Little Falls, N.J. (Navy BuShips Contract NObs 66965), October, 1956.

11
Nuclear Materials and Problems

JOHN E. HOVE

DIRECTOR, MATERIAL SCIENCES LABORATORY
AEROSPACE CORPORATION
LOS ANGELES, CALIFORNIA

It is probably worthwhile to present a brief discussion of nuclear-reactor principles in general, even if only to clarify terminology. In so doing, only fission-type reactors will be considered, even though fusion or thermonuclear reactions yield a several-fold increase in energy per unit weight; it is only the fission reactions that can be controlled and hence used. A free neutron penetrating a uranium[235] nucleus will usually cause it to split into two unequal nuclei, called fission products or fragments, with the release of two or three secondary neutrons and about 200 Mev of energy. Under the proper conditions, at least one of the new neutrons will cause another fission event and so on, producing a self-sustaining reaction. Of the 200 Mev of energy released, 166 Mev goes into kinetic energy of the fission products, which is almost entirely converted into heating the solid uranium fuel element. These heavy particles are stopped in a distance of the order of $\frac{1}{2}$ mil. Of the remaining energy, some 10 Mev goes into direct gamma radiation, which is frequently an annoying by-product. It is difficult to shield against introducing health-hazard and structure-heating problems. The remainder of the fission energy goes into neutron kinetic energy and radioactive radiation from the fission products (the latter, of course, also contributes to the gamma-radiation problem). As a comparative figure, it may be of interest to note that the heat-energy equivalent of fissioning 1 kg of uranium[235] produces almost 20 billion kcal, which is some 2 million times greater than the heat energy produced by burning 1 kg of kerosene.

Uranium[235] (and the other possible fuels, thorium[233] and plutonium[239]) may be fissioned by neutrons of thermal, intermediate, or fast energies. However, the probability of fission increases with decreasing neutron energy, and thus most reactors operate with neutrons of thermal energies (another reason for this is the relative ease of control of thermal reactors). At birth, the secondary neutrons have energies ranging between 1 and 2 Mev. These neutrons are slowed down to thermal energy by a material known as a moderator. This moderator must be highly efficient in accepting kinetic energy from a neutron by inelastic collisions without, at the same time, capturing or absorbing the neutron and thus removing it as a possible fission producer. If we consider only normally available materials, the possible moderator materials are dense forms of hydrogen (deuterium), beryllium, and carbon. In order to achieve a sustained, or chain reaction, there obviously must be some minimum amount of fissionable fuel in the reactor. This minimum amount, called the critical mass, depends on the efficiency with which the secondary neutrons are preserved so that they can function as fission producers. The loss of neutrons by escape from the reactor is minimized by use of a blanket material, called the reflector, whose function is to scatter as many escaping neutrons back into the system as possible. The other major loss of neutrons occurs by absorption into nuclei of the reactor materials *not* resulting in useful fission. This aspect severely limits the types of materials that can be used in a reactor. Many undesirable "poison" materials cannot be economically eliminated. The plentiful isotope uranium[238] is one such, and so are many of the fission products. This makes it all the more imperative not to build in deliberately such poisons, except, of course, as control rods. Such rods, which can be inserted into the reactor, utilize highly absorptive materials, such as boron or cadmium, to control the neutron flux level and hence the reactor power. Table 11.1 gives a résumé of the tolerances of the normal elements (except those used for control purposes) in a thermal-reactor core and hence an indication of what materials can be used. It should be pointed out that, in many cases, the extreme undesirability of the naturally occurring element is due to the presence of a single isotope. This is true in the cases of boron and lithium, both of which are so intolerable that they do not appear in Table 11.1. If the undesirable isotope can be almost completely eliminated (with reasonable economy), either material could be used in large amounts. In fact, this is being done at present with lithium in order to explore its usefulness as a liquid-metal coolant for certain high-temperature reactors.

Aside from space or atmospheric flight uses, the major applications of nuclear reactors have been for stationary power-producing plants (either for commercial utilities or remote military use), stationary process heat production, and marine propulsion. While it is naturally desirable to keep such reactor plants as small and compact as possible, this is clearly not the major requirement. Economy, in both construction and operation, is usually the ruling factor, along with accessibility and reliability.

Table 11.1   Element Tolerances in Thermal-reactor Cores
(All percentages in volume per cent)

1. Elements tolerable in large amounts (greater than 25%):

   $_2$He, $_4$Be, $_6$C, $_8$O, $_9$F, $_1$H†

2. Elements tolerable in moderate amounts (less than 25%):

   $_{12}$Mg, $_{13}$Al, $_{14}$Si, $_{15}$P, $_{40}$Zr,
   $_{82}$Pb, $_{83}$Bi

3. Elements tolerable in small amounts (less than 5%):

   $_7$N, $_{10}$Ne, $_{11}$Na, $_{16}$S, $_{18}$A, $_{19}$K,
   $_{20}$Ca, $_{24}$Cr, $_{26}$Fe, $_{30}$Zn, $_{31}$Ga,
   $_{32}$Ge, $_{37}$Rb, $_{38}$Sr, $_{39}$Y, $_{41}$Nb,
   $_{42}$Mo, $_{44}$Ru, $_{50}$Sn, $_{56}$Ba, $_{58}$Ce, $_{86}$Rn

4. Elements tolerable in traces (less than 0.1%):

   $_{22}$Ti, $_{23}$V, $_{25}$Mn, $_{28}$Ni, $_{29}$Cu,
   $_{33}$As, $_{34}$Se, $_{35}$Br, $_{46}$Pd, $_{51}$Sb,
   $_{52}$Te, $_{53}$I, $_{57}$La, $_{59}$Pr, $_{76}$Os,
   $_{78}$Pt, $_{81}$Tl, $_{90}$Th, $_{92}$U

5. All other elements are essentially intolerable.

† $_1$H is an exception because of its excellent moderating properties.

This is not generally true for flight or space utilization, where small size and weight (coupled with high power requirements) become factors of critical importance. Especially in the fields of direct flight or space propulsion, these requirements impose severe restrictions on the materials. It may truthfully be said that materials requirements are slightly beyond the present limit of capabilities. The requirements of such systems will be discussed later, but one basic shortcoming of all present reactor-propulsion designs, as compared with those of chemical propulsion, will be mentioned here. This involves the prevalent method of heating the propulsion medium (whether air, hydrogen, or something else) by heat transfer from the reactor or heat-exchanger surfaces. When chemical fuel is burned in conventional propulsion engines, liberation of heat occurs throughout the chamber and the temperature of the combustion products can be considerably higher than that of the walls. Furthermore, the walls can be cooled with relative ease. If, on the other hand, the gas is being heated by heat transfer from a surface, that surface has to be at least 50 to 100°C hotter than the gas. Thus, the gas temperature is limited by the temperature that the walls can maintain. In order to overcome this difficulty, various schemes to inject the fission products directly into the gas have been considered to avoid the basically inefficient process of heating a solid in order to heat a gas. There are serious difficulties in such an undertaking. Any scheme involving the use of a fissionable gas or powder (either using a reactor as a source of neutrons or having the gas at critical densities) encounters the problem of either dumping intolerable amounts of expensive fuels out the exhaust or having such a constricted gas-flow path that the thrust becomes very small. A successful design of this type would be of extreme value for many aspects of nuclear flight.

Applications of Nuclear Power to Atmospheric Craft and Spacecraft

Manned Aircraft. Although this use of nuclear power does not strictly fall in the province of this chapter, it is one of a family of applications, all of which have similar materials problems. The outstanding advantage of aircraft nuclear propulsion is the possibility of very long range. As an example, a supersonic aircraft weighing 120 tons could fly around the world with nuclear power using about 0.5 kg of uranium[235]. If the same aircraft were chemically powered, about 1,000 tons of fuel would be consumed and this would require approximately 15 refuelings. Thus, the successful construction of a nuclear-powered manned aircraft of supersonic capability appears desirable. Aside from the reactor materials difficulties, two major problems here involve radiation protection of the flying personnel and ground personnel, especially during landing and takeoff. The first requires shielding and hence introduces a weight problem. This implies that military bombers would be the first such craft built because it is easier to shield a small crew than a large number of passengers. The protection of ground personnel involves protection against the release of radioactive materials in any large quantities. Since the activation of dust or normal air-constituent atoms (of which argon is the only worrisome one) is of minor importance, this problem implies that loss of the fission products by diffusion into the airstream must be avoided. The reactor problems will be discussed later, but the heating surfaces must reach temperatures of 1100 to 1400°C for supersonic flight. Naturally, the hotter one can run such a reactor reliably, the better, since the efficiency is improved and the size is reduced.

Unmanned Ramjet Missile. The nuclear ramjet engine represents a relatively simple type of power plant. It amounts to a "flying reactor" with a diffuser in the nose and a jet nozzle in the rear. The reactor can look essentially like a swiss cheese, and there need be no moving parts except the control mechanisms. Since there is no crew, shielding problems are reduced to those of protecting instrumentation. The ramjet operates efficiently only at supersonic velocities, so it is necessary to launch such a missile with a booster. This has the effect of minimizing takeoff health hazards because the reactor can be held at very low power until a high altitude is reached. Work in this country on such a reactor has been conducted under the code name Pluto (see *Nucleonics*, August,

1960, page 24).   The missile is designed to operate around Mach 3, probably at low altitudes.   It is, of course, at very low altitudes and high speeds where the range advantage of a reactor engine over a chemical engine becomes great.   The specific thrust of a nuclear ramjet is likely to be less than that of a chemical engine, because in the latter case the air is heated to around 1500°C.   This means that the reactor-coolant wall temperature would have to be around 1600°C to achieve the same specific thrust, and this is stretching present-day materials technology a little too much for comfort.   The total thrust, however, of a reactor ramjet can be equal to or greater than that of the chemical unit if the dimensions are increased so that the total flow is greater.   In the nuclear engine, there is little penalty in fuel consumption when this is done. However, especially for low-altitude flight, the size is limited because of the increased aerodynamic drag associated with increasing the reactor diameter.   Thus, it is desirable to attain high temperatures (as close as possible to the 1500°C mentioned above) and a high power density. The latter means a high heat flux per unit area and hence a high temperature gradient near the heating surface.   These conditions impose somewhat more severe restrictions on the reactor materials than in the case of manned aircraft, even though other problems are somewhat alleviated.

Nuclear Rocket Missile.   In using a nuclear reactor for rocket propulsion, the usually suggested advantage is the very large energy capacity it provides.   However, for propulsion, the nuclear rocket, like the chemical rocket, must still carry an enormous quantity of a working medium aboard; and when this medium is gone, propulsion stops.   Thus, unlike atmospheric missiles, the nuclear rocket does not necessarily have a superior range.   There is the advantage that, whereas the chemical rocket requires a store of both fuel and oxidizer, the nuclear rocket requires only a store of inertial mass material.   Furthermore, this material may be in the most desirable form (such as, perhaps, pure hydrogen) used because no chemical reaction products are formed.

If the nuclear rocket is used to power a first stage, the advantage mentioned above becomes worthwhile if the rocket is large enough and the reactor heating-surface temperature high enough (of the order of 2500°C). Even though the duration of use is quite short for this application, the reactor materials difficulties are very severe.

The other projected use of nuclear rockets involves long-range space flights, using low power and starting from orbit.   Here the advantage lies not so much in achieving a range markedly superior to that of a chemical system, but in carrying a higher payload.   This advantage can be quite great.   Thus, if it is assumed that a 75-ton spacecraft is in an earth orbit and is propelled into an orbit around Mars and back, the payload with a chemical rocket would be 3,000 lb while that with a nuclear rocket would be 20,000 lb. This is largely due to the absence of an oxidizer material, but partially due to the somewhat greater efficiencies that are possible.

Auxiliary Power for Spacecraft. It is in this area that nuclear systems seem to show the greatest advantage and, in fact, it may be that they form the only hope for some uses. The two general applications involve (1) power for communication and other electronic equipment on satellites and (2) power for electrical propulsion systems. At the present time, the only practical energy sources for such devices are solar and nuclear energy. Solar energy appears useful only for low powers, that is, for auxiliary applications up to about 10 to 20 kw. Missions requiring much greater energy levels would seem to have to depend on the nuclear sources that are presently being developed by the Atomic Energy Commission in their Systems for Nuclear Auxiliary Power (SNAP) program. Such reactor systems must be as small and light as possible and extremely reliable. The importance of the last point is suggested by the fact that a one-way trip to Mars would take approximately 1 year with the 30-kw SNAP-8 system presently under development. Thus, a useful mission requires some 2 years of continuous reactor operation with no attention or servicing.

Crucial Materials Requirements in Nuclear Applications. Before discussing available materials and their problems and progress, it may be worthwhile to review briefly the requirements imposed on these materials by the nuclear systems mentioned previously. The most striking general feature of the various reactor systems is the requirement for small size coupled with as high a power level as possible. In the case of SNAP, high power is necessary for future missions, but some present missions can utilize relatively low power. However, in the case of the propulsion reactors, most missions will not succeed at all unless the power is high. A typical large stationary power reactor, such as Atomics International's sodium graphite reactor, has a power density in the core of about 1 megawatt/ft^3. It is not difficult to estimate that the aircraft and ramjet reactors must have a power density about ten times greater, while the nuclear rocket (used as a first stage) must be around fifty to one hundred times greater. In essence this means that the temperatures will be high (say 1200 to 1500°C for the air breathers and 2000 to 2500°C for the rocket); the temperature gradients will be high and the nuclear radiation level will be high. The radiation level is about proportional to the power density; hence radiation damage is about ten to one hundred times more serious than in presently operating commercial reactors. This may not be so serious as it sounds, because the very high operating temperatures will probably cause sufficient annealing to alleviate the damage.

In most cases, the small-size requirement also implies the need for a homogeneous reactor concept rather than a heterogeneous design. In the former case, the fuel and moderator are, as the name implies, intimately mixed, whereas in the latter, of course, the fuel is in the form of separated elements. A homogeneous design is comparatively expensive, but this is not the principal guide for the applications of the kind discussed herein. Furthermore, the heat-transfer requirements are such that there must be a void volume of the order of 50 per cent in the reactor core. This means that it is imperative to keep down the amount of nonessential material; i.e., one cannot afford the luxury of strengthening the structure with material that adds to the weight but does not function as a fuel or moderator.

The coolant material cannot be arbitrarily selected. In the case of the air breathers, air must be the coolant, although to be sure it is possible to use an intermediate coolant in the reactor and heat the air by a secondary heat exchanger. Because of the high temperatures involved, the question of compatibility of materials and the atmosphere becomes a critical one. This whole problem gets into the area of high-temperature chemistry in a crucial way. In most cases the phase diagrams of the possibly useful materials at the necessary temperatures are not even well known. It is clear that great practical difficulty could be involved if one should encounter an unsuspected ternary compound with a low melting point. Questions of diffusion in the solid state and plastic deformation become exceedingly important, particularly in the presence of high temperature gradients. The influence of this last variable on the properties of materials is almost a new field. Although not in the realm of the present discussion (this will be discussed in Chap. 13), the possibility of thermionic direct-conversion reactors brings up the subject of high-temperature electrical insulators and a new aspect of materials compatibility. If we are concerned with space flight, the time of reliable operation must be long, and even relatively small amounts of diffusion into a good insulator are quite likely to change it into a semiconductor, with possibly disastrous results. It is also clear that for any of the applications being discussed, excessive grain growth or other changes in material microstructure could be of great importance. The difficulty here is that, especially in the area of relatively little-known high-temperature materials, the factors governing microstructural changes and their rates are not well understood. Unfortunately, as in almost all systems programs, there is never enough time to do the sensible thing, i.e., to acquire a good foundation of basic knowledge so that predictions of the final performance of a material can be made with assurance. Despite this, it must be said in fairness that the nuclear flight programs have involved a large amount of basic and applied research on materials. This has been more essential than in other programs because in pushing the material performance to its limit, it is rarely possible to rely heavily on ingenious systems design.

Materials Problems

Useful Types of Materials.   The choice of useful reactor materials for nuclear flight applications is restricted to those substances whose properties are reasonably known.   First of all, the neutronic requirement of major use (excluding fuel thin coatings or other minor volume constituents) in a thermal-reactor core is restricted to the elements in categories 1 and 2 in Table 11.1.   This statement naturally neglects the deliberate use of poison materials for control purposes.   The next restrictive requirement is that of refractoriness; i.e., useful materials should be solid and still retain some strength up to at least 1500°C.   These two conditions alone restrict the choice of usable solids pretty much to those shown in Table 11.2.   Strictly speaking, the zirconium hydride system

Table 11.2   Useful High-temperature Materials

Element	C	O	H	Be
Be	Be_2C	BeO		
Mg	. . . . .	MgO		
Al	Al_4C_3	Al_2O_3		
Si	SiC	SiO_2		
Zr	ZrC	ZrO_2	Zr-H	$ZrBe_{13}$

does not belong in this group because it loses hydrogen rapidly at temperatures well below 1500°C.   However, this problem may be alleviated sometime in the future if a suitable cladding can be developed to withstand high enough hydrogen pressures at high temperatures.   Furthermore, at the high hydrogen side of the zirconium-hydrogen system (say at H-Zr of about 1.9), the density of hydrogen atoms is some 10 per cent higher than that of hydrogen in water, and about twice that of liquid hydrogen.   This property makes zirconium hydride of great interest. Both carbon and zirconium are set apart in Table 11.2 because their elemental solids qualify by our standards.   To date, there is not a great deal known about the zirconium beryllide system, but it may well be a very interesting system.   It should also be mentioned that there is a stable set of uranium beryllide compounds, some of which are very refractory (e.g., UBe_{13}) and, at least according to the Russian literature, quite stable to radiation-damage effects.   Other useful refractory fuel compounds include UO_2, UC, some of the uranium silicides, and possibly some of the sulfides.   Both the beryllium and the aluminum carbide systems are difficult to use because of high vapor pressures and because they are highly reactive materials.

Aside from the materials mentioned in the previous paragraph, it can be seen that available materials are relatively few in number. There may be ternaries and higher compounds, but generally these tend to be less refractory. We cannot necessarily, of course, exclude the possibility that some hitherto unknown compound may be found of equal or superior qualities, although neither can this possibility be counted on. Furthermore, if the ambient atmosphere is air (as in two of the applications being considered), only the five oxides are inherently stable. Both SiC and $ZrBe_{13}$ can, however, be used in an oxygen atmosphere because both form a tenacious oxide film that prevents further oxidation. Many attempts, with varying degrees of success, have been made to coat graphite with SiC so that it can be used in an oxidizing atmosphere. Although it appears that such coatings may be feasible, there is usually an inherent distrust of them under conditions where the failure of the coating would be catastrophic. On one occasion, such a dependence was likened to the building of a boat out of sugar and depending on a paint job to provide seaworthiness. If we recall that beryllium, hydrogen, and carbon form just about the entire stock of useful moderating materials and, further, that it is imperative in nuclear flight applications to eliminate as many nonessential materials as possible, it is clear that BeO, graphite, and ZrC (excluding beryllides since little is known about them) stand out clearly. Over the last several years, much has been learned about BeO and graphite, and some of the properties of these materials of direct interest to nuclear flight will be discussed further.

Properties of Graphite. The factors that make graphite of interest are its very high stability as a solid (it sublimes at about 3600°C), its properties of increasing strength with temperature, and its high thermal conductivity as compared with other high-temperature materials. Both its specific heat and thermal conductivity have been measured in the laboratory up to its sublimation point. It also has a low coefficient of thermal expansion. These properties combine to give graphite a high resistance to thermal shock. Table 11.3 shows a comparison of a thermal stress figure of merit for graphite, BeO, Al_2O_3, and stabilized ZrO_2. The values shown are typical but not necessarily representative of each material. There is a statistical variation of the properties, especially the strength and, for graphite, also the thermal expansion. However, the values do represent an average and may be compared on an order-of-magnitude basis. It can be seen that graphite and BeO are about comparable at 500°C, but graphite is considerably better at 1200°C. This is largely due to the fact that the thermal conductivity of BeO drops more rapidly with temperature than does that of graphite.

Table 11.3 Index of Thermal Stress Resistance, $R = \sigma k/\alpha E$

Material	Temp., °C	σ, psi	k, cal/(sec)(cm)(°C)	α per °C	E, psi	R
BeO	500	35,000	0.22	9.4×10^{-6}	53×10^6	15.5
	1200	22,000	0.053	9.4×10^{-6}	48×10^6	2.6
Al_2O_3	500	40,000	0.035	7×10^{-6}	53×10^6	3.8
	1200	20,000	0.015	10×10^{-6}	48×10^6	0.6
ZrO_2	500	20,000	0.0044	9×10^{-6}	22×10^6	0.4
(stabilized)	1200	13,000	0.0050	11×10^{-6}	18×10^6	0.3
Graphite	500	3,800	0.22	4×10^{-6}	1.2×10^6	17.4
	1200	4,400	0.10	4×10^{-6}	1.4×10^6	7.9

There is considerable graphite research underway to evaluate the relationship between manufacturing methods and properties. Much work has gone into dense-graphite preparation. This last point is of considerable importance to flight reactors, aside from the possibility of having improved properties. The best of the commercial graphites still have about 20 per cent void space, which is essentially wasted. Work is also underway to make SiC-bonded graphite, which gives some promise of increasing the strength as well as helping the oxidation resistance. Future graphite bodies may be expected to bear little resemblance to the material now being used.

Properties of Beryllia. Beryllium oxide has been the subject of intensive research effort in the last few years, largely because of the nuclear flight programs. Prior to about 1956, the strength data as a function of temperature that appeared in the literature showed the BeO rupture modulus falling off to essentially zero above about 1100°C; this made it quite unattractive. Since that time, fabrication research, primarily on problems involving purity and density, has increased the useful-strength region beyond the temperatures needed for flight propulsion. At 1200°C, strengths of 20,000 to 30,000 psi can be reproducibly obtained; at 1400°C, the strength is still in the range of 10,000 to 15,000 psi. There is still considerable room for improvement; samples have been made of very-fine-grained (of the order of 1 μ) BeO that have strengths over 40,000 psi at 1200°C. On a single sample at 1200°C (well below the region of appreciable creep), the specimen bent about 10°, but did not break under the rapidly applied load. The possibility of some ductility was thereby indicated.

The thermal conductivity and thermal expansion of BeO have been measured up to about 2100°C. The behavior of the thermal conductivity above around 1800°C is quite interesting (even though this is above the present temperatures of interest, we may be certain that future applications will always want an increased use temperature). The conductivity apparently starts to increase above 1800°C in an exponential manner with T^{-1}. Without knowing what it means we may determine an *activation energy* for this process of about 2 ev. Aside from the basic question of the mechanism leading to this behavior, it is clear that such behavior might be of considerable technological interest, particularly since small additions of MgO tend to lower the temperature at which such an increase in thermal conductivity occurs. There is another phenomenon in some BeO samples which is also not understood but which can be annoying to the designer. At about 2100°C, samples have been observed to decrepitate and to show rather extensive grain growth. Whether the grain growth and the decrepitation represent the same phenomenon or not remains to be seen. Since the cracking has been observed to occur at high temperature (where creep is fairly easy), it is not immediately clear that grain growth alone could be the cause. Attempts to detect a possible phase transition at this temperature have failed. While BeO as a nuclear material will probably never be deliberately used at this temperature, it may well be so used as a reentry material. Another interesting observation, which again has not yet been sufficiently investigated, is what appears to be an appreciable first-stage (i.e., short-time) creep when minor additions of MgO are added. This could be of considerable importance for thermal stress resistance.

Considerable work has been done on BeO in the field of fabrication research and development. Both extrusion and hot-pressing have been investigated more thoroughly, probably, than ever before, and considerable success in making reproducible shapes has been realized. Pressure welding of dense pieces is in an early stage of development, but shows exceedingly high potential. The biggest single problem in fabrication is still that of properly preparing and characterizing the powder. However, at the present rate of research and development progress, it may be anticipated that BeO will become one of our most useful new materials in just a few years.

12

Materials for Direct Conversion—
Theoretical Considerations

CLARENCE ZENER

DIRECTOR, WESTINGHOUSE RESEARCH LABORATORIES
PITTSBURGH PENNSYLVANIA

An attempt is made in this chapter to present what appear to be the essential features of direct-conversion heat engines and of their materials of construction. This subject is introduced by discussing certain general features of continuous heat engines, features which are accentuated in direct-conversion heat engines but which seemingly have not been previously discussed in relation to conventional heat engines.

The thermal efficiency is conventionally defined by

$$\eta = \frac{\text{net power output}}{\text{gross heat intake}}$$

The net power output is the gross power generated minus the power needed to run the various necessary auxiliaries. The gross heat intake is the heat that must be supplied by an external reservoir.

Considerable insight into the problems encountered in designing continuous-flow heat engines is gained by an explicit separation of both the power output and the heat intake into reversible and irreversible parts. Thus

$$\text{Power output} = p_{\text{rev}} - \Delta p$$
$$\text{Heat intake} = q_{\text{rev}} + \Delta q$$

Here p_{rev} is the power that would be delivered in the absence of all irreversible power losses; q_{rev} is the heat intake in the absence of all irreversible heat fluxes. One objective of good design is to minimize both the irreversible power loss Δp and the irreversible heat flux Δq. This design objective may be formulated in mathematical terms by introducing the

336

dimensionless parameters

$$x = \frac{\Delta p}{p_{rev}}$$
$$y = \frac{\Delta q}{q_{rev}}$$

(12.1)

Thus the thermal efficiency may be written as

$$\eta = \frac{p_{rev}}{q_{rev}} \frac{1 - x}{1 + y}$$

(12.2)

We have thereby expressed the thermal efficiency as the product of a cycle efficiency

$$\eta_c = \frac{p_{rev}}{q_{rev}}$$

(12.3)

and of a degradation factor

$$\epsilon = \frac{1 - x}{1 + y}$$

(12.4)

introduced by irreversible processes. One design problem is the maximization of the degradation factor ϵ.

In a wide range of heat engines, x may be reduced to a very small value, and y may also be reduced to a very small value, but they cannot be reduced simultaneously. In fact, x and y are so related that their product is a constant with respect to any design changes.

As an example, consider a continuous-flow heat engine whose working medium goes through the cycle depicted in Fig. 12.1. In an unsophisticated design, the power output per unit cycle is equal to the area of the closed loop shown in Fig. 12.1a; the heat input is equal to the area of the shaded region in this figure. In a more sophisticated design, the heat input can be greatly reduced by using part of the heat rejected in the fourth stage as the heat input to the second stage. If such a transfer of heat suffered no impedances, such as those imposed in reality by finite heat conductivities, then the heat intake would be the area of the shaded region in Fig. 12.1b. This heat intake is q_{rev}. A transfer of heat from the working medium in stage 4 to that in stage 2 must take place through some system of heat exchangers, preferably by a counterflow system. Heat flow must, however, be driven by a temperature gradient. The existence of a temperature gradient means that the working medium leaving the heat exchanger in stage 2 will be at a lower temperature than the working medium that enters the heat exchanger in stage 4. An additional heat intake Δq is necessary to raise the temperature of the working medium in stage 2 to the value it would have if this temperature gradient did not exist. This additional heat intake could be reduced even more by extending the length of the heat-exchange tube, but such an extension would raise the power Δp necessary to push the working medium through the tubes. A simple analysis shows in fact that Δq is inversely proportional to this length, while Δp is proportional to the length, and hence that the product $\Delta q \, \Delta p$ is a constant. The design

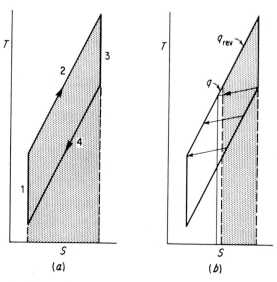

Fig. 12.1 Graphs illustrating cycle of working medium in continuous-flow heat engine.

problem of maximizing the degradation factor ϵ may thus be expressed in the following mathematical language. The problem is to find the values of x and y that will maximize the ratio

$$\epsilon = \frac{1 - x}{1 + y}$$

subject to the condition that

$$xy = \text{const}$$

Since the degradation factor will be larger than the smaller product xy, the reciprocal of this product is known as the figure of merit f of the system:

$$xy = \frac{1}{f}$$

The solution of this purely mathematical problem leads to the following:

$$\epsilon = \frac{\sqrt{1 + f} - 1}{\sqrt{1 + f} + 1} \qquad (12.5)$$

A plot of the solution is presented in Fig. 12.2. Note that ϵ is proportional to f as long as f is small compared with unity, and it asymptotically approaches the value of unity as f becomes large.

In the example illustrated in Fig. 12.1b,

$$f \sim M^2$$

where M is the Mach velocity of the fluid in the heat-exchanger tubes. The coefficient of M^2 is of the order of magnitude of unity, depending upon the slope of the heat-exchanger tubes but not on any absolute dimensions. The coefficient of M^2 also is proportional to the Prandtl number, namely, the ratio of the thermal diffusivity coefficient to the

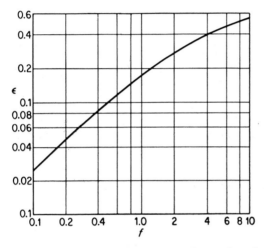

Fig. 12.2 Degradation factor ϵ versus figure of merit f.

momentum diffusivity equation—a ratio that is almost unity for most gases. It will be shown later that the proportionality of f to the ratio of two basic constants (such as of two diffusivity coefficients) is a characteristic feature of the direct-conversion heat engines that will be studied.

In direct-conversion heat engines, the thermal efficiency may always be expressed in the form

$$\eta = \frac{J(\text{emf} - RJ)}{J\pi + K\,\Delta T} \tag{12.6}$$

The first terms in both numerator and denominator represent reversible quantities, the second terms irreversible quantities. The cycle efficiency is thus

$$\eta_c = \frac{\text{emf}}{\pi} \tag{12.7}$$

and the figure of merit is given by

$$f = \frac{\text{emf } \pi}{RK \, \Delta T} \tag{12.8}$$

When appropriate use is made of the value of $\rho K/T$ for metals, namely, $2(k/e)^2$, the figure of merit may be rewritten in the following form:

$$f = \frac{1}{2} \frac{(RK)_{\text{metal}}}{RK} \frac{e \text{ emf}}{k \, \Delta T} \frac{e\pi}{kT} \tag{12.9}$$

This form is particularly useful because each of the three factors is dimensionless and is of the order of magnitude of unity.

In most heat engines, including direct-conversion heat engines, the product xy is a constant only when the range ΔT is small compared with T itself. The author has previously shown† how to treat the general case where ΔT is no longer small compared with T. In this general case

$$\eta = 1 - e^{-A} \tag{12.10}$$

where

$$A = \int_{T_c}^{T_h} \epsilon(T) \, d \ln T \tag{12.11}$$

Next to be presented is a discussion of the basic features of direct-conversion heat engines. A direct-conversion heat engine is one that converts heat directly into electric power without going through the intermediary stage of mechanical power. The term direct conversion has, however, a much deeper significance. An appreciation of this requires a slight acquaintance with the basic features of a conventional continuous-flow heat engine. The essential parts of such an engine are the compressor, the heater, the turbine, and finally the heat extractor or condenser. The appellation *condenser* is misleading. In order to condense the working medium, the combined action of the condenser and turbine are necessary. The situation is similar to that of compressing a spring resting vertically upon a table. When the spring is pressed down, the table exerts an equal but opposite force at the bottom of the spring, and thus it plays an important role. So likewise in a conventional heat engine, the so-called compressor exerts a force upon the working medium in the direction of flow of the working medium, and the turbine exerts a force upon the working medium in a direction counter to its flow. The combined action of these two forces results in a compression of the intervening working medium.

Direct-conversion heat engines have elements that correspond to compressors and turbines. The distinctive difference between conven-

† C. Zener, in P. Egli (ed.), "Thermoelectricity," chap. 1, John Wiley & Sons, Inc., New York, 1960.

tional continuous-flow and direct-conversion heat engines lies in the nature of the forces with which the "compressors" and "turbines" act upon the working medium.   In the conventional heat engines, the compressors and turbines exert only indirect boundary-layer forces upon the working medium.   In direct-conversion heat engines the compressor and turbine elements exert direct body forces upon the working medium. Since turbulence is inevitably associated with boundary-layer forces, the "compressors" and "turbines" of direct-conversion heat engines have potentially higher efficiencies than do their counterparts in conventional heat engines.

The main advantage of direct-conversion heat engines, however, lies in their simplicity rather than in their potentially greater efficiency.   When an electron gas is used as a working medium, the compressor and turbine functions are performed by electric fields.   Not only are these fields stationary, and hence require no moving parts, but nature automatically creates them at the interfaces of materials of different composition. When the two materials are solids, the interface electric field gives rise to the well-known contact differences of potential.   A direct-conversion heat engine utilizing such fields for the compressor and turbine functions is called a thermoelectric heat engine.   When the two materials are a metal and a vacuum, or a metal and a plasma, the interface electric field gives rise to the well-known work function of metals.   A heat engine that utilizes such fields for the compressor and turbine functions is called a *thermionic heat engine*.

The formal analysis of the thermal efficiency is identical for thermo-electric and thermionic heat engines.   At least over limited temperature ranges, the thermal efficiency of each may be represented as the product of a reversible efficiency η_c and of a degradation factor $(1 - x)/(1 + y)$. In each, x is that fraction of the internally generated emf that is lost in the internal RI drop, and y is the ratio of the rate of irreversible heat flux to the rate of the irreversible heat absorption.   In each type of heat engine, one is continually struggling to minimize the irreversible flux of heat, as represented by y, without at the same time raising too far the internal RI drop.   The technical problems encountered in the two types of direct-conversion heat engines are, however, quite distinct. On the one hand, the figure of merit f of the thermoelectric heat engine is determined solely by the internal composition of the two opposing materials.   The nature of their interface is irrelevant, except that it must not constitute an appreciable thermal or electrical impedance.   On the other hand, the figure of merit of a thermionic diode is ultimately limited by the characteristics of the metal-vacuum interfaces.   The material problems encountered with these two types of direct-conversion heat engines will be discussed next.

The figure of merit f of a thermoelectric heat engine may be expressed as a simple function of the material parameters provided that the two opposing materials have matched properties, i.e., identical electrical resistivity ρ, identical thermal conductivity K, and Seebeck coefficients S identical in magnitude but opposite in sign. This function is then

$$f = \frac{T}{\rho K} S^2 \tag{12.12}$$

In the thermoelectric literature, the figure of merit is commonly denoted by Tz,

$$f = Tz$$

where, of course,

$$z = \frac{S^2}{\rho K} \tag{12.13}$$

A detailed analysis of this expression for the figure of merit reveals that f may be expressed as a function of the ratio of two thermal conductivities. One of these is that part of the thermal conductivity contributed by the lattice, as distinct from that contributed by the electrons. This thermal conductivity will be denoted by K_L. The second thermal conductivity is that part contributed by the electrons or holes when their concentration is such as to give a Seebeck coefficient of 172 μv/°C. This particular value of the Seebeck coefficient is just $2k$, where k is Boltzmann's constant. This second thermal conductivity is denoted by K_e^*. Thus

$$f = f\left(\frac{K_e^*}{K_L}\right) \tag{12.14}$$

A plot of this function is presented in Fig. 12.3.

During the past two years, a great deal has been learned about the factors that influence the two conductivities K_e^* and K_L. The second of these, K_L, was discussed at length in an earlier publication.† In this paper, the importance of Bragg reflection of lattice waves in lowering the mean velocity of the phonons (namely, of the lattice-wave packets which transport heat) was emphasized. Such Bragg reflections might be introduced by long-range ordering or by complexity of unit cells.

To repeat, K_e^* is the electronic contribution to the thermal conductivity when the charge-carrier concentration is such as to give a Seebeck coefficient of $2k$, or 172 μv/°C. This charge-carrier concentration has a unique characteristic. If electrons are regarded as wave packets with each packet having a spatial extension of one thermal wavelength, this electron

---

† *Trans. ASM*, 1961, p. 1052.

concentration is just enough to fill the space completely with nonoverlapping electrons or, more precisely, with nonoverlapping wave packets. Below this concentration, the classical Boltzmann statistics are applicable. Above this concentration, the Fermi statistics must be used. The optimum charge-carrier density for maximum figure of merit is just about equal to this critical concentration, namely, about $10^{19}/cm^3$. For this reason the author has named such materials *transconductors*. They have charge-carrier concentrations midway between the value of 10^{16} (or less for standard semiconductors) and 10^{22} (or more for metals).

During the past three years, an intensive effort has been made to raise the electron thermal conductivity K_e^* and to lower simultaneously the

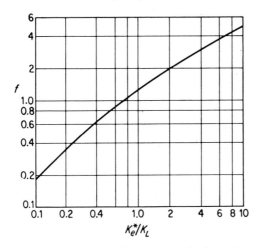

Fig. 12.3 Figure of merit f versus ratio of electronic thermal conductivity to the lattice thermal conductivity, K_e^*/K_L.

lattice thermal conductivity K_L. The present state of progress is best exemplified by showing the degradation factor ϵ of the best thermoelectric materials developed in the Westinghouse Research Laboratory under the Bureau of Ships contract. Figure 12.4 shows the n-type materials, where the charge carriers are electrons; Fig. 12.5 shows the p-type materials, where the charge carriers are holes. Each material is shown over that temperature range in which its degradation factor is higher than that of any other material. The detailed characteristics of the various materials shown here are from the *Quarterly Thermoelectric Review* issued by the Naval Research Laboratory.

A wide diversity of opinion is held by the experts as to the future of the thermoelectric heat engines. Perhaps the safest way to form an opinion is to look at the past history, which is summarized in Table 12.1. The material efficiency is the maximum possible thermal efficiency of a

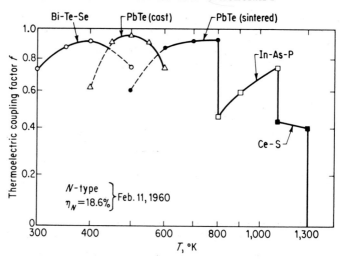

Fig. 12.4　Thermoelectric coupling factor versus temperature for *n*-type materials.

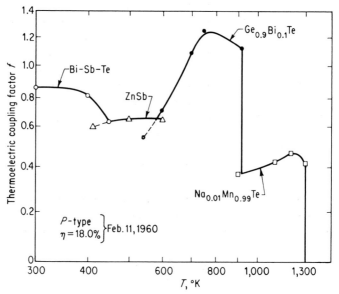

Fig. 12.5　Thermoelectric coupling factor versus temperature for *p*-type materials.

thermoelectric heat engine constructed out of the materials available;
all extraneous losses due to contact resistance, parallel heat leaks, etc.,
have been neglected. Calling such losses extraneous does not alter
the sad fact that they are extremely difficult to minimize.

While no attempt will be made to predict the performance characteristics of future thermoelectric materials, it is believed that the intense

Table 12.1

Date	Material efficiency, %	Maximum capacity of units, watts
1957	6	1
1958	10	10
1959	14	100
1960	18	5,000

efforts to raise this performance will greatly expand our understanding of the basic factors that determine the electrical and thermal characteristics of solids.

Material problems in a thermionic heat engine will be the next subject discussed. As has been previously mentioned, the compressor and turbine functions are performed at metal-vacuum interfaces. The electric field at these interfaces gives rise to the well-known work functions. The physics of thermionic power generation is identical to the physics of any continuous-flow heat engine. The electron gas experiences a force acting in the direction of flow at the vacuum-anode interface. Upon entering the anode, the electron gas gives up its heat of condensation and so a means must thus be provided for extracting heat from the anode. The electron flow is from the anode to the cathode via an electric conductor. The electric conductor guides the electrons through an appropriate load. At the cathode-vacuum interface, the electrons evaporate across an electric field which exerts a force counter to their direction of flow. The cathode-vacuum interface thus performs the turbine function. The evaporating electrons absorb heat, and so means must be provided for supplying heat to the cathode.

The work delivered by the electron gas, per cycle per electron, is just the heat absorbed during evaporation from the cathode minus the heat of condensation at the anode. The cycle efficiency is thus

$$\eta_c = \frac{w_c - w_A}{w_c} \tag{12.15}$$

In order that the electron flux through the vacuum be from the cathode to the anode, the cathode and anode temperatures must satisfy the following relation:

$$\frac{T_c}{T_A} \geq \frac{w_c}{w_A} \tag{12.16}$$

The cycle efficiency is thus essentially equal to the Carnot efficiency $(T_c - T_A)/T_A$. The actual efficiency is obtained by multiplying the cycle efficiency by an appropriate degradation factor. This factor takes into account the internal RI drop of potential as well as the irreversible heat leaks. One irreversible heat leak is so large, and so difficult to combat, that most material problems in a thermionic heat engine are centered around this one problem—how to minimize the degradation of the cycle efficiency caused by this single heat leak. The heat leak referred to is the thermal radiation from the cathode to the anode.

This radiation loss is given by

$$R = 5.7 \left(\frac{T_c}{1,000}\right)^4 \epsilon \qquad \text{watts/cm}^3 \qquad (12.17)$$

where the cathode temperature T_c is in degrees Kelvin and where ϵ is the cathode emissivity. The anode also emits thermal radiation to the cathode. Under the usual conditions this is negligible compared with the radiation emitted from the cathode. A nonnegligible correction is, however, the reflection of radiation from the anode back to the cathode. When due consideration is taken of the reflectivity of both the anode and the cathode, we find that ϵ must be given the value

$$\epsilon = \frac{\epsilon_c \epsilon_A}{\epsilon_c + \epsilon_A - \epsilon_c \epsilon_A} \qquad (12.18)$$

If the thermal-radiation heat leak is not to cause a serious degradation of efficiency, it must be several times less than the reversible heat absorbed by the electrons evaporating from the cathode. This reversible-heat absorption is Jw_c or, more precisely, $J\mu_c$, where J is the electric current in amperes and μ_c is the chemical potential in volts. The chemical potential μ_c and w_c are identical in the case of pure metals where the Richardson equation

$$J = 120T^2 \epsilon^{-w_c/kT}$$

is valid. Irrespective of the cathode material, the thermionic current always obeys the Richardson equation with the chemical potential substituted for the work. In fact, Richardson's equation can be regarded as defining the chemical potential, and this term is identical to the work function in the particular case where it is independent of temperature.

The condition that the radiation heat leak not cause a serious degradation of efficiency may thus be expressed as

$$J\mu_c \gg R$$

or, more precisely, as

$$(120T^2 e^{-\mu_c/kT})\mu_c > 5.37 \left(\frac{T}{1,000}\right)^4 \qquad (12.19)$$

A detailed analysis shows that this equation is satisfied provided that

$$\frac{\mu_c}{kT} < 16 \qquad (12.20)$$

Serious degradation by the radiation heat leak may thus be avoided by raising the cathode temperature to a sufficiently high value. Although the radiation increases rapidly with a rise in temperature, the thermionic current (and hence the reversible-heat absorption) increases at a still higher rate.

As an illustration, a particular example will be given. For a high cycle efficiency, a low value of μ_A and a high value of μ_c are required. The lowest μ_A for a pure metal is that for cesium, 1.9 volts. Designing for a cycle efficiency of 50 per cent and choosing μ_c to be 3.8 volts causes the inequality for T_c to reduce to

$$T_c > 2800°K$$

Unfortunately, however, the rate of evaporation of any metal at this temperature is excessive. A review of the analysis reveals that the thermal-radiation leak was well below the reversible-heat absorption, and because of this the temperature had to be raised to a value consistent with the inequality

$$kT > \frac{\mu_c}{16} \qquad (12.21)$$

For the value of μ_c selected, this inequality required an excessive cathode temperature.

Is it possible that, by an appropriate choice of initial conditions, a practical cathode temperature can be attained? To investigate this possibility, a search was made for usable materials having chemical potentials lower than the value for Cs. Certain oxide films were found to possess such characteristics, but such especially prepared film would soon become spoiled because of evaporation. A similar problem, of course, arises with the use of a cesium anode. However, the evaporation difficulty can be overcome by introducing a cesium plasma in the vacuum space. By keeping the anode at a sufficiently low temperature, the plasma will condense upon the anode and thereby maintain a clean cesium surface.

The only alternative is to lower the chemical potential of the cathode below 3.8 and thus be satisfied with a cycle efficiency of less than 50 per cent. A very rough correlation exists, however, between low chemical potentials and high vapor pressures. The question therefore arises as to the possibility of simultaneously satisfying the basic inequality $kT > \mu_c/16$ and the requirements of only moderate rate of evaporation.

The rate of evaporation of a solid is determined primarily by the ratio H/kT, where H is the heat of evaporation of the solid. The lower this ratio, the higher is the evaporation rate. In order to find whether or not it is possible to satisfy simultaneously the two requirements of efficiency and long life, a critical lower limit for the ratio H/kT must be obtained, and then this lower limit must be checked to see if it is consistent with the upper limit of 16 for the ratio μ_c/kT.

The rate of evaporation of atoms from a solid is equal to the rate at which atoms bombard the solid from its own vapor at an equilibrium pressure. Thus if r is the number of atoms that evaporate from a square centimeter of area per second, n the number of atoms per cubic centimeter of the equilibrium vapor, and v the mean velocity normal to the surface of those atoms moving toward the solid, then

$$r = \frac{n}{2} v \qquad\qquad (12.22)$$

Statistical mechanics provides a method of estimating the density n in terms of the heat of vaporization of the atoms, the Debye temperature of the solid, the mass of the atoms, and a quantity known as the statistical weight of the isolated atoms. Of these various parameters, the density depends critically only upon the heat of evaporation or, more precisely, upon the ratio H/kT. As an example of the critical way in which n varies with this parameter, in the case of iron at 2000°K a variation of H of 10 per cent introduces a factor of 10 in n. Thus if an upper limit is set for the rate of evaporation, this establishes a lower limit for the ratio H/kT, this lower limit being very insensitive to the parameters such as mass and Debye temperature. A reasonable requirement for the rate of evaporation is that less than 1 mm be vaporized per year. The lower limit that this requirement places upon the ratio H/kT is 42. Our two inequalities for the cathode,

$$\frac{H}{kT} > 40$$

$$\frac{\mu}{kT} < 16$$

can be satisfied simultaneously only if

$$\frac{H}{\mu} > 2.5$$

The ratios H/μ for the pure metals are given in Table 12.2. It can be seen that no pure metal satisfies this inequality. That is, there is no pure metal for which a temperature of operations can be found that is high enough to make the irreversible heat leak due to radiation small

Table 12.2

Element	H/μ	H,[†] kcal/mole	μ[‡], ev
Nb	2.01	184.5	3.99
Ta	1.95	185	4.13
W	1.93	201.6	4.53
C	1.71	172	4.36
Os	1.66	174	4.55
Re	1.65	189	4.97
Mo	1.60	155.5	4.24
U	1.58	125	3.45
Ir	1.57	165	4.57
Ru	1.54	160	4.52
Pr	1.40	87	2.7
Zr	1.38	125	3.93
Rh	1.29	138	4.65
Ce	1.28	85	2.88
V	1.27	120	4.11
Sm	1.18	87	3.2
Ti	1.16	112	4.16
La	1.16	88	3.3
Nd	1.15	87	3.3
Co	1.07	105	4.25
Si	1.07	88	3.59
Pt	0.99	121.6	5.36
B	0.92	97.2	4.6
Fe	0.91	96.7	4.63
Ni	0.90	101.6	4.91
Be	0.85	76.6	3.91
Pd	0.81	93	4.98
Cr	0.80	80.5	4.45
Cu	0.79	81.5	4.48
Al	0.78	75.0	4.20
Au	0.76	82.3	4.71
Mn	0.75	68.3	3.95
Ge	0.74	78.4	4.62
Ba	0.72	41.96	2.52
Sn	0.71	72	4.39
Ga	0.69	66.0	4.16
Li	0.65	37.1	2.46
Ag	0.64	69.1	4.70
Ca	0.63	46.0	3.20
Sr	0.62	39.2	2.74
Sb	0.58	60.8	4.56
Bi	0.50	49.7	4.34
Pb	0.50	46.3	4.04
Na	0.50	26.0	2.28
Tl	0.46	43.3	4.05
Te	0.44	47.6	4.73
Se	0.43	48.4	4.87
Mg	0.42	35.9	3.76
Cs	0.42	18.8	1.94
Rb	0.42	20.5	2.13
K	0.41	21.5	2.25
Zn	0.32	31.2	4.27
Cd	0.29	27.0	4.04
Hg	0.14	14.5	4.53

† From *Natl. Bur. Std. (U.S.), Circ.* 500.
‡ From Landolt-Borstein, Zahlenwerte und Funktionen aus Physik. Chemie. Astronomie. Geophysik. Technik, vol. 1:4, pp. 759–761, 1950.

compared with the reversible heat absorbed by the evaporating electrons and yet at the same time is sufficiently low so that the evaporation rate of the atoms is within tolerable limits.   It must be concluded, therefore, that if thermionic diodes were constructed by using a pure metal as a cathode, the life would be short if the efficiency approached the cycle efficiency, or the efficiency would have to be degraded considerably below the cycle efficiency if long life were required; simultaneous high efficiency and long life are not possible.

Two approaches can be adopted for developing cathode materials that will simultaneously satisfy the two basic requirements.   One approach is to develop alloys that will have a higher value of the ratio H/μ than any pure metal.   This approach is being pursued at Los Alamos.   Their preliminary results indicate that a uranium cathode has an appreciably higher ratio than any pure metal.   A second approach is to learn how to prepare surfaces with a low sticking coefficient.   Previously the rate of evaporation of atoms from a surface was taken as equal to the rate at which atoms bombarded the surface from an equilibrium vapor.   It was implicitly assumed that every vapor atom that bombarded the surface stuck to it and could leave only by evaporation.   It is conceivable, however, that only a small fraction will so stick to the surface and that the majority will be reflected by the surface.   Under such circumstances, the rate of evaporation will be much less than otherwise calculated. Specifically, if α is the fraction of atoms that stick to the surface, the rate of evaporation contains a factor $(1 - \alpha)$.   Current experiments at the Bureau of Standards indicate that appropriate treatment may reduce α several orders of magnitude.

Considerable time has been devoted to a discussion of the cathode-material problem; there seems to be little doubt that it will be solved in the next several years.   It therefore seems pertinent to inquire as to what will be the efficiency of the thermionic heat engine once a suitable cathode material (i.e., one for which the degradation due to thermal radiation losses is negligible) has been found.   Substituting into the cycle efficiency

$$\mu_c = \frac{\mu_c \mu_A}{\mu_c}$$

the value of 1.9 volts for μ_A, and the inequality

$$\frac{\mu_c}{kT_c} \leq 16 \qquad \text{for } \mu_c$$

gives the following:

$$\mu_c \leq \frac{T_c - 1,400}{1,400} \qquad (12.23)$$

The cycle efficiency is thus that of a Carnot cycle whose upper temperature is T_c and whose lower temperature is $1400°K$. The cycle efficiency will therefore not be improved by operating the anode at a temperature below $1400°K$.

Looking next at the degradation due to irreversible RI drops and thermal leaks other than radiation, we must consider the RI drops and heat leaks along the external conductors connecting cathode and anode as well as the losses across the cesium plasma in the space between cathode and anode. The cesium plasma is necessary in order to maintain a low work function at the anode. Proceeding along the lines indicated in the introduction to this chapter, we obtain a value of about 32 for the figure of merit of the thermionic heat engine when radiation loss is neglected. The corresponding degradation factor is 80 per cent.

In both thermoelectric and thermionic heat engines an electron gas is used as a working medium. Direct-conversion heat engines may also use other types of working media. Two examples will be briefly discussed. Consider a membrane that is permeable to the ions of a gas but is impermeable to free electrons. Physicists call such an element a semipermeable membrane; chemists call it an electrolyte. Suppose that the pressure of the gas is different on the two sides of the membrane, e.g., p_h and p_1. If 1 mole of gas could be transported reversibly from the high-pressure side to the low-pressure side, there would be a gain of free energy equal to

$$\text{Work per mole} = RT \ln \frac{p_h}{p_1}$$

In order to be consistent with the terminology previously used this expression should be rewritten

$$\text{Work per molecule} = kT \ln \frac{p_h}{p_1}$$

One practical way of achieving this reversible transfer is to coat both sides of the semipermeable membrane with porous electrodes and then to join these two electrodes by metallic conductors to the two sides of a battery of voltage V, where

$$zeV = kT \ln \frac{p_h}{p_1} \tag{12.24}$$

Here e is the electronic charge and z is the number of electrons that must pass through the battery for each molecule that passes through the semipermeable membrane. Thus for a cesium-metal gas, z is unity; for an oxygen gas, z is 4.

It is of particular pertinence that the voltage is proportional to T. This proportionality enables us to construct a direct-conversion heat engine by joining two such semipermeable membranes in series. The high-temperature membrane performs the role of a turbine. The low-temperature membrane performs the role of a compressor. The greater voltage across the turbine element enables it to drive the compressor element and still have a net emf available for a load.

The above-described direct-conversion heat engine may be described as a recycling concentration cell. Its cycle efficiency is the Carnot efficiency. The actual efficiency is, of course, degraded by certain irreversible RI drops as well as heat leaks. A brief discussion of these irreversible losses furnishes an excellent example of the degradation discussed in the introduction. An irreducible RI drop occurs along the leads that join the high- and low-temperature membranes. An irreducible heat leak occurs along these same two leads. At first sight it would seem that an appropriate choice of dimensions for these leads would render such irreversible losses negligible. Closer inspection reveals that these two losses are conjugate in that they cannot be reduced independently. If a reasonable pressure ratio, say 100:1, is taken, then in the particular case of oxygen where z is 4, the figure of merit of the system is 0.2 and the corresponding degradation factor is 0.05. In practice such high degradation could be avoided by joining a large number of high-temperature concentration cells in parallel with respect to the flow of gas ions and in series with respect to the electric current, with a similar arrangement for a set of low-temperature concentration cells. The figure of merit is proportional to the square of the number of such concentration cells joined electrically in series.

In conclusion, several kinds of direct-conversion heat engines are potentially applicable for space use. Each type of engine has its own characteristic materials problem. In the thermoelectric heat engine, material development has extended the upper temperature limit to only 1300°K. Materials must be developed that can operate at several hundred degrees higher temperature. In the thermionic heat engine, cathode materials must be developed that have either a higher H/μ ratio or a sticking coefficient several orders of magnitude less than unity. The self-cycling concentration cell is still in the conceptual stage. Suitable semipermeable membranes have yet to be developed. It would be premature to focus development efforts upon only one of these types. It is possible that in the coming decade all three types will be operational in space.

13

Materials for Direct Conversion

D. E. THOMAS

MANAGER, MATERIALS DEPARTMENT
ASTRONUCLEAR LABORATORY
WESTINGHOUSE ELECTRIC CORPORATION
PITTSBURGH, PENNSYLVANIA

The purpose of this chapter is to examine the materials problems involved in the nuclear production of heat and the direct conversion of that heat into electric power for space applications. In order to keep the subject within bounds and in order to reflect advanced thinking, it will be necessary to speak only of large power supplies utilizing nuclear heat. It is generally agreed that nuclear power plants are superior to others when large amounts of power (megawatt range) are required for extended periods of time (10,000 hr) in space. The present generation of space power systems is characterized by small size and large weight per unit output. For example, the SNAP-10 system has an output of 300 watts and weighs 400 lb. Thus, the weight per unit output is 1,300 lb/kw. This is in contrast to the figure of about 10 lb/kw that is desired. While some improvement can be brought about by clever design innovation, it is clear that the present SNAP systems cannot be directly scaled up to large, efficient sizes by using the present materials, because operating temperatures must be increased. This leads to the keynote of the materials problem: high-temperature capability.

In order to examine the need for high temperatures, it is pertinent to turn to the radiator because this component of the system constitutes a large fraction of the total plant weight. The size of the radiator for a given plant size depends upon its operating temperature. This is shown in Fig. 13.1, wherein the maximum cycle temperature has been fixed at 1115°C and the radiator temperature varied. It is seen that the optimum radiator temperature is about 750°C. If the maximum cycle temperature is increased, then the optimum radiator temperature also increases, while the size of the optimum radiator decreases. In fact, the optimum

353

radiator temperature is found to be about 75 per cent of the maximum cycle temperature expressed in absolute temperature units.   The situation shown in Fig. 13.1 represents a combination of temperatures that is believed to be consistent with reasonable materials development, and so 750°C will be adopted for the purposes of discussion as a minimum radiator temperature.   This is the temperature of the heat sink, and all

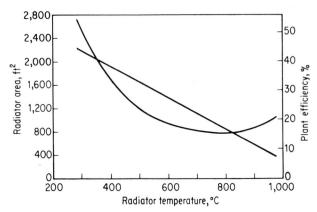

Fig. 13.1   Effect of radiator temperature on radiator size; 75 per cent of Carnot efficiency (1115°C maximum cycle temperature, 1,000 kw output).

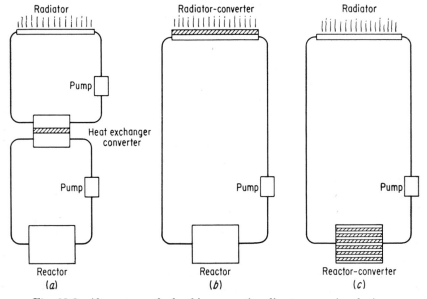

Fig. 13.2   Alternate methods of incorporating direct-conversion devices,

the temperature drops of the system must be added in order to arrive at the maximum temperature encountered in the heat source.

The various ways that the energy converter can be incorporated in the power-plant system are illustrated in Fig. 13.2. The heat exchanger–converter is shown at a, and this arrangement requires two coolant pumps because there are two coolant circuits. In this case, it is easy to match the heat-transfer areas of the converter and the radiator. The radiator-converter is shown at b. This system is simple, having only one pump. However, it is difficult to achieve satisfactory matching of the heat-transfer areas of the converter and the radiator. The reactor-converter is shown at c. This system provides easy area matching, but it has the disadvantage of exposing the converter materials to high radiation levels. Furthermore, the reactor core has a high content of parasitic material, complicating the design and requiring extra fuel. Not shown is the conductivity type which relies on conduction of heat from the fuel directly through a converter-radiator. This design is suitable for small sizes. The significance of these arrangements, insofar as materials problems are concerned, will become apparent in the ensuing discussion; both thermoelectric and thermionic conversion will be considered.

Materials for Nuclear Thermoelectric Systems

Nonintegral Type. The term "nonintegral" means that the thermoelectric material is not located inside the reactor. Heat is transferred from the fuel elements to a fluid and thence either to a thermoelectric heat exchanger or to a thermoelectric radiator. Let us consider the materials of the system, starting with the fuel material, fuel-element cladding, etc., and ending with the thermoelectric material.

Fuel Material. Those familiar with reactor problems will immediately recognize that the development of fuel materials having high-temperature capabilities represents a difficult problem. It is expedient to treat this subject in some detail at this point, because the discussion applies as well to the other systems that will be discussed. As a consequence of the radiator temperatures analysis, it is evident that the fuel surface temperature must exceed 1000°C. At the same time, it is desirable to have as high a fuel center temperature as possible in order to extract heat at the highest possible rate. The melting temperatures of some refractory uranium compounds and dispersions are shown in the lower part of Fig. 13.3. Incidentally, a variety of compounds of uranium can be considered as possible fuel materials, because the reactors of interest are of the highly enriched types. The materials having the highest melting temperatures are the solid-solution carbides (10 mole per cent UC). Next in order are UO_2, a dispersion of UO_2 in tungsten, a dispersion of UO_2 in molybdenum, UC, and $BeO-UO_2$. The last-mentioned material exhibits eutectic melting at 2060°C.

While a high melting temperature is desirable, it is only part of the story. It is pertinent also to factor thermal conductivity into the picture, and this is done by means of the so-called "heat integral":

$$\int_{\theta_s}^{\theta_c} k(\theta)\, d\theta$$

where $k(\theta)$ = thermal conductivity of fuel as function of temperature θ

      θ_C = center temperature

      θ_S = surface temperature

This integral is a measure of the power-handling capability of a particular fuel, in units of watts per centimeter of length or equivalent. Some estimated values of the integral in which the surface temperature is taken as 1000°C and the center temperature is taken as the melting temperature

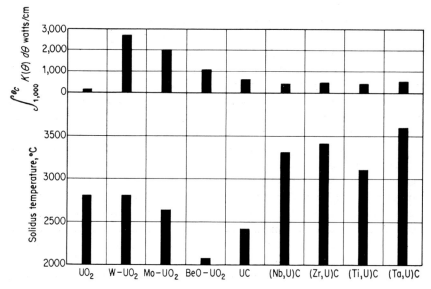

Fig. 13.3 Solids temperatures and relative power-handling capabilities of high-temperature fuel materials.

are shown in the upper part of Fig. 13.3. It is to be noted that UO_2, the material that serves so well in low-temperature terrestrial power plants, has a rather low power-handling capability. Because of the high thermal conductivity of molybdenum and tungsten, the dispersions with these metals have outstanding values of the heat integral. Similarly, $BeO-UO_2$ shows up well, whereas the solid-solution carbides do not look so good as one would expect from their high melting temperatures. It should be pointed out most emphatically that the values given for the heat integral in Fig. 13.3 are only rough estimates. The calculations were based upon low-temperature thermal conductivities, because high-temperature values were not available. Also, no allowances were made for irradiation effects. An idea of the uncertainty involved can be gained by considering cases in which the thermal conductivity of irradiated material is known as a function of temperature, or in which the heat integral has been measured experimentally. Thus, a value of 100 watts/cm is calculated for UO_2, whereas experimentally the value is about 35 watt/cm for a surface temperature of 1000°C. In the case of UO_2-BeO, a value of 1,020 watt/cm is shown in Fig. 13.3, whereas a value of only 138 watt/cm is calculated when the temperature variation and irradiation effect are taken into account. Thus, it is obvious that additional data are needed on fuel material properties.

The effect of irradiation upon the fuel material is of major concern. The principal phenomenon is that of the production of fission-product inert gases (Kr and Xe) and their subsequent migration. Hopefully, these gases may be retained in the lattice; but given sufficient mobility, they may diffuse out of the fuel material or they may collect locally within the fuel material as bubbles. If they diffuse out of the fuel material, space may have to be provided somewhere in the fuel element to limit the pressure to a value that will not deform the cladding. If, on the other hand, bubble formation occurs, the tendency for the fuel to increase in volume (swell) must be considered. If such swelling cannot be restrained by the cladding, the fuel is of little use. Obviously, a detailed quantitative knowledge of the behavior of fission gas in a fuel material is required in order to set the temperature and burnup capabilities of a fuel. Since such information is not available for the temperature range in question, we must be content to speculate a little. Dense UO_2 retains most of its fission gas at high burnups when the surface temperature is 500°C or less, as has been the case in most irradiations. It is known that above 1000°C, the diffusion rates of Kr and Xe in UO_2 increase very rapidly with temperature. In a few irradiations at about 1500°C, gas bubbles were observed to form. These observations suggest that bulk UO_2 with a surface temperature of 1000 to 1100°C, and center temperature near the melting point, may evolve a considerable amount of fission gas and exhibit a tendency for swelling. The above remarks concerning gas evolution also apply to UO_2 dispersed in a refractory metal such as tungsten or molybdenum. In this case the question is whether the matrix metal would be strong enough to resist the gas pressure without significant swelling. It may be necessary to alloy the matrix metal to provide additional high-temperature strength. Uranium monocarbide is currently receiving a great deal of attention as a fuel material. The irradiations carried out to date on this material have been at lower temperatures.   At 845°C center temperature, negligible fission-gas evolution and small volume changes have been observed.   This is encouraging. It is expected that the strengthening and elevation of the melting point provided by alloying UC with the refractory metal monocarbide will be beneficial.

An attempt to summarize the fuel situation is shown in Table 13.1. The data shown were selected either because they were obtained at high temperatures or because they represent very high burnup rates. Although there is reason to hope that some of these materials will perform satisfactorily at surface temperatures of about 1000°C, it must be recognized that none of them have been shown experimentally to be capable of doing so.

Table 13.1   Representative Irradiation Data for Potential
High-temperature Fuels [1–3]

Fuel material	Irradiation temperature, °C		Burnup, fissions/cm³	Remarks	Reference
	Surface	Center			
BeO-UO₂ (25 w/o) (100–140 μ UO₂)	400	< 540	11–13 × 10²⁰	2½% volume increase; 7% gas release	1
UC	540	845	6.5 × 10²⁰	1.9% volume increase	2
	805	1000	2.14 × 10²⁰	1.2% volume increase	
Bulk UO₂	400	< 540	20–26 × 10²⁰	5% volume increase; 20–25% local volume increase	1
UO₂ powder	<540	<1490	7–130 × 10²⁰	Volume increase not determined; fission gas release 2–68%	3

Another aspect of the fuel material that is of concern is the possibility of adverse effects arising from the contact of the fuel material with the fuel-element cladding.   This can take the form of excess interdiffusion, with or without formation of new phases or eutectic formation. The data available concerning the compatibility of the fuel materials previously mentioned and the refractory metals are scarce and cursory in scope. Table 13.2 summarizes the available data.   The UO₂ containing dispersion and UO₂ itself appear to be reasonably free from undesirable interaction.   To judge from the behavior of BeO, the BeO-UO₂ fuel may also be expected to be compatible with the refractory metals at interface temperatures of about 1000 to 1100°C.   The data on the carbides also look encouraging but they are too sparse, particularly in view of the probable role of deviations from stoichiometry in determining the activity of carbon in these compounds.

The compatibility of the fuel material with the coolant is of importance in the event that the fuel-element cladding becomes defective and thus allows the coolant to come into contact with the fuel.   Here, again, the data are few, qualitative, and of short-time nature.   As may be seen in Table 13.3, UO_2 looks promising, as do the carbides.   The dispersion

Table 13.2   Fuel Material–Cladding Material Compatibility [4–6]

Fuel material or fuel base	Cladding material			
	W	Mo	Ta	Nb
UO_2	OK, 2800°C	OK, 2622°C	OK, 2800°C	OK, 2415°C
W-UO_2	OK, 2800°C			
Mo-UO_2	....	OK, 2622°C		
Nb-UO_2	....	....	....	OK, 2415°C
BeO	Gross effect, at 2100°C	Gross effect at 1900°C OK, 1800°C	....	Reaction at 1800°C
BeO-UO_2				
UC	....	Some reaction at 120°C	OK, 1800°C (2 min)	Some reaction at 1200°C
(Zr, U)C	OK, 2400°C (15 min)			
NbC	....	....	....	Eutectic at 1900°C
TaC	....	....	Eutectic at 2800°C	

may be expected to be compatible with Na, NaK, or Li on the basis of the behavior of UO_2 shown in Table 13.3 and the behavior of the refractory metals shown in Table 13.4.

Fuel-element Cladding.   The foregoing discussion has indicated that the refractory metals have been selected for consideration as fuel-element cladding.   We have but to examine the mechanical properties of the stainless steels and the nickel-base superalloys to be convinced that it is necessary to use the refractory metals or their alloys for service at 1100°C.

The reaction between the cladding material and the coolant is of concern.   The temperature regime, as well as cycle considerations, leads to the selection of liquid metals as potential coolants.   In dynamic liquid-metal corrosion, several modes of attack are observed: dissolution of the solid metal in the liquid metal, interdiffusion of constituents of the solid and liquid phases, and mass transport associated with temperature or activity gradients in the system.   The data available, summarized in

Table 13.4, are neither definitive nor systematic; so the behavior at higher temperatures cannot be predicted. The situation does look hopeful, however.

To return to the question of high-temperature strength, we find that the literature is notably deficient in the long-time creep data so necessary

Table 13.3   Fuel Material–Coolant Compatibility [6–8]

Fuel material or fuel base	Coolant†	
	Na or NaK	Li
UO$_2$	OK, 1000–1500°C	
W-UO$_2$		
Mo-UO$_2$		
Nb-UO$_2$		
BeO	OK, 800°C	OK, 800°C
BeO-UO$_2$		
UC	OK, 1000°C (720 hr)	
(Zr, U)C		
(Nb, U)C		
(Zr, U)C		
(Ta, U)C		
ZrC	OK, 840°C (100 hr)	OK, 840°C (100 hr)
TiC	OK, 840°C (100 hr)	OK, 840°C (100 hr)

†Blank spaces in the coolant columns indicate that no information is available on compatibility data.

Table 13.4   Cladding Material–Liquid Metal Compatibility [9, 10]

Cladding material	Liquid metal	
	Na or NaK	Li
W	OK, 900°C	OK, 900°C
Mo	OK, 900°C	OK, 900°C
Ta	OK, 1010°C	OK, 1000°C
Nb	OK, 900°C	OK, 900°C

for the designing of fuel-element cladding. An estimate of the strength of a number of the refractory metals and their alloys can be obtained from Fig. 13.4, in which is plotted tensile strength as a function of temperature. There is a great deal of activity in the development of refractory-metal-base alloys, and it would be beyond the scope of this chapter to review it. Although the operating temperatures are far above the

meter of hydride $\times$ 10^{-22}) versus temperature at 1 atm pressure. It can be seen that an N_H of 4 to 5 is maintained by zirconium hydride up to about 870°C and by yttrium hydride up to about 1200°C. The hydrides are characteristically difficult to fabricate into engineering shapes with controlled hydrogen content.

Thermoelectric Materials. Keeping in mind that the discussion is confined to the case in which the thermoelectric material is not integral with the reactor core, we examine first the structure of thermoelectric heat exchangers and a thermoelectric radiator. A section of a thermoelectric

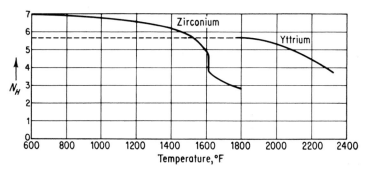

Fig. 13.5 Hydrogen density versus temperature for ZrH_x and YH_x at 1 atm hydrogen pressure [12].

heat exchanger is shown schematically in Fig. 13.6. Located midway between the hot and cold sides are the thermoelectric materials, alternately n and p types. The current-collecting straps are shown without cross-hatching, and these are arranged for series connection of the thermoelectric materials. The straps are insulated from the cold and hot plates, and the thermoelectric materials are insulated from each other as indicated by the cross-hatching. The compatibility requirements involved are immediately obvious. The hot and cold plates must be compatible with the primary and secondary coolants; the insulating material must be compatible with the hot and cold plates, the straps, and the thermoelectric materials; and the thermoelectric materials must be compatible with the strap material. "Compatibility" is used broadly here to denote such considerations as diffusion, chemical reaction, expansivity, bondability where required, and strength.

Essentially the same compatibility problems are present in the thermoelectric radiator shown in Fig. 13.7 as were shown in the thermoelectric heat exchanger. The problem of area matching is evident here. In general, the geometric cross-sectional area of the thermoelectric materials is not the same as the optimum radiator surface area. The design shown represents an area ratio of essentially unity. A moment's reflection will show that we cannot manage to get area ratios very far from unity by manipulating the geometry of the thermoelectric cells and of the radiator. The radiator area should be the greater.

The thermoelectric materials on which an appreciable amount of work has been performed are represented in Figs. 12.4 and 12.5. These figures show the thermoelectric coupling factor (f) as a function of

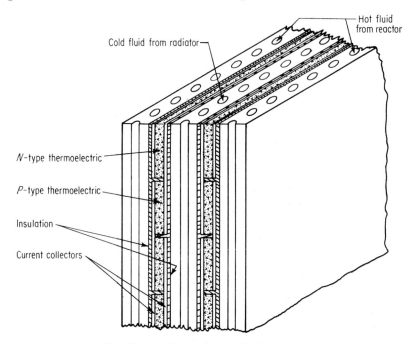

Fig. 13.6   A thermoelectric heat exchanger.

temperature for both n- and p-type materials.   Recalling that the radiator temperature should be of the order of 750°C (1023°K), we can see that the only materials having interesting values of f at temperatures above this value are CeS and $Na_{0.01}Mn_{0.99}Te$.   However, the temperature drop available is so small that the efficiency of these two materials is too low.   It must be concluded, therefore, that thermoelectric materials having higher temperature capabilities will be needed for large space applications.   It is possible that n-type CeS can be extended to higher temperatures, perhaps to 1300°C.   A p-type material, possibly having this same temperature capability, is ThS.   Gadolinium selenides (Gd_2S_3 doped with GdSe) and other rare-earth compounds are believed to hold promise.

The bonding of the thermoelectric materials to the current collectors is difficult inasmuch as the junction not only must have adequate strength but also must have low thermal and electrical resistivity. The dissimilar metal at the junction should not affect the thermoelectric properties unfavorably. Lead telluride can be bonded to iron or copper. Copper, however, affects thermoelectric properties adversely, while iron appears to be satisfactory in this respect. Various solders and brazing compositions have been used, but much of this information remains undisclosed.

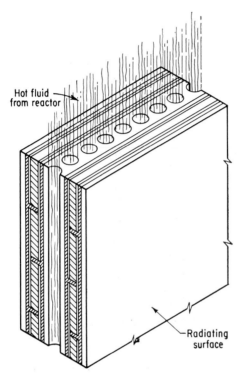

Hot fluid
from reactor

Radiating
surface

Fig. 13.7   A thermoelectric radiator.

In connection with the development of swaging techniques at the Westinghouse Atomic Power Department [13], compatibility tests were conducted on lead telluride and germanium telluride in contact with a number of materials. Lead telluride appears to be compatible up to 650°C with low-carbon steel, iron–7% aluminum, and iron–7% aluminum–4.3% chromium. It was also found to be compatible with Type 304 stainless steel up to 700°C and with niobium, aluminum, and Zircaloy-2 below 600°C. Germanium telluride appears to be compatible with aluminum, tungsten, Type 304 stainless steel, and molybdenum at 650°C. However, catastrophic reactions were exhibited with low-carbon steel, iron–7% aluminum, and iron–7% aluminum–4.3% chromium.

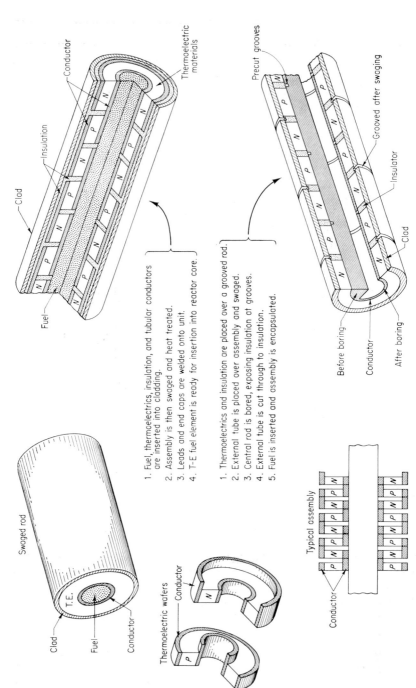

Fig. 13.8 Methods of fabrication of multiple-junction thermoelectric elements.

1. Fuel, thermoelectrics, insulation, and tubular conductors are inserted into cladding.
2. Assembly is then swaged and heat treated.
3. Leads and end caps are welded onto unit.
4. T-E fuel element is ready for insertion into reactor core.

1. Thermoelectrics and insulation are placed over a grooved rod.
2. External tube is placed over assembly and swaged.
3. Central rod is bored, exposing insulation at grooves.
4. External tube is cut through to insulation.
5. Fuel is inserted and assembly is encapsulated.

Swaging as a technique for fabricating thermoelectric units offers some interesting possibilities [13]. Several alternative approaches are shown in Fig. 13.8. The process shown on the left involves swaging of an assembly of an inner and outer tube with powder of the thermoelectric material previously packed into the annular space. This operation has

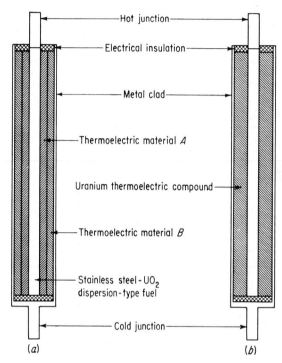

Fig. 13.9 Structure of thermoelectric fuel elements. (*a*) Cascaded-type element (two *n*- or *p*-type thermoelectric materials); (*b*) uranium compound fuel and thermoelectric material.

been performed with copper, stainless-steel, and aluminum tubes, with germanium telluride and both *n*- and *p*-type lead telluride. Reduction of 35 to 65 per cent in area was employed, and densities of 94 to 98 per cent have been obtained in the swaged thermoelectric material after suitable sintering. A direct bond is produced by this method of fabrication. The swaged tubes are machined into wafers and brazed or silver-soldered into assemblies as shown at the left in Fig. 13.8.

A further extension of the swaging technique is shown at the upper right in Fig. 13.8. Cold-pressed rings of thermoelectric powder of about 96 per cent density are sintered at 600°C for 6 hr. Powdered Lavite or Mycalex is cold-pressed to the various shapes required. The parts are then assembled with two metal tubes as shown. (The figure shows fuel at the center.) The assembly is swaged lightly (hot or cold) and annealed at 600°C. The attachment of leads and end caps completes the assembly. An alternative procedure is illustrated at the lower right in Fig. 13.8. This involves a grooved mandrel which is later bored to expose the

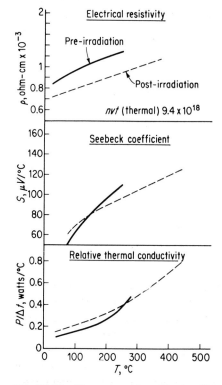

Fig. 13.10 Changes produced by irradiation on properties of thermoelectric material ($Bi_{0.05}Ge_{0.95}Te$, p-type).

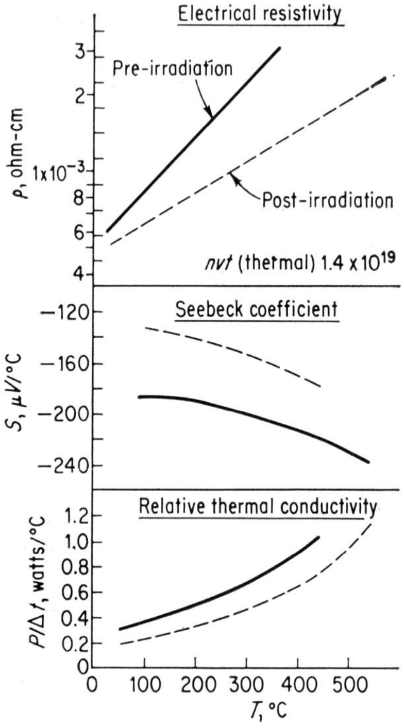

Fig. 13.11 Changes produced by irradiation on properties of thermoelectric material (PbTe, n-type).

grooves. The principal difficulty in swaging is the tendency for the various components to shift position. Hot swaged elements containing n- and p-type lead telluride have been on test for 1,750 hr, with the hot side at 500°C and the cold side at 100°C, the thermoelectric properties comparing favorably with those of conventionally fabricated couples.

Integral Thermoelectric Systems. In integral thermoelectric systems, the thermoelectric materials are contained within the reactor core. A further important distinction (see Fig. 13.9) can be made between the case where the fuel and thermoelectric material are separate and the case where the fuel and thermoelectric generation functions are combined in a single material. In the former case, consideration must be given to the effect of neutron irradiation upon the performance of the thermoelectric couples. In the latter case, consideration must be given not only to the effect of neutron irradiation per se but also to the effects of fission-fragment damage and chemical effects of fission product upon the properties of the thermoelectric fuel. Since the materials considerations in the balance of the system remain unchanged, discussion will be limited to irradiation effects in thermoelectrics.

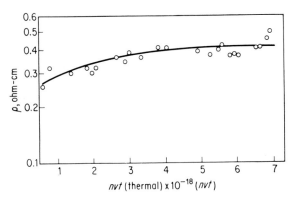

Fig. 13.12 Resistivity of $Li_{0.05}Ni_{0.95}O$ versus nvt (thermal) at 464°C.

Fuel and Thermoelectric Material Separated. Irradiation experiments [13, 14] have been performed on a limited number of thermoelectric materials. Measurements on p-type $Bi_{0.05}Ge_{0.95}Te$ performed before and after exposure to 9.4×10^{18} nvt (thermal neutrons) are represented in Fig. 13.10. The changes observed in the Seebeck coefficients (S), electrical resistivity (ρ), and effective thermal conductivity (K) are such that the thermoelectric figure of merit or coupling factor f is essentially unchanged. (f is defined by the equation $f = TS^2/\rho K$.) Similar measurements (see Fig. 13.11) made on n-type lead telluride after an exposure of 1.4×10^{19} nvt (thermal) indicate that an improvement of about threefold in the figure of merit is brought about by neutron irradiation. The foregoing measurements were made before and after irradiation. Measurements have been made during irradiation of $Li_{0.05}Ni_{0.95}O$ at 464°C. Figure 13.12 shows the electrical resistivity of $Li_{0.05}Ni_{0.95}O$ increasing with neutron exposure, the resistance measurement being made so that the resistance of the bond is included. However, the resistance measurements taken by means of probes located on the thermoelectric material itself show that resistivity decreases with increasing neutron exposure (see Fig. 13.13). The Seebeck coefficient of this material is decreased slightly with increasing exposure as shown in Fig. 13.14. On postirradiation annealing at

600°C, the slight change in the Seebeck coefficient induced by irradiation did not recover, whereas the electrical resistivity changes did recover. It is believed, therefore, that if $Li_{0.05}Ni_{0.95}O$ were irradiated in the range of 700 to 1100°C, its range of probable usefulness, the damage would tend to anneal out *in situ*.

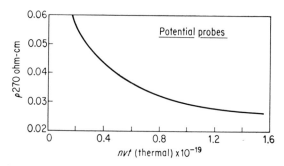

Fig. 13.13   In-pile resistivity data for $Li_{0.05}Ni_{0.95}O$.

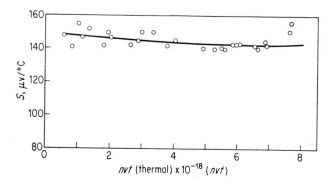

Fig. 13.14   Seebeck coefficient versus nt (thermal) at 464°C for $Li_{0.05}Ni_{0.95}O$.

While the effect of irradiation upon the thermoelectric material has not been extensively studied, it is encouraging and somewhat surprising that the changes in the figure of merit are small and sometimes in a favorable direction.

Combined Fuel and Thermoelectric Material.   Requiring a single material to perform the functions of fuel and thermoelectric is a rather large order.   The lattice damage occasioned by high-energy fission fragments is many times greater than that produced by fast neutrons.   In addition, the fission products effectively introduce an assortment of foreign atoms that would be expected to alter the thermoelectric parameters because thermoelectric materials are sensitive to impurities and doping agents. The other considerations about fuel materials that were discussed earlier

apply here also.   The requirement that the material have good thermoelectric properties and also contain uranium, of course, severely limits

Table 13.5   Preparation of Thermoelectric Materials [13]
(Uranium thermoelectric compounds)

Compound	T_H, °C	T_c, °C	S, μv/°C	Ohm-cm at 25°C
US_x	45	29	−67	0.016
US_x	77	34	−305	0.070
USe_x	82	39	−171	0.019
UTe_x	102	29	−1.4	5.1×10^{-4}
UC_x	93	29	+43	1.9×10^{-4}
UC_x	135	53	+22	1.03×10^{-4}
$UTe_x + US_x$	151	87	+140	0.07

the number of candidate materials.   Some materials of possible interest
are shown in Table 13.5, together with some preliminary measurements
of Seebeck coefficients.   While the
values of the subscripts in most of
the compound formulas are uncertain at present because of the
extreme difficulty in performing
the chemical analyses involved, it
is evident that some of the compounds should be studied further.
Most of the materials are difficult
to prepare and handle because of
the volatility of the anions, a factor
that may also complicate their application.   The   resistivity   and
Seebeck   coefficient   of   one   of
the   more   interesting   materials,
UTe + US, are shown as a function of temperature in Fig. 13.15.
No   irradiation   testing   has   been
performed.

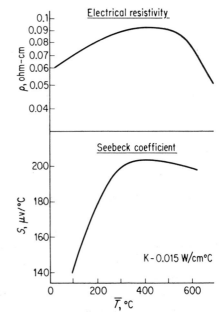

Fig. 13.15   Seebeck coefficient and electrical resistivity versus temperature for
$UTe_x + US_x$.

Materials for Nuclear
Thermionic Systems

In the introduction to this chapter, distinctions were made concern-
ing the several ways in which the unit converting heat to electricity could
be incorporated into the power plant.   In a thermionic converter, the

cathode temperature must exceed about 1400°K, and preferably it should be hundreds of degrees higher. This requirement is based on considerations of the emitting properties of the cathode, as described in Chap. 12, whereas in the case of the thermoelectric converter, the maximum temperature involved is primarily determined from consideration of the radiator area-temperature relationship. Since locating the thermionic converter anywhere outside the reactor core involves the transport of heat by a transfer fluid, which is an unattractive scheme at temperatures much above 1400°K for reasons already discussed, the present discussion will be limited to the case where the thermionic unit is combined with the fuel element.

Table 13.6   Theoretical Efficiency and Cathode Evaporation Rate [15]
(Tungsten cathode)

T, °K	J_A, amp/cm²	Efficiency, %	Evap. rate, mm/1,000 hr
2300	0.041	0.215	0.00015
2500	0.298	1.05	0.0038
2700	1.63	3.81	0.0592
2900	7.31	10.7	0.642
3100	26.5	21.7	4.96
3300	84.4	33.8	29.9

The principles underlying the thermionic conversion of heat to electricity were presented in Chap. 12. In connection with the high-vacuum diode, it was pointed out that the rate at which electrons are emitted from the cathode must be considerably in excess of the rate of evaporation of the cathode material if sustained operation is required. This is further illustrated in Table 13.6, in which efficiency and tungsten-cathode evaporation rate are listed as a function of cathode temperature. It is obvious that at temperatures at which interesting efficiencies are obtained, the evaporation rate has already become excessive. In the high-vacuum diode it is desirable to have cathode and anode materials having low work functions. The work functions of a number of materials are shown in Table 13.7. With the exception of the carbides, the cathode materials either have vapor pressures that are too high or involve a cesium coating which would be unstable in a vacuum. The carbides, however, are considerably less volatile than the metals. The carbides will be discussed in more detail later.

Among the anode materials shown are the specially coated materials such as BaO on nickel. Such coatings, or for that matter any anode material, would soon become covered with condensed cathode material. Another very important aspect of the vacuum diode is the fact that the spacing between anode and cathode must be of the order of 0.001 to 0.002 cm in order to avoid the formation of a space charge. It would be very difficult to imagine a practical device involving the maintenance of such a small clearance between two surfaces, particularly in view of the high temperatures involved. Consequently, more emphasis has been placed upon the cesium diode in which a spacing of 0.01 cm or more is tolerable.

In the cesium diode, cesium vapor is introduced into the space between the anode and cathode. Although both anode and cathode operate at temperatures in excess of the saturation temperature associated with the

Table 13.7 Work Functions of Several Materials [16, 17]

Material	Work Function, ev
Cathodes:	
Tungsten	4.53
Barium-impregnated tungsten (900–1200°C)	1.7
Thorium on tungsten (1800–2000°C)	2.55
Cesium on tungsten (1400–1600°C)	1.7
ZrC	3.8
UC	3.1–4.57
$(Zr_{0.8} U_{0.2})C$	4.3
Anodes:	
BaO and SrO on nickel	1.0
Cs on AgO	0.75
Cs on WO	0.71
Cs on nickel	1.81
Nickel	4.91

pressure of cesium, the anode becomes covered with at least a monolayer of cesium and the cathode may be partially or completely covered. This has the effect of reducing the apparent work function of the surfaces, as may be seen in Table 13.7. In operation, cesium in the interelectrode space becomes ionized both thermally and by contact with the cathode surface. The latter process depends upon the work function of the cathode material being greater than the ionization potential of cesium (3.89 ev). Since the work function of tungsten is 4.53 ev, cesium atoms can be ionized by collision with a tungsten surface. This is true of the other refractory metals also. In an irradiation field, additional ionization would be expected. Since the cesium is positively charged, it serves the important function of neutralizing the space change due to electrons. This permits larger interelectrode spacing in the cesium diode.

Insofar as the selection of a cathode material for the cesium diode is concerned, it must resist corrosion attack by cesium, it must have a work function greater than 3.89 ev, and in addition it must have a low evaporation rate. The last-mentioned requirement is somewhat relaxed because interesting efficiencies develop at lower cathode temperatures than is the case in the vacuum diode. These and other considerations, such as strength and dimensional stability, lead to the selection of such high-temperature materials as the refractory metals tungsten, tantalum, molybdenum, and niobium, and the solid-solution carbides such as (Zr, U)C. Among the refractory metals, niobium is attractive from the point of view of neutron capture cross section, and this is of some importance because a thermionic reactor core would contain substantial amounts of the material. In the temperature range of interest, it is quite probable that higher strengths than can be provided by the pure metals will be required. The solid-solution carbide (Zr, U)C has a work function (or chemical potential) high enough to be effective in ionizing cesium and has sufficiently low volatility (or dissociation pressure) to be attractive. The (Zr, U)C solid solution has a lower vapor pressure than do its constituents, ZrC and UC. The emission properties have proved to be highly variable, and this is probably associated with uncontrolled deviations from the stoichiometric composition. The solid-solution carbides, some of which were mentioned in connection with fuel materials, have not been studied in detail. The use of a fueled cathode with the fuel present in the surface introduces the possibility of fouling the thermionic diode with fission products. Many of the less volatile species would undoubtedly condense on the anode and insulating components.

There is a need for systematic, quantitative data on the reactions between cesium and the various potential cathode and anode materials. Table 13.4 shows that the refractory metals generally stand up well in sodium and lithium; this may also be true with cesium.

Fuel materials and possible fuel-element cladding materials for high-temperature service have been discussed. In the present context, the fuel-element cladding also performs the function of the thermionic cathode. Further, the metallic cathode materials that have been discussed are the same materials that were previously discussed as cladding.

Another necessary component in the thermionic diode is the insulation necessary to position the anode and cathode. The compatibility of the metals discussed with the insulating materials must be considered. Some upper limits are set by the fact that tungsten exhibits gross reactions with alumina at temperatures in excess of 2000°C, with beryllia above 2100°C, with magnesia above 2000°C, and with thoria at about 2300°C [18, 19]. Molybdenum shows gross reactions with alumina above 2000°C, with beryllia above 1900°C, with magnesia at temperatures higher than 1800°C, and with thoria at 2200°C. No reaction occurs at 1800°C between molybdenum and these oxides. Nickel, which has been used as an anode material, is reported to be compatible with the previously mentioned oxides and with titania at 1800°C. Alumina appears to be a good candidate material, but its use is limited to the temperatures below 2000°C. Thoria may be useful at the highest temperature. Referring back to

Table 13.2, we see that uranium dioxide could be considered for very high temperatures. In this case, depleted material would have to be used to avoid fissioning. Joining of alumina to tungsten and nickel has been performed successfully with a nickel-titanium braze.

Irradiation effects in the case of the fueled thermionic diode present no problems other than those that have already been discussed, with the exception of possible effects of transmutation upon the work function and a possible increase in the rate of evaporation through irradiation-induced sputtering.

In a nuclear thermionic system such as those that have been described, the heat delivered to the anode would be transferred through an electrically insulating layer to an outer cladding and thence to a liquid-metal system that would transport the heat to a radiator. Here the materials considerations are similar to those previously discussed in conjunction with nuclear thermoelectric systems.

No attempt has been made to make a judgment as to the best materials for nuclear thermionic applications. It is felt that too little is known about the properties of the materials involved and about the physics of the thermionic devices to permit well-founded materials selections.

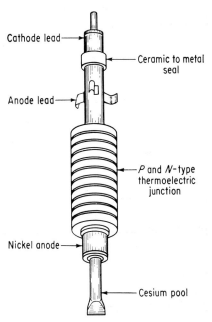

Fig. 13.16 Nuclear-heated thermionic-thermoelectric unit in thermal series.

An example of a thermionic diode that has been run in-pile [20] is shown in Figs. 13.16 and 13.17. This particular device was a combined thermionic-thermoelectric generator, the latter being fitted around the former, as indicated in Fig. 13.17. The thermionic section was fueled with UO₂ clad with a tantalum cathode, operating at about 1600°C. The anode was made of nickel and was spaced 0.025 cm from the cathode. Cesium vapor was supplied from a pool at the bottom of the device at 260°C. The thermionic section produced an open-circuit potential of 0.6 volt and a closed-circuit current of 600 to 700 ma. The thermoelectric section produced an open-circuit potential of 0.26 volt and a closed-circuit current of 400 to 500 ma. The device was operated in-pile for 40 hr, at which time a reactor incident terminated the experiment.

In discussing materials for direct conversion of nuclear heat to electric power for space applications, it has been necessary to bring in a large variety of materials and materials considerations, and it has therefore been impossible to present a great deal of detailed information about any

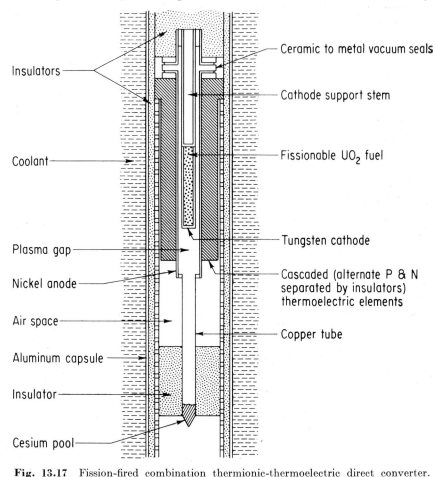

Fig. 13.17   Fission-fired combination thermionic-thermoelectric direct converter.

given material.   There are many uncertainties involved in materials for large direct-conversion systems.   It is hoped that this presentation has served to bring about an increased awareness of the materials problems that need attention.

REFERENCES

1. *Bettis Tech. Rev.*, BTR 18, April, 1960; BTR 20, September, 1960.
2. Pearlman, H.: Effect of Radiation on Massive Uranium Monocarbide, NAA-SR-Memo 4631.

3. Weber, C. E.: Radiation Damage in Non-metallic Fuel Elements, *Proc. Second UN Intern. Conf. Peaceful Uses At. Energy*, vol. 5, p. 619, 1958.
4. Gangler, J. J., W. A. Sanders, and I. L. Drell: Uranium Dioxide Compatibility with Refractory Metals, Carbides, Borides, and Oxides between 3500 and 5000°F, NASA-TND-262, February, 1960.
5. Quarterly Status Report of the LASL Plasma Thermocouple Development Program for the Period Ending Dec. 20, 1959, LAMS-2396.
6. Rough, F. A., and R. F. Dickerson: Uranium Monocarbide: Fuel of the Future, *Nucleonics*, March, 1960, p. 74.
7. Tipton, Jr., C. R., (ed.): "Reactor Handbook," vol. 1, "Materials," Interscience Publishers, Inc., New York, 1960.
8. Barney, W. K.: Irradiation Effects in UO_2, A/Conf., vol. 6, 1958.
9. Reeds, E. L.: Stabilities of Refractories in Liquid Metals, *J. Am. Ceram. Soc.*, vol. 37, p. 146, 1954.
10. Mausteller, J. W., and B. G. Voorhees: The Liquid Metals Handbook, Sodium and NaK Supplement, TID-5277.
11. Tantalum and Tantalum Alloys, *Battelle Memorial Institute, DMIC Rept.* 133, 306, Columbus, Ohio, 1960.
12. Funston, E. S.: Physical Properties of Yttrium Hydride, *Nuclear Metallurgy (AIME)*, vol. VII, p. 51, 1960.
13. Thermoelectric Nuclear Fuel Element, *Westinghouse Atomic Power Department, Quart. Progr. Rept.* WCAP-1376, WCAP-1545, WCAP-1596, and WCAP-1647.
14. Danko, J. C., G. R. Kilp, and P. V. Mitchell: Irradiation Effects of Thermoelectric Materials, *ARS Preprint* 1276-60, 1960.
15. Hernqvist, K. G., M. Kanefsky, and F. H. Norman: Thermoinic Energy Converter, in Kaye, J., and J. A. Welsh (eds.): "Direct Conversion Heat to Electricity," John Wiley & Sons, Inc., New York, 1960.
16. Hernqvist, K. G.: Thermionic Converters, *Nucleonics*, July, 1959, p. 49.
17. Bowman, M. G.: Chemistry of Fuel Element Cathode Materials, *ARS Preprint* 1286-60, 1960.
18. Johnson, P. D.: Behavior of Refractory Oxides and Metals Alone and in Combination in Vacua at High Temperature, *J. Am. Ceram. Soc.*, vol. 33, p. 168, 1950.
19. Economos, G., and W. D. Kingery: Metal Ceramic Interactions: II, Metal-Oxide Interfacial Reactions at Elevated Temperatures, *J. Am. Ceram. Soc.*, vol. 36, p. 403, 1953.
20. Danko, J. C.: Private communication, Westinghouse Atomic Power Department.

14

The Economic Aspects of Materials
and Their Applications
in Missiles and Spacecraft

MORRIS A. STEINBERG

MANAGER, MATERIALS AND PROPULSION RESEARCH
MISSILES AND SPACE DIVISION
LOCKHEED AIRCRAFT CORPORATION
PALO ALTO, CALIFORNIA

The economic aspects of materials and their applications in missiles and spacecraft present such a broad spectrum of potential discussion that only the highlights can be touched in this chapter. Comments have, therefore, been limited to a selected few of the material problems and requirements of ballistic missiles and spacecraft.

In the area of materials for ballistic missiles, the economic considerations will be discussed for material selection and fabrication methods for reentry vehicles, for motor cases, and for nozzles and vector-control hardware.

In the case of materials for spacecraft, the presentation will be even more general and limited to the material aspects involved in temperature control of spacecraft, auxiliary power problems as they affect temperature control, moving mechanisms, and finally material problems inherent in the use of electronic components in the environment of space.

The Importance of Materials Aspects to Missiles and Spacecraft Development

This chapter will cover the economic aspects of materials and their applications to missiles and spacecraft. In many respects much of the material to be presented herein has, in one form or another, been presented in the preceding 13 chapters. However, a slightly different emphasis will be placed on this material in that it will be reviewed from a different aspect, namely, the economic one. Economic aspect does not

378

necessarily mean the aspect of lowest cost. Furthermore, this factor is not confined just to the raw-material cost but involves also the cost of the finished part installed in the missile or spacecraft.

The aim is not to build the cheapest possible missile or spacecraft but rather to build, at least cost, a structure equal to the capabilities of the other components of the system—the power plant, guidance controls, propellant, and the reentry vehicle. This means, in general, that the structure must be designed to the lightest weight at a tolerable cost. The problems are (1) to find the value of saving a pound of weight and (2) to know how materials, fabrication, and installation costs vary from material to material. Finding the solutions of these two problems is the essence of missile materials engineering [1].

The above comments are even more important in the case of a development of space systems utilizing space vehicles. Considerably more knowledge is needed before these vehicles can be designed to function in a useful and reliable fashion for a long time and to perform rather complex missions while in orbit. As a final element, our knowledge of the performance of basic materials in space must be increased. If networks of military satellites are to be placed in orbit, ways must be found to ensure the uninterrupted operation of their complex electronic equipment. Before examining the economic factors affecting material selections for both missiles and spacecraft, it will be well to examine the status of development of our ballistic missiles systems and our present space programs and the projected growth of these programs.

The spending for space programs, both civilian and military, from 1958 through 1961† is given in Fig. 14.1. It is evident that the United States has really been seriously involved in the space field for only about 3 years [2].

While there are 19 major programs for which the Ballistic Missile Division of the Air Force is responsible today, only five are directly concerned with ballistic missiles. The others all involve studies for space projects. At the present time, ballistic missiles are already entering the United States Air Force inventory. By 1963, the development of our new missiles will be pretty well completed. At that point, between 60 and 80 per cent of the Ballistic Missile Division's research and development activities will be concerned with space projects [3]. Only the remainder will involve ballistic missile work. From a dollar point of view, the Air Force space program today is on about the same level as the ballistic missile effort was in fiscal 1958. Major emphasis on the present

† NOTE: These figures represent the best available data as of January 1, 1961. Since that time the military space program has been augmented and the civilian space program has been accelerated and supplemented so that the total will be some 50 billion dollars in the next nine years.

generation of ballistic missiles will be on improvements that will continue to perpetuate themselves through new developments. This will include improving existing missiles by using new approaches that will stress reliability, simplicity, and lower cost. Fiscal 1960–1961 funding for

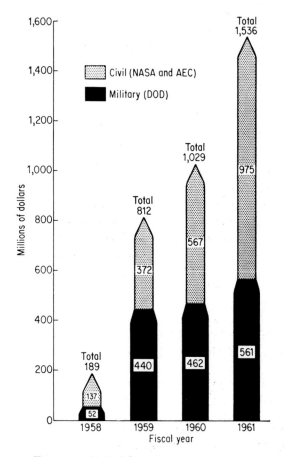

Fig. 14.1   United States spending for space.

ballistic missilery for the Air Force included some $2\frac{1}{2}$ billion dollars, and something over 500 million dollars on space projects [2].

The immediate goal in space for the Air Force is satellites for early-warning observations and communications. The rapidity with which the military utilizes space will in part depend on the cost of placing payloads in orbit. It is necessary to reduce this by an order of magnitude or more. There are a number of ways that this can be accomplished, one of which includes the development of recoverable boosters as a possibility of cost cutting.   Another possibility is more economical boosters, which could provide lower cost per pound of payload.   Other requirements must be met by spacecraft designs; these include high reliability and adaptability.

Missiles	Spacecraft
STL direction:	Discoverer
Atlas	Midas
Titan	Samos
Minuteman	Transit booster
Aerospace Corp. direction:	Tiros booster
Midgetman	Courier booster
Scaled-down polaris	Mercury booster
Anti-missile missile	Dyna-Soar booster
	WS-609A booster
	Able probes
	Advent and Flag communi- cations satellites
	Interceptor satellites

Fig. 14.2   Major Air Force ballistic missile program.

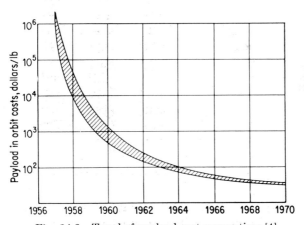

Fig. 14.3   Trend of payload cost versus time [4].

Figure 14.2 has a listing of some of the major missile and spacecraft programs under development at the present time by the Air Force [3].

The present trend in the area of orbital techniques is illustrated by Fig. 14.3, where the expected payload cost per pound of payload in orbit is plotted versus time.   Although this is guesswork only, and not the author's, it indicates the direction that must be taken. A considerable improvement from an initial cost of a million dollars per pound to about a hundred dollars per pound, a reduction of four orders of magnitude, cannot be achieved without effort. This improvement is expected to result from several combined influences: by increasing vehicle size, by using more powerful propellants, by establishing higher firing rates, and finally by recovering boosters and reusing the recovered and rejuvenated hardware [4]. Many other contributions will assist in further reducing

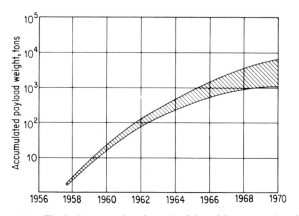

Fig. 14.4 Typical accumulated payload in orbit versus time [4].

the overall cost per unit weight. The cost of materials is not insignificant, and one method by which cost can be reduced is by proper selection of materials.

It is interesting to look at an estimation of the accumulated payload in orbit as a function of time for the next decade as given in Fig. 14.4. It is evident that if the mutual tasks that have been outlined for this coming decade are to be accomplished, cost must be lowered.

A breakdown of the total costs of placing a useful payload into orbit can be represented on a relative scale as is shown in the chart of Table 14.1.

Table 14.1 Typical Cost Distribution per Firing for a Large Vehicle [4]

Item	Per cent of cost
Transportation firing range operation	15
Assembly test checkout	25
Payload cost	5
Upper stages manufacturing	25
Booster manufacturing	30
Total firing cost	100

In terms of the civilian space programs, the 10-year plan outlined by NASA through 1970 indicates expenditures totaling 13 to 15 billion dollars from 1960 through 1970, and a total of some 260-odd launches [5]. Table 14.2 gives a list of the total launches projected for the 10-year pro-

Table 14.2   Ten-year Launch Program [5]†

	Fiscal year														Total
	1960		1961				1962	1963	1964	1965	1966	1967	1968	1969	
	3	4	1	2	3	4									
Redstone	...	1	2	3	2	...	...	...	...	...	...	...	...	...	8
Atlas	...	1	2	1	2	1	6	1	...	...	...	...	...	...	14
Juno II	1	...	1	3	...	...	...	...	...	...	...	...	...	...	5
Thor-Able	2	...	...	...	...	...	...	...	...	...	...	...	...	...	2
Atlas-Able	...	1	1	...	...	...	...	...	...	...	...	...	...	...	2
Scout	...	4	2	...	2	...	6	6	6	6	6	6	6	6	56
Thor-Delta	1	1	1	2	1	1	5	...	...	...	...	...	...	...	12
Thor-Agena B	...	...	...	...	...	...	1	6	6	6	6	6	6	6	43
Atlas-Agena B	...	...	...	...	1	...	3	4	5	6	3	12	12	12	58
Atlas-Centaur	...	...	...	...	...	1	5	4	5	6	9	...	...	...	30
Saturn	...	...	1	...	...	...	3	5	1	4	4	4	4	4	30
Nova	...	...	...	...	...	...	...	...	...	...	...	...	1	2	3
Total	4	8	10	9	8	3	29	26	23	28	28	28	29	30	263

† Total cost, 13 to 15 billion dollars.

gram. These launches are for three major efforts: (1) the Mercury program to place a man in orbit, (2) deep space missions, and (3) a 3-year satellite program for scientific, meteorological, and communications work. These are shown in Table 14.3.

This program is to culminate in the 1970s with manned flights to the moon as well as manned permanent near-earth space stations (1965–1968).

With the development of the larger boosters under the NASA program, the projected growth of individual payload weights that can be placed into a near-earth orbit as a function of time is given in Fig. 14.5.

With the above short summary of the scope and size of both major missile and space programs over the next decade, it would be well to review the impact of these major programs on the materials industry. There are several anachronisms that stand out when we talk of materials and their application to missiles and spacecraft. The missile industry uses a small tonnage of metals but requires the utmost in metal properties. Missile development is calling for the best efforts of engineers and scientists in every field, including materials engineers.   While the application of metals to missiles and spacecraft is but a very small portion of the total of the metalworking picture in the United States, paradoxically, missile and spacecraft applications are probably the greatest single current

Table 14.3 [5]

a. Project Mercury Schedule

	Fiscal year						Total
	1960		1961				
	3	4	1	2	3	4	
Little Joe......	1	1	...	...	...	...	2
Redstone.......	...	...	2	3	2	1	8
Atlas..........	...	1	2†	2†	2†	5†	12

† Orbital.

b. Deep Space Missions

	Fiscal year							
	1960		1961				1962	1963
	3	4	1	2	3	4		
Thor-Able.....	I							
Thor-Delta....								
Atlas-Able.....	I	L	L	L				
Atlas-Agena...	...	...	...	...	...	...	L	4L	2
Centaur.......	...	...	...	...	...	...	...	2P

L—lunar; P—planetary; I—interplanetary.

c. Three-year Satellite Program

	Fiscal year							
	1960		1961				1962	1963
	3	4	1	2	3	4		
Juno II.............	S	...	S	2	S			
Thor-Able..........	M	...	...	...	...			
Scout..............	...	S	S	S	2S	...	2S	2S
Delta..............	C	M	S	S	...	...	C	3S
Thor-Agena B.......	...	...	...	...	...	...	2M	S
							S	
Atlas-Agena B......	...	...	...	...	...	...	...	C
							...	2S

S—scientific; M—meteorological; C—communications.

stimulant to materials research and development.   Estimates have been made that the 1959 metal consumption by the United States metalworking industries totaled over 100 million tons whereas in comparison, the total annual metal requirement for the aircraft and missiles industry, decreasing every year for the past six years, was estimated to be about 95,000 tons, and the missile applications are but a small part of even this unimpressive total [6].

Nevertheless, this tiny fraction of the country's metal consumption is probably responsible for more materials research than any other industry. The reason, of course, is that the Department of Defense expects that spacecraft and missile developments and improvements will be made, and this demands improved fabrication techniques and new materials.

Two striking trends in material developments have marked the missile and space fields. These are (1) a rapid increase in the types of materials being considered and (2) a marked increase in the number of physical properties of concern. Table 14.4 lists the types of materials and their

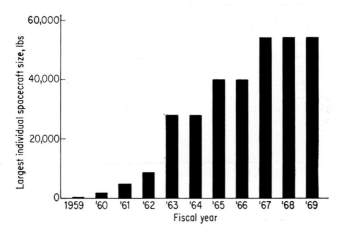

Fig. 14.5 Payload weights in terms of the weight of a near-earth satellite [5].

order of importance for the period from 1954 to 1960; and what is evident is the large number of newer materials that are of prime importance for consideration in missile and spacecraft technology, as compared with the standard structural materials that we have been so used to, particularly in the aircraft field, over the last few decades. Table 14.5, which is even more illuminating, indicates a large increase in variety of physical properties concerned for applications in missiles and spacecraft in terms of their importance for the period from 1954 to 1960. Again, the point of significance is the fact that we are now interested in many properties of materials that were of no concern to us in the past, and for which there is a paucity of data. Many of these properties are of prime importance for applications that are presently at hand. As can be seen, many of these properties have to do with the interaction of materials and the space environment, as well as the environments produced by propulsion and reentry conditions of ballistic missiles. Not only are these properties not well defined, as compared with common materials properties, but the environments that these materials have to live in them-

Table 14.4   Construction Materials for Missiles and Spacecraft [7]

Material	1954	1956	1958	1960
Aluminum alloys.................	1†	1	1	1
Magnesium alloys...............	2	2	2	2
Titanium alloys..................	2	2	2	2
Alloy steel......................	2	1	1	1
Stainless steel...................	3	1	1	1
Glazing and dielectric plastics......	2	2	1	1
Copper.........................	...	1	1	3
Nickel alloys....................	...	2	1	1
Cobalt alloys....................	...	2	1	1
Ceramics.......................	...	2	1	1
Powder metal products...........	...	2	1	1
Ablating materials...............	...	2	1	1
Beryllium.......................	...	3	1	1
Graphite........................	...	3	1	1
Molybdenum alloys...............	...	...	2	1
Chromium alloys.................	...	...	3	1
Niobium alloys..................	...	...	3	2
Tungsten alloys..................	...	...	3	2

† Numbers indicate order of importance.

Table 14.5   Significant Properties of Structural Materials for Missiles and Spacecraft [7]

Property	1954	1956	1958	1960
Density.........................	1†	1	1	1
Strength........................	1	1	1	1
Ductility.......................	1	1	1	1
Stiffness........................	1	1	1	1
Corrosion resistance..............	1	1	1	1
Fatigue strength.................	1	1	1	1
Creep strength...................	3	1	1	1
Thermal expansion...............	2	1	1	1
Thermal conductivity.............	3	1	1	1
Specific heat....................	...	2	1	1
Thermal-shock resistance..........	...	2	1	1
Ignition characteristics...........	...	3	1	1
Emissivity......................	...	3	1	1
Ablation characteristics...........	...	3	1	1
Radiation resistance..............	...	3	2	1
Meteorite-strike resistance.........	...	...	3	1
Reaction to ionized gas...........	...	...	3	1

† Numbers indicate order of importance.

selves have not been well and clearly established. Finally, materials engineers must learn the language and technology of our aerospace engineers in order to interpolate requirements into best material choices.

In order that long-life satellites can be designed so as to operate usefully in orbit for their intended life, the reliability of these vehicles must be improved. In large portion, to ensure reliability requires a clear understanding of the effect of the complete space environment on materials, an environment which, as has been indicated, is at present only poorly defined.

Economic Considerations of Materials for Spacecraft

Space systems, composed of satellite networks linked to earth-based communication and command stations, offer a unique and practicable means for gathering, processing, and transmitting information about near and deep space [8].

Space systems have already been utilized as data-gathering platforms during single early satellite and space flights; but until the operations for getting into orbit and, once there, routinely performing the orbital functions necessary to fulfilling all mission requirements have become commonplace, we cannot hope to exploit fully the information-gathering potential of space systems. The performance with satellites is becoming increasingly successful; knowledge is increasing, as is confidence in our vehicles. However, there is still a good deal of ground to cover before a level of reliability that will routinize every phase of satellite operations from launch to long-term complex-orbital-mission capabilities can be obtained.

A most critical area of inquiry, which must be explored before such reliability can be established, is that of materials application. It will be necessary to know in much greater detail what the environment of space really is, what its effects are upon materials, and how criteria for improving and selecting materials can be established so that they will stand up to the special environmental stresses of space. Lacking final solutions to a multitude of problems that hamper space-system design, high-confidence (but not overconservative) systems must be produced.†
In the first 13 chapters in this book, you have been apprised of the progress made to date.

The motivation for pursuing materials research lies in the need to produce these systems and to apply the systems to stated objectives without compromise due to fear of the unknown and possibly deleterious effects of the space environment upon any system components.

Environmental Factors in Space.   At this time, the effects of some of the following forces can be estimated and specific needs for greater knowledge of these forces can be indicated.

† In large measure, portions of this section have been taken from Ref. 8.

1. Electromagnetic radiation from the sun and earth and from the solar spectrum including the UV and X-ray regions

2. Primary cosmic radiation

3. Local radiation regions, as in the Van Allen belts, as well as the auroral-zone radiation and its dependence upon the strength of solar activity

4. Dust-particle concentration from meteoric and earlier corpuscular matter, atomic and molecular matter in the earth's vicinity

5. Corpuscular radiation from the sun, for normal and intense solar-activity periods, its energy spectrum and density; and the effect of earth shielding by the earth's magnetic field; as well as measurement of neutral and charged particles for many atomic weights

6. Low vacuum and its effects upon the vehicle of chemical reactions, sublimation, evaporation, sputtering, and dust collisions

Nuclear bursts in space and internally generated nuclear radiation represent perturbations of the natural environment and constitute special problems.

These environmental conditions may exist singly or in combinations. They may be casually related; for example, a major solar flare and its associated phenomena will perturb several environments. They may act with varying force upon materials, one environment accelerating or compensating for the degrading effects of another. They may be of unequal force over periods of time; the cycle of intense solar-flare activity over the past few years, for instance, will probably be followed by a cycle of quiescence. Finally, some environments will exert only a momentary force as a vehicle passes through on the way to orbital altitudes.

In designing high-confidence space systems we are confronted on the one hand by a limited ability to simulate, at one time, all these special environments and on the other by the absolute need to study and plan against their complex interworking. Further, we should know time-space average values, novations over the earth (large-scale and small-scale), novations in time, etc., for a number of possible orbits.

Successful spacecraft design is a result of successful test activity, and this depends upon a well-defined integrated program, a firm understanding of problems that have to be overcome or allowed for in space materials, and an unabating test effort, both on the ground and in space.

In order to clarify the full meaning of all these and relate them to economic factors, a few selected topics will be discussed, for example,

1. Problems posed by the environment
2. Implications of thermal-control design
3. Problems of testing

4. Choice of APU, and the relationship of material selection to these factors

5. Electronic components

Problems Posed by the Environment.   The following list is a representative one, which includes problems of varying severity.   Lower-risk problems have been included with the knowledge that uncertainty about these should soon be removed by ground or space experiments.

1. Erosion of surfaces and finishes by meteoric matter.   The removal of surface layers degradates thermal control, and pitting distorts optical characteristics, minimizes scattered light, etc.

2. Long-term radiation effects of such backgrounds as the Van Allen radiation on solid-state materials, dielectrics, and organic materials like lubricants or Teflon.

3. Sublimation and evaporation of materials in high vacuum.   Surfaces and substrata may be affected by the modification of the gas layer on the vehicle.   Organics are particularly sensitive to material loss.

4. Friction on bearing surfaces, switching contacts, gear trains, etc. Questions here are: What is the best method of preventing seizing where metal parts come in contact?   What is the significance of changes in the surface-gas film?   What are lubrication requirements?

5. Degradation of organic materials by the short-wave end of the solar spectrum.   We need to investigate the inhibitive force of a vacuum on the degradation, photoionization of surface layers of solids, and mechanisms of charge transfer between the vehicle and the environment.

6. Permeability of thin shells such as space structures made rigid by internal pressure.

7. Behavior of thin films of material.   These are used to control transmissive characteristics or emissive or radiative properties of vehicle and component surfaces.   Even within the vehicle they may be influenced by environmental factors.

8. Sputtering of materials by incident atomic and molecular surface bombardment of an intensity to change surface properties and cause system malfunctions.   To assess all the difficulties, we must determine yield ratios (surface atoms removed per incident particle) and measure factors, such as pressure and surface preparation, that influence yield ratios for several incident particle types at the actual energy of the encounter.

9. Solar plasma or corpuscular radiation which produces these varied effects relative to altitude and location: high-energy-sputtering [9] radiation damage to plastic surfaces and a consequent hydrogen evolution, charring, and carbonizing at high exposures.   One source pessimistically

suggests that a single major flare could accelerate both sputtering and radiation damage, either one of which may result from normal events [10].

10. Special problems that can arise because of leakage radiation produced by nuclear devices that have requirements for thermal dissipation of energy. But these are merely noted since they depend on specific details of source design, shielding properties, etc.

The effects of these are uncertain and may turn out to be phantom problems; however, any one has the potential to damage electrical, mechanical, or optical properties of the vehicle and its components. Until uncertainty about environmental forces is eliminated, answers to these three determinative questions must be sought: What are actual environmental conditions? What are the effects of these upon materials? How can improved materials be selected for use in space?

Implications of Thermal-control Design. Thermal control is a major factor affecting the economics of spacecraft. The work yet to be accomplished before satisfactory answers to thermal-control problems become available can best be gauged by reviewing some of the aspects of temperature control needed to satisfy requirements of internal instruments as payload packages, since it has been established that positive measures of thermal control are essential for the satisfactory operation of all types of instrumented and manned aerospace vehicles. This subject was discussed in detail in Chap. 8. However, some repetition is worthwhile because this is one of the most serious of space materials problems. The methods by which control of temperature might be achieved can be classified as either active or passive. Active techniques are those by which electrical, mechanical, chemical, or nuclear mechanisms are utilized within the vehicle to generate and distribute heat energy. Passive techniques are those measures that are static in nature, incorporated at the time of design and, therefore, not readily amenable to change while the vehicle is in operation. Passive methods include selection of the basic materials of construction, insulation, and various types of surface treatments [11].

Of all the methods for controlling the temperature of spacecraft and satellites, the most important are passive techniques involving coatings for the vehicle surface to control the exchange of heat. In the vacuum of space, all exchange of heat between a body and space must be by electromagnetic radiation. If excess heat is generated within a space vehicle by its power sources, this excess must be dissipated radiantly from the vehicle to space; or if, on balance, the vehicle radiates energy at a higher rate than it absorbs heat from the sun and earth reflection, then the deficiency must be made up from its internal power sources. Also, if the vehicle's solar absorptivity is greater than its own emissivity, it will overheat [12].

The complexity of controlling the heat balance is made more difficult

by orbit and space factors and the radiation characteristics of the surfaces
—the α_s (solar absorptivity), the ϵ (low-temperature emissivity), and the
α_s/ϵ ratio—all of which affect the satellite heat balance in a complex
fashion.   The effects of uncertainties and variations in orbit geometry,
such as those brought about by orbit injection errors, regression of the
nodes, and changes in either the day or hour of launch, affect the estimate
of the thermal irradiation of the vehicle and yield uncertainties in the
estimate of the heat balance, thus causing deviations from the predicted
satellite temperatures.   Radiation characteristics and methods of developing and maintaining stable finishes also yield uncertainties.   If stable
finishes are made available, the temperature-control problem is then
reduced to one of optimizing designs on the basis of such factors as
reliability, weight, and power requirements.   The major challenge to the
materials engineer is to provide such stable surfaces.

Design Philosophy.   The present design philosophy relies upon passive radiation techniques in which the desired average orbital temperature is achieved by properly balancing the absorptivity of the surfaces
for solar radiation, α_s, with their emissivity for infrared radiation, ϵ.
Analysis reveals that the average orbital temperature varies as the fourth
root of the α_s/ϵ ratio, as indicated by the equation

$$\sigma \bar{T}^4 = \frac{\alpha_s}{\epsilon} (\bar{F}_s S + \bar{F}_r R) + \bar{F}_e E + \frac{1}{\epsilon} P_i \tag{14.1}$$

or, for a prescribed orbital geometry, the following equation where the
term α/ϵ is normally dominant:

$$\bar{T}^4 = \frac{C_1 \alpha}{\epsilon} + C_2 \frac{P_i}{\epsilon} + C_3 \tag{14.2}$$

where $\bar{T}$ = average orbital temperature for external surface
σ = Stefan-Boltzmann radiation constant
α = coefficient of solar absorptivity
ϵ = coefficient of infrared emissivity
$\bar{F}_s, \bar{F}_r, \bar{F}_e$ = radiant interchange geometrical factors for solar insolation,
earth radiation, and albedo
S, R, E = incident radiation energy due to solar insolation, earth
emission, and albedo
P_i = internal power generation

The space-time average skin temperature as a function of α_s/ϵ for a
typical noon circular polar orbit, with no internal power, is given by the
curve shown in Fig. 14.6.

Oriented-cube Space Vehicle.   Perhaps the best way of indicating
the thermal-control problem is by a specific example in which certain of

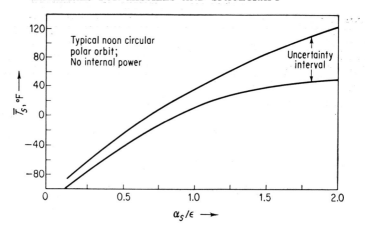

Fig. 14.6   Space-time average skin temperature $\bar{T}_s$ versus α/ϵ.

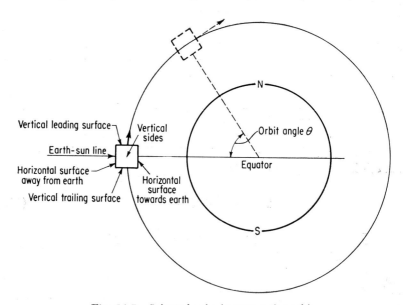

Fig. 14.7   Oriented cube in noon polar orbit.

the variables can be changed, such as altitude, thermal capacity. Wc and δ/ϵ (terms defined below), and the equilibrium temperatures can be obtained.   This is most easily done by an example with an oriented cube in a noon polar circular orbit as shown in Fig. 14.7.   All faces are assumed to lie thermally isolated to simplify the calculations.   That it is an oriented cube means that all faces maintain a fixed orientation with respect to the instantaneous inertial velocity vector.   The horizontal surface away from the earth receives only direct solar insolation (Fig. 14.8), while the horizontal surface facing the earth (Fig. 14.9) receives mostly earth shine and earth-reflected solar radiation with some direct solar insolation just prior to and after eclipse.   The leading and trailing vertical

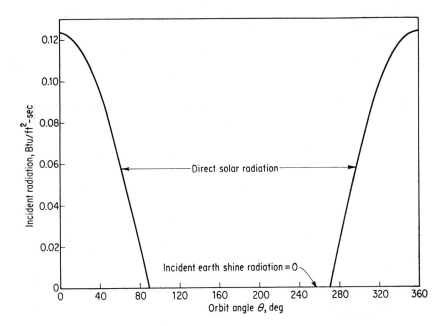

Fig. 14.8   Irradiation of horizontal surface away from the earth.

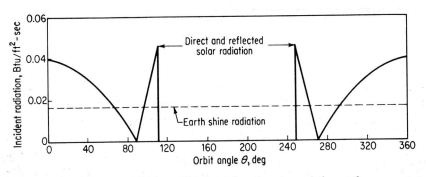

Fig. 14.9   Irradiation of horizontal surface toward the earth.

sides see a combination of all three sources of radiation, while the other two vertical faces receive only earth shine, albedo, and earth-reflected solar radiation at a low level of intensity.

Transient temperature responses of each face—assuming all surfaces thermally insulated—have been calculated for these parameters:

1. Orbital altitudes: 300 and 2,300 miles
2. Ratios of solar absorptivity to infrared emissivity, α_s/ϵ: 0.15, 0.30, 1.00, 2.00, 4.00
3. Thermal capacity parameter $Wc\ \delta/\epsilon$: 0.1, 1.0, 10.0, where $W =$ specific weight, $c =$ specific heat, and $\delta =$ thickness

Figure 14.10 shows the periodic temperature variation for the horizontal surface facing away from the earth in a 300-mile noon orbit for

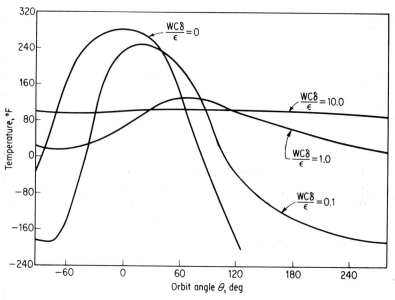

Fig. 14.10 Transient temperature history of horizontal surface away from the earth.

a range of thermal capacities. Included for interest are the analytical results for an infinitely thin plate of zero capacity. Note that for plates of small thermal capacity, the peak temperature is a measure of the ratio of α/ϵ, while in the eclipse the temperature response can be simply calculated as that of the $\bar{T}^4$ radiation to free space of a finite-thermal-capacity plate and is only a function of the infrared low-temperature emissivity ϵ.

It is difficult to ascertain the minimum temperature that may be encountered when a vehicle of very low thermal capacity is in the shadow of the earth. For a space research device such as the Echo I balloon, which consisted of a film of Mylar bearing an evaporated aluminum coating as well as a silicon monoxide coating, it has been estimated that a minimum temperature was reached within 5 min of the time it passed into the shadow of the earth.   The minimum temperature is not known, but may have been well below $-100°C$.   Most organic materials at such low temperatures are very brittle.   Hence, it may be that in space, low temperatures will have a relatively greater influence on the serviceability of organic coatings than will the maximum temperatures likely to be attained.

Maximum and minimum temperatures that could potentially be reached by thin plates with variable α/ϵ ratios are shown in Fig. 14.11. α/ϵ ratios in the range from 0.1 to 0.3 can be achieved with special paints, while ratios of 2.0 to 3.0 are typical of polished metals; higher values can be achieved by special spectrally selective solar absorbers.   The effect of spatial orientation upon the maximum temperature oscillations experienced is shown in Fig. 14.12 for the four thermally distinct cube surfaces.

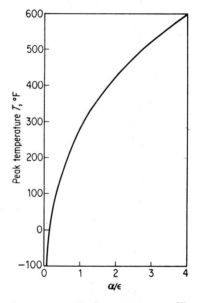

Fig. 14.11   Peak temperature, Wc $\delta/\epsilon = 0$.

Correlation of preferred thermal orientations with preferred environmental orientations permits certain conclusions to be drawn.

1. Solar irradiation.   Greatest dosage of X rays and short-wavelength ultraviolet radiation will be on the horizontal surface facing away from the earth and the vertical leading and trailing sides.

2. Sputtering.   Greatest inpact by nitrogen and oxygen atoms at lower orbital altitudes will be upon the vertical leading face of the cube.

3. Micrometeoritic erosion.   Micrometeorites are mostly confined to the plane of the ecliptic and are attracted by the earth's gravitational field so that they travel in spiraling paths toward the earth's surface. These trajectories, relative to the earth, when combined with the satellite motion at velocities of approximately five-sevenths of the velocity of the most probable micrometeoritic particles, imply that the surfaces of the cube will experience widely separated fluxes of particle impacts.   The leading vertical edge has by far the highest flux of particles impacting, while the horizontal surface facing the earth and the trailing vertical side receive almost none.   The other sides will experience approximately equal numbers of hits, but at a reduced flux.

4. Solar corpuscular radiation.   The earth's magnetic field will perturb this to some extent and complicate orientation statements.

5. Auroral radiation.   Electrons in the 30-kev and protons in the 100-kev range will not disturb the horizontal surface facing the earth. Protons in this energy range may cause surface sputtering as nominally experienced in the laboratory.

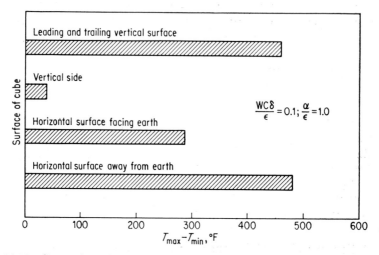

Fig. 14.12   Comparison of temperature oscillations of four faces of cube in 2,300-mile noon orbit.

6. Van Allen belt and solar flare protons.   Two additional sources of radiation show only a limited degree of orientation effect because of complex interactions of the particles with the earth's magnetic field.   However, these particles are thought to be generally so highly energetic that they penetrate into the material rather than cause surface sputtering.

Different materials exhibit characteristically different values of the α/ϵ ratio; these values vary from 10.0 or more for polished metallic surfaces to 0.3 for certain classes of painted surfaces.   The particular value of the α/ϵ ratio corresponding to a desired temperature is achieved by constructing a mosaic of materials that has the properly weighted average α/ϵ ratio.   This concept has been discussed by Camack and Edwards [13] and was discussed in other chapters.

The four basic classes of thermal-control surfaces from which a suitable mosaic may be constructed are given below; and the coatings, to be used in amounts as indicated by thermal analysis of the vehicle and its trajectory, are of these types:

1. Flat absorber.   High emissivity at all wavelengths
2. Solar absorber.   High ratio of emissivity in the solar region to emissivity in the infrared region
3. Flat reflector.   Low emissivity at all wavelengths
4. Solar reflector.   Low ratio of emissivity in the solar region (below about 4 μ wavelength) to emissivity in the infrared region

Programs to determine the stability of these under combined vacuum, temperature, ultraviolet radiation, and rapid-ascent heating are needed.

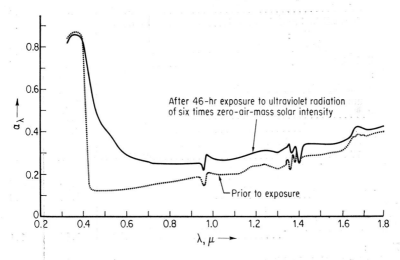

Fig. 14.13   Spectral absorptivity α_s versus wavelength for TiO$_2$–pigmented epoxy-base paint.

Investigations should include the development and formulation of inorganic coatings and semi-inorganic paints to incorporate stability with the other advantages of organic paint.   A typical example of what can happen to paints with organic vehicles is shown in Fig. 14.13, which indicates that α_s increases 50 per cent while ϵ remains the same, therefore increasing the temperature.

The flat absorbers currently used are black paints and anodizing treatments resulting in black matte surfaces.   Characteristic emissivities are 0.9 throughout the spectral range from 0.2 to 25 μ.   The flat reflector presently in use is an aluminum-pigmented silicone paint.   Reflectance of incident energy is approximately 70 per cent throughout the spectral range of interest.

Highly polished metallic surfaces are used as solar absorbers.   Surfaces of polished aluminum (a representative material) have α/ϵ ratios between

Table 14.6 Representative Material Radiative Properties†

Materials	α‡	ϵ§	α/ϵ ratios
Metals:			
Aluminum 6061 alloy:			
As received..................................	0.41	0.04	10.3
Machine-polished and degreased..............	0.35	0.04	8.8
Sandblasted, 120 size grit...................	0.60	0.41	1.5
Aluminum 2024 alloy:			
As received..................................	0.27	0.02	13.5
Machine-polished and degreased..............	0.31	0.06	5.2
QMU beryllium alloy:			
Rolled plate, chem. milled..................	0.48	0.11	4.4
Rolled plate, chem. milled, chem. polished.....	0.50	0.09	5.6
Gold:			
Vacuum deposit gold on aluminum...........	0.24	0.04	6.0
Vacuum deposit gold on buffed titanium......	0.33	0.05	6.6
Nickel.......................................	0.45	0.17	2.6
Electroless nickel.........................	0.63	0.66	0.95
Special surfaces on metals:			
Dow 17 on magnesium.....................	0.53–0.72	0.50–0.82	0.95
Foils and adhesive-backed metals:			
Fascal chrome aluminized Mylar film.........	0.25	0.09	2.8
Bright gold foil...........................	0.29	0.23	1.3
Paints (according to vehicle):			
Vinyl (phenolic):			
Dull black Micabond......................	0.93	0.84	1.1
Epoxy:			
Skyspar (untinted white)...................	0.26	0.86	0.3
Silicone:			
Fuller gloss white silicone...................	0.30	0.81	0.37
Fuller flat black silicone....................	0.89	0.81	1.1
Fuller aluminum silicone...................	0.23	0.20	1.2
Acrylic:			
Kemacryl lacquer (white)...................	0.26	0.75	0.35
Kemacryl lacquer (black)...................	0.94	0.83	1.1
Miscellaneous:			
Silica oxide:			
5 mils of silica on magnesium..............	0.21	0.83	0.25
Adhesive-backed dielectrics:			
Scotchcal (white) on aluminum..............	0.24	0.83	0.29
Ceramics:			
Cermet (ceramic containing sintered metal)....	0.65	0.58	1.1

† Values listed are averages of several determinations. Accuracy of the tabulated values is variable, but usually reliable to 10 per cent, except for very low emissivities.

‡ Solar absorptivity, extraterrestrial.

§ Total hemispherical emissivity at 500°R.

6.0 and 12.0.   The variation in α/ϵ ratio is indicative of the pronounced effect of surface finish and cleanliness.   This class of thermal-control surface requires specialized protection techniques throughout the manufacturing process.

At present, solar reflectors are approximated by white paints.   Various pigment-vehicle combinations are used.   The lowest practical values of α/ϵ are congruent to 0.25.

Solar reflectors are used in areas where it is desired to maintain a very low equilibrium temperature or where it is necessary to dissipate large amounts of internally generated power.   Solar absorbers are, of course, used for exactly opposite reasons.   Flat absorbers and reflectors are required to minimize orbital-temperature fluctuations and, in conjunction with the solar reflectors and solar absorbers, to establish the temperature level.   Typical values of various coatings are given in Table 14.6.

Temperature Effects on Operational Characteristics of Certain Important Electronic Components.   As stated previously, the economic value of the use of satellites for military missions is enhanced if their reliability can be ensured and their lifetime extended.

Control of temperature of operating components is one important method of ensuring this.   Some important examples can be discussed.

To begin with, allowable temperature variations differ from component to component.   Electron tubes and transistors can operate over a temperature range between 0 and 100°C with relatively small variation of failure rate.   On the other hand, paper capacitors and film resistors may increase in failure rate to a factor of about 5 as the ambient temperature rises from 0 to 100°C.   Photographic devices or film can become seriously affected unless the temperature range is held to rather small limits with a reasonable mean temperature.   Some of these effects are due to the nature of film materials, others to thermal perturbations of optical properties.

Similarly, there is a relatively significant effect of temperature on semiconductor devices used for photovoltaic solar-energy conversion.   Silicon-cell efficiency is roughly halved as the temperature rises from 0 to 100°C.   Other equipment, by contrast, operates most effectively at extremes of the temperature range.   For example, in an ideal thermal receiver approximating an infrared radiation detector, the minimum detectable power (and signal-to-noise ratio) varies approximately as the five-halves power of the absolute temperature.   Such high sensitivity to temperature has been essentially demonstrated by experiments with photoconductive materials in which the main noise was generation-recombination noise (this being the dominant noise at the temperatures considered—100 to 300°K).   Consequently, there is a positive benefit in operating photoconductive devices at rather low temperatures, particularly in a passive fashion which would allow us to take advantage of this characteristic of photoconductive detectors without an active complex system [14].

Conventional bearings are also relatively temperature-sensitive. Their mean operating life can degrade rapidly in 200°F local temperatures, while gyros, clocks, or generators of very stable frequencies will function precisely only within close temperature limits.

Thermal-control methods, whether in active or passive systems, must be of high confidence level, a level attainable only through considerable data gathering and testing. At this time, passive techniques seem most capable of building confidence because, first, they operate with less degradation than active ones and, second, they can perform supplementally in the complex active systems. But whichever technique is employed, it must evolve slowly and surely through a program of testing.

Factors Affecting Choice of Materials. Although radiation characteristics are of primary importance, they are by no means the only factor involved in choosing a material for thermal control of spacecraft. The radiation characteristics must be reproducible in the shop, and they must be stable not only during the launch, orbit, and reentry phases for which the vehicle is designed, but they must also be stable during all phases of manufacture, handling, checkout, and storage prior to the actual launch. Reproducibility of thermal control surfaces necessitates careful specification of substrate composition and finish, plating or coating processes, and all mechanical treatments to which the surface may be exposed.

Prelaunch environmental factors that affect the radiation characteristics of materials and tabulated by Gaumer [15] are:

1. High ambient temperatures
2. Mechanical wear and tear during handling which necessitates both excellent adhesion and adequate abrasion resistance of a material
3. Oxidation in air, which causes the formation of a surface coating of oxide on a material with resultant change in the α/ϵ ratio
4. Corrosive atmospheres, which cause actual chemical changes in some materials, particularly magnesium
5. Physical contamination from dirt and dust, various organic oil film deposits, and, perhaps most important, the fingerprints of workers handling thermal control materials

The launch, orbit, and reentry stages are those that usually are discussed in connection with spacecraft materials work. Both the launch and reentry stages are characterized by high temperatures produced by aerodynamic heating and by shear stresses due to atmospheric friction.

The temperatures reached by external control surfaces during the ascent phase are frequently of the order of 1000°F. There is an urgent need to develop paints that are stable in this environment. Silicone-base paints, both white and black, exhibiting adequate stability up to about 800°F have been developed.

The orbital stage subjects spacecraft to a number of important environmental factors that can affect the radiation parameters of materials. Arranged in order of increasing importance with regard to their effect upon thermal-control materials, these factors, stated previously and reiterated in summary, are:

1. Micrometeorite erosion
2. Sputtering of materials by atmospheric ions and protons and possibly electrons
3. High-energy radiation and high-energy particles, both those in the Van Allen belt and corpuscular radiation emanating from the sun
4. Temperature extremes from -200 to $+600°F$ and the mechanical and thermal stresses induced by orbital cycling between these extremes
5. The high-vacuum environment (10^{-10} mm Hg) and resultant deterioration of volatile materials
6. The ultraviolet component of solar radiation and resultant changes in emissivity of most, if not all, materials exposed to ultraviolet for prolonged periods of time

Other than temperature-control surfaces, a number of other material problems in spacecraft are concerned with the following:

1. Surface coatings
2. Materials and parts
3. Lubrication
4. Mechanical properties

These have been treated *in general*, and now a summary is in order.

Surface Coatings. No organic coating can be expected to resist the combined forces of radiation, temperature change, and high vacuum. Ultraviolet radiation causes molecular changes which produce crosslinked, low-soluble refractory structrues. An oxygen absence plus an efficient UV-reflecting pigment will inhibit UV radiation, but the degrading effects of high vacuum cannot be contravened since they are a function of the finite vapor pressures of such materials. These are greatly increased by the formation of low-molecular-weight scission fragments in elevated-temperature regimes. The data in the following table show the weight losses of a wide range of organic coatings exposed for 24 hr to various temperatures in vacuum of 10^{-5} mm Hg (a 90-mile-altitude equivalent). Note that only a straight silicone resin and Kel-F did not suffer a rapid and severe loss of integrity.

Coating type	Per cent loss in vacuum after 24 hr at:	
	300°F	500°F
Polyurethane.................	66	100
Epoxies (four species).......	7–14	61–83
Alkyd.....................	17	39
Silicone....................	7	7†
Acrylic....................	43	62
Phenolic...................	6	15
Kel-F......................	2	3‡
Nitrocellulose..............	82	88
Polysulfide.................	63	65

† Nine per cent at 600°F.
‡ Ninety-eight per cent at 600°F.

Other Materials and Parts.   Organic materials have a number of functional applications in spacecraft, and their use requires the retention of properties under conditions quite dissimilar from those on earth. Seals and gaskets, for example, must provide tight joints and be unreactive with materials with which they come in contact, such as high-energy fuels or other special fluids. These conditions must be obtained even though one side of the seal or gasket is exposed to an ultrahigh vacuum and the entire body is subjected to direct space radiation or to secondary radiation induced by it. Adhesives must also maintain tight, leakproof joints and structural strength under similar conditions. Where adhesives are used to cement optical components together, the effect of the space environment on their refractive indices is another consideration. Electrical applications of organic materials, such as insulation on wires, dielectrics for capacitors, relay structures, and circuit boards, require that such parts not undergo degradation in space [16].

A recent summary of radiation data obtained from United States and U.S.S.R. space probes suggests these facts about the resistance of parts in space. Structural metals will be relatively insensitive to radiation [17]. Elastomers and organic fluids will be quite prone to radiation damage. So, too, will transistors and diodes, but their normal cladding and location in space vehicles will protect them even in the more intense radiation zones. Semiconductor devices and other sensitive electronic components are subject to change with time, and they have low permanent-damage thresholds. Solar cells are generally directly exposed to space unless a more complex scheme of reflected or piped light is used. Proton experiments with solar cells at RCA and at Lockheed indicate that an appreciable decrease in power output can occur after a few months in the midst of the intense Van Allen proton belt. Relief can be obtained by use of protective windows, to a point dictated by weight restrictions.

Lubrication. Lubrication (the subject of Chap. 10) of moving parts is essential to minimize power requirements and to prevent gross seizures. The surface films of adsorbed gases present on all surfaces in the atmosphere are irreparably removed by wear and evaporation in space. As a result, base-metal surfaces make direct contact and may cold-weld together. The potential danger of this affects bearings, gears, cams, and electric parts like sliding contacts, relays, and switches. Lubrication in a vacuum is difficult because of the increased evaporation rate and because fatty acids, lacking oxygen, cannot form protective metallic soaps.

Low-vapor-pressure oils and greases, such as the oils used as pumping fluids in vacuum diffusion pumps, have low evaporation rates but are lacking in good lubricating qualities. Used in a bearing test in vacuum conditions on the order of 10^{-6} mm Hg, these gave lives of only about 1,000 hr. Projected bearing tests planned for both ground and space will measure the running torque by strain-gauge transducers to obtain torque-time histories. Pressure in the bearing tester will be measured by an ionization gauge to give pressure-time history, and motor power consumption will be measured.

Other approaches to lubrication problems in space include the study of thin-film solid lubricants—vacuum-deposited plates of soft metals like silver and gold and of bonded films of laminar solids; of self-lubricating solids—plastics such as Teflon and porous compacts impregnated or filled with molybdenum disulfide; and of dissimilar materials—sapphire, Pyroceram, or carbides in contact with hardened steels [18].

Mechanical Properties. Experiments to measure atmospheric-induced changes such as fatigue and creeping-rupture strength in mechanical properties of materials require a high degree of simulation. Information of this type is needed if large-area low-mass structures are to be built which could find use as passive communications antennas, optical reflectors, and radiation collectors. The statics and dynamics of tori-stiffened circular membranes have been studied in preliminary fashion [19]. Studies on materials, pressurization, and modes of rigidification are needed. A number of methods of rigidification have already been proposed. These include (1) gas-reaction rigidification of a flexible membrane consisting of a linear polymer which will undergo a cross-linking reaction to form a rigid network under stimulation of a reactive vapor; (2) the use of water-soluble silicates which, on inflation of the structure in space, will lose water to yield a rigid network of silicic acid (the reaction can be augmented by using carbon dioxide as an inflation propellant); (3) the rigidification of organic films by the loss of volatiles, primarily high-vapor-pressure plasticizers; (4) rigidification by chemical-reaction foams or by volatilization foams. Each will have to be investigated on the ground, and plans toward space experiments will have to be made in the not-too-distant future.

Economic Aspects of Materials Applications As They Affect Electronic Components for Missiles and Spacecraft. Not too well known is the fact that almost 60 cents of each dollar in the missile and spacecraft industry is spent in the area loosely connected with the field of electronics.

Aerospace electronics is undergoing very rapid changes forced, on the one hand, by engineers and scientists who are making electronic devices smaller and more efficient and, on the other hand, by the systems engineers, who always want more functions done electronically. While circuits are shrinking in size and complexity, the systems in which they are used are becoming larger and much more complex—almost beyond any hope of reasonable reliability and maintainability [20].

The number of components of many aerospace systems runs into the millions and is still increasing with the accelerating design trend to digital systems for many functions besides computing. Even though circuit redundancy and derating techniques are used to achieve some measure of reliability because of their large number, electronic components are at the crucial point for system reliability.

The problem of reliability has triggered the biggest component research and improvement programs the electronic industry has yet seen and is developing a new class of ultrahigh-quality components tailored to aerospace requirements.† Materials research and application play a major role in these developments.

These special components differ from the general line of electronic parts in at least five respects [20].

1. Environmental characteristics. Aerospace components must be rugged enough to stand the rigors of the ground, air, and/or space environments in which they will operate as reviewed above. These factors have already been detailed. Many of these environments can be attenuated by cooling, isolation, shielding, etc.; but the more rugged the component, the less the penalty that must be paid for environment-proofing. Also, protective systems can fail, and then the rugged component has the better chance of survival.

2. Reliability in the operational environment. A requirement of 0.001

† Much of the information of this section was taken from Ref. 20.

per cent mean time between failures per 1,000 hr is becoming quite common for missile components. Generally, the standby and operational lifetimes of aerospace vehicles are increasing sharply. What is now wanted is equipment with 15,000 hr of continuous operational life without failure. Soon this figure will double. For extended space missions, continuous operational lifetimes of 5 to 10 years will not be unusual.

3. Superior performance. Because of the many extremely difficult jobs they must do, and because designers are always trying to cut down on the number and complexity of parts, aerospace components in most cases must give considerably higher performance than "commercial" components.

4. Small size and weight and low power drain. These are obvious but highly important and ever-present factors of consequence.

5. Low cost. A fifth factor, which lately has become more important, is cost. An aerospace component may cost anything from two to a hundred times as much as a functionally similar "commercial" part. No big reductions in cost can be expected until the industry learns how to mechanize component assembly and testing. Mechanization should provide higher yields and better parameter uniformity. Also, the effect of minimum weight cannot be overstressed in terms of economics of the total system. The same is true of power requirements.

Microelectronics. The greatest gains in component development will be provided by microelectronics. Intensive efforts are under way to find ways of building micro-sized electronic circuits that can perform their functions in much less space than is required by conventional electronics design. Reductions of 50 to 99 per cent are desirable. Reduced size, weight, and power drain are not the only aims. Simplicity, reliability, easy environment-proofing, elimination of most circuit connectors, and low cost are also important objectives.

High-density packaging, thin-film techniques, and integrated circuits are the three basic techniques of microelectronics. Microelectronics will ultimately lead to molecular electronics, which does away with the discrete components functions that are performed by the interaction with the molecular properties of the solid. Microelectronics is applicable to 80 to 90 per cent of the circuits in aerospace electronic equipment [20].

A comparison of the characteristics of microminiaturization techniques is given in Table 14.7. Size reductions of the three major techniques are indicated. The time element projected for the growth of these techniques from research through development and production is given in the chart of Fig. 14.14.

The choice of materials and the methods of application perhaps play almost as major a role in the development of microsystem electronics as does the circuit designer. It is now possible to prepare almost all passive

Table 14.7 Characteristics of Microminiaturization Techniques

Techniques and some developers	Est. practical size reduction over conventional components	Practical parts densities, parts per cubic foot	Special skills and technologies required	Cost of first model	Adaptable to semiautomatic production	Adaptable to automatic production	Circuit design flexibility†	Breadboarding by designer
High-density packaging:								
One dimension controlled (Hughes, Thompson Ramo-Wooldridge)	1.5–6	150,000–600,000	No	Moderate	Yes	Yes	Good	Yes
Two dimensions controlled (RCA)	2.5–10	250,000–1,000,000	No	Moderate	Yes	Yes	Good	Yes
Thin-film circuits:								
Screened or chemically deposited (Centralab, DOFL, Lockheed, Sprague)	10–30	1,000,000–3,000,000	Yes	High	Yes	No	Limited	No
Vapor-deposited (Bell Labs, GE, IBM, International Resistance, Sylvania, Servomech, Varo)	20–40	2,000,000–4,000,000	Yes	High	Yes	No	Limited	No
Integrated circuits: (Fairchild, GE, IBM, Motorola, RCA, Texas Instrument, Westinghouse)	20–80	2,000,000–8,000,000	Yes	Very high	Yes	No	Limited	No

† Denotes adaptability to a wide range of communications and computer circuits.

circuit elements (resistors, capacitors, inductors, conductors, and joints) in thin-film form. Programs are now underway to extend these methods to the active elements. Specifically, efforts have turned to semiconductor thin films and to the study of the effects of thickness on their properties.

Four Techniques. There are four basic techniques used for the deposition of thin films on a variety of substrates including glasses, polycrystalline ceramics, single-crystal ceramics, metals, heat-resistant plastics, and semiconductors [20]. The deposition techniques include evaporation,

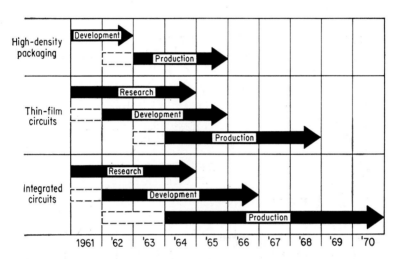

Fig. 14.14 Timetable for microminiaturization techniques.

sputtering, pyrolytic deposition and cracking, and electrodeposition or plating.

The technique chosen for a given application will depend largely on the film material. Evaporation, as in metal film resistors, and pyrolytic cracking, as in deposited carbon resistors, are widely used commercially because they are amenable to mass-production techniques. But since most materials are also better suited to evaporation, this may well be the most important deposition method in the future. A typical example, showing the construction of an *RC* oscillator, is given in Fig. 14.15.

In microminiaturization by molecular electronics, materials phenomena are used instead of assemblies of individual parts to perform functions. A typical integrated circuit formed in a single silicon crystal is shown in Fig. 14.16.

Materials Problems for Spacecraft Auxiliary Power Units. In the space field the need for compact, lightweight, long-life sources of electric power for exoatmospheric applications is well known. The type of unit most suitable depends primarily on the mission.   Secondary factors which determine the most suitable device for advanced space vehicles

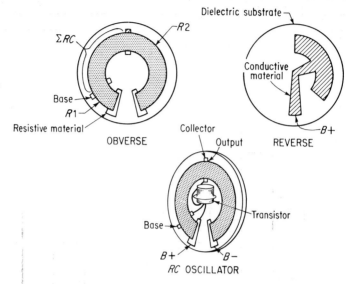

Fig. 14.15   *RC* circuit thin-film techniques.

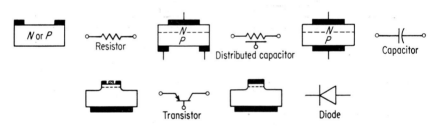

Fig. 14.16   Molecular electronic circuit.   Typical integrated circuits formed in a single silicon crystal.   The resistor is formed by applying ohmic or nonrectifying contacts to a semiconductor wafer; the capacitor, by the capacitance of a relatively large area of *p-n* junction; the distributed capacitor, by the combination of resistive and capacitive elements; the transistor and the diode, by diffused-base techniques. Similar circuits can be formed in other semiconductor crystals [20].

depends on watts per pound, the duration of the mission, and the reliability of the device, effects of a malfunction (particularly if a nuclear reactor is used), the source of thermal energy, the availability of the system, its cost, and environment and other usual considerations.

The power requirements for space vehicles can be divided into two categories: (1) secondary power applications and (2) propulsion requirements.   Secondary power requirements may range from 1 to 15 kw for periods of from 4 hr to 1 year.   For electrical propulsion systems, however, depending on the length of the mission and the boost thrusts available, the power will vary from 50 to 600 kw.   Up until the present time all power requirements for space vehicles have been supplied either by silver-zinc or nickel-cadmium battery systems, or by solar cells in connection with storage cells of the type just mentioned.

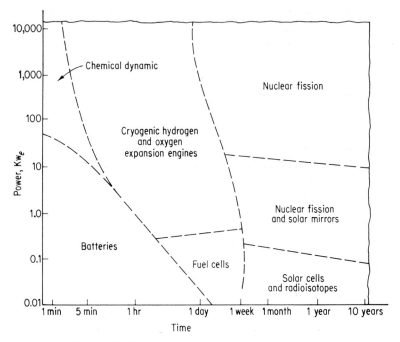

Fig. 14.17   Useful-energy requirements versus time.

A rather extensive survey by W. C. Cooley of NASA [21] has compared nuclear and solar power systems along a number of important lines.   For purposes of comparison, a 3-kw power source was used as a basis.   To obtain some information of the useful regimes of energy sources that can generate electric power in space, attention is invited to Fig. 14.17.   This clearly delineates the power level and time of availability for a number of actual and expected nuclear power sources.

A few words should be said concerning present systems.   At the present time, the use of silicon solar cells and silver-zinc batteries in space vehicles has proved to be very helpful, and the technology is improving rapidly. Presently available cells are usually rectangular, 1 cm wide by 2 cm long and about 10 to 20 mils thick.   They are made of pure silicon crystals built to produce a surface having a *p-n* junction.   The conversion efficiency at ambient temperature is approximately 8 per cent, corresponding to a power of about 10 watts/ft^2 of normal incidence of solar radiation outside the earth's atmosphere.   For a 3-kw average output in an orbit with 65 per cent of the time in the sun, a total power of at least 4,600 watts must be produced.   With a solar-cell array oriented toward the sun within $\pm 10°$, an area of at least 460 ft^2 of cells will be required.   If we assume predicted 1960 production costs of silicon solar cells of about $125 per watt, the cost of cells will be $575,000 per system.   If the cells are only 2 cm^2 in area, over 200,000 cells are required to be connected into series and parallel circuits.   The reliability of such a system is subject

Table 14.8   Comparison of Power Systems

System	Thermal cycle efficiency, %	Solar collector diam., ft	Estimated system weight, lb
Reactor-turboelectric............	8	...	1,930
Solar-turboelectric..............	10	34	850
Solar–Stirling engine............	30	20	555
Solar-thermoelectric.............	6	43	1,250
Solar-thermionic................	8	37	1,000–1,500
Solar-photovoltaic...............	8†	24‡	600–1,450

† Overall.
‡ Equivalent.

to question in view of the large number of electrical connections and the fragility of the cells which are connected to lightweight structures.†
    The system is subject to severe accelerations and vibrational loads during launch and to cyclic thermal stresses while in orbit.   Weight of such a system would be between 300 and 600 lb, exclusive of energy storage or attitude control.   If nickel-cadmium batteries are used for storage, they will weigh about 700 lb.   The attitude-control system is estimated at 100 lb; therefore, the entire power system might weigh up to 1,400 lb.
    Data for various power systems are given in Table 14.8, which compares a reactor-turboelectric of the SNAP-2 variety with the solar-photovoltaic system just discussed and with other potential solar-source energy-conversion systems.
    A 3-kw nuclear-reactor system such as the SNAP 2 includes a small reactor weighing about 220 lb; a primary coolant liquid of sodium; and a mercury Rankine-cycle turbogenerator, plus a radiator requiring about

† These data were taken from Ref. 21.

100 ft², with the mercury condensing in it at 600°F. The problems of such an APU include safety, radiation scattering, shielding, and the problems of orbital start-up of the turbine and reactor since it is not practical to operate the turbogenerator during the boost phase. All these problems complicate this type of power system. However, it is the most advanced of the nuclear systems that should be available in the next few years.

In all the systems described, material problems and economic factors are foremost. They begin primarily with the cost of obtaining 1 lb of useful payload in orbit. This payload will also include auxiliary power equipment. The reliability and endurance capability of the auxiliary power unit, the vehicle and mission compatibility of the auxiliary power unit, the safety, and the development and production costs are all part and parcel of the usefulness of such a system. The cost of electric energy in outer space is now running at about $1,000 per kilowatthour, if the booster-vehicle costs are included, compared with a few cents per kilowatthour near the earth. The difference of five orders of magnitude provides ample opportunity for cost reduction. Even though the cost of development and production of space power systems may be only of the order of 5 to 10 per cent of the cost of the booster vehicle, the power-system development is still a multimillion-dollar effort. The weight of the power system is particularly important, and it may determine the size and cost of the booster vehicle required for the specific mission. With nuclear turboelectric, nuclear thermionic, and nuclear thermoelectric systems, all the problems inherent in operating the systems on the ground from a materials point of view are also obtained in space but are compounded by the environment of space, as has been discussed previously.

The major problem that we are facing in the direct conversion of electric power from thermal energy is that the right kinds of materials are not available for use at the elevated temperature which characterizes these systems. Materials research holds the key to future progress in the field of direct energy conversion. In the equations discussed earlier, concerning thermal control, P_i stood for generated internal heat that had to be dissipated. With batteries and solar cells and the electronic equipment operated from these sources, it is at a minimum. However, with the development by auxiliary power units of large amounts of thermal energy that must be radiated into outer space, major problems may develop. The effect of the environment on the methods of dumping this energy may also be drastic, particularly if liquid or gas systems are used for removing heat from the energy source or energy converter. A typical example of a nuclear APU is shown in Fig. 14.18, which is a schematic of the SNAP-2 nuclear-turbogenerator system. The esti-

mated timetable for use of three nuclear auxiliary power systems for
spacecraft is given in Fig. 14.19.

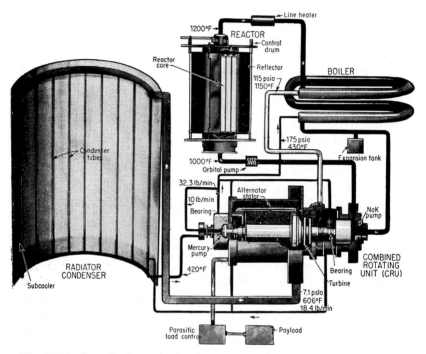

Fig. 14.18   Snap-2 schematic showing reactor-turbogenerator and condenser.

Economic Considerations of Materials for Missiles

As stated previously, the second part of this chapter will discuss the
three critical materials considerations of the ballistic-missile reentry
vehicle, motor cases, and nozzle and vector control of hardware.

The discussion will be limited to solid-propellant rockets, and the
remainder of the chapter is concerned with economic aspects and the
trend toward the second- and third-generation missiles which are and
will be solids.   There are a number of reasons that favor the solid-propellant rocket motor.   Since weight is a premium, optimization studies
have disclosed the best shapes for the lightest structures.   Also, operating motor conditions and other load conditions such as launch and lateral
loads determine the design criteria imposed on these structures.

The last five years have shown a continuing emphasis on solid-propellant rockets in competition with the liquid engines because of the many

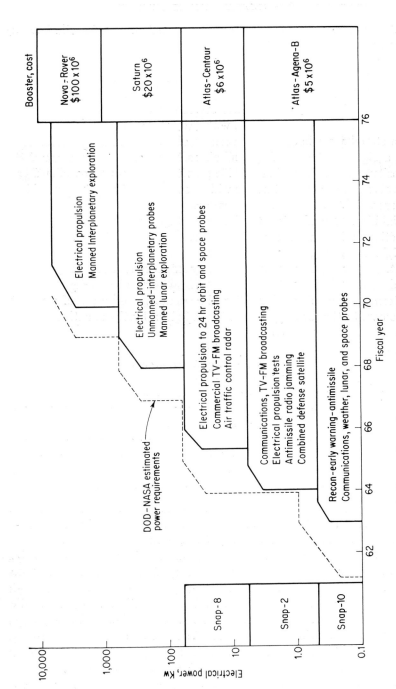

Fig. 14.19 Comparison of power systems based on missions and power sources.

413

advantages offered by solid propellants. A list of qualities that favor the solid-propellant application is as follows:[†]

Readiness. Less preparation required before firing.

Simplicity. The rocket motor depends on a mechanism with very few components to be operated.

Handling. Propellant and motor are one easily moved unit.

Storage. The solid propellant, with proper care for the environment, can be stored for a long time. Because of compactness it requires less space, a big advantage in ships and aircraft.

Density. With the higher specific gravity of the solid propellant, the total volume for the rocket motor will be smaller. It results in a vehicle with less weight.

Reliability. In addition to the advantages above, solid-propellant production rockets are more reliable, having a reliability of 99 per cent and higher.

Cost. The overall expense is generally less because development costs are reduced.

In terms of propulsion dynamics, the overall performance of a rocket vehicle can, to the first approximation, be given by the equation

$$V_B = g \left(I_{sp} \ln \frac{W_B}{W} - t_b \right)$$

where W = takeoff weight

W_B = weight at burnout

t_b = time to reach burnout condition with acting loads keeping thrust and gravitational forces

The velocity V_B at the end of the powered flight is an indication of the overall performance of the rocket vehicle and can, therefore, be transformed into ranges or altitudes obtainable.

Disregarding the generally small second gravitational term, the equation demonstrates how the velocity depends on the specific impulse I_{sp} and the mass-weight ratio W/W_B. This latter parameter shows the importance of keeping the inert weight of the vehicle small by efficiently utilizing the structure and the materials. If a certain mass-weight ratio cannot be achieved, it may result in a complete failure of the intended mission.

A major portion of the effort in materials application work for ballistic missiles is concerned with obtaining a minimum inert-weight fraction by taking maximum weight out of the main areas to be discussed—motor cases, reentry structures, inert hardware, nozzle, insulation, and vector control mechanisms. The economic factors are based on this as a first consideration.

[†] This analysis is taken from Ref. 22.

A further refinement in efficiency is possible by introducing staging which conserves energy that would be expended by carrying aloft unnecessary structural components.

Material Selection for Motor Cases. The design of very light motor cases requires full utilization of materials with high strength properties. Up to now, steels have been used for the fabrication almost exclusively, because their use offers certain advantages in formability and weldability. A variety of good steels are available; and a continuous improvement, resulting in increased strength and better properties, has been going on over the last several years.

A list of materials being used or seriously considered would include (1) the low-alloy steels such as 300 M, AMS 6434, SA 4340, and SA 4130; (2) the hot-worked die steels such as H 11 and Laddish D6A; and, finally, (3) the precipitation-hardening stainless steels of the AM 350 and the 17-7 PH variety.

A second category of materials is the titanium alloys, such as the 6% aluminum–4% vanadium variety or the alpha-beta alloy; and the all-beta alloy, such as the 13% vanadium–11% chromium–3% aluminum alloy. The final category, besides the high-strength homogenous steels and the titanium alloys, is the composite materials exemplified by the glass-reinforced plastics. In any design of a missile to meet specific range and payload requirements within a specific time, a certain gross weight is generally established. The strength level required for the various components, including the motor case, is then determined.

The importance of metallurgical factors has been repeatedly discussed. You may have the feeling that a clear understanding of the variables involved does not at present exist in the missile industry. You could not be more correct. All the metallurgical factors, including the fabricability and the reliability, enter into the acceptance criteria of any material chosen for a pressure vessel. These considerations in turn determine the economics of the system or the cost of production of a motor case.

Recently a tremendous effort has been made in the United States to produce cases of steels capable of being stressed to pressures equivalent to 200,000 to 240,000 psi. This strength level can be reached consistently and repeatedly provided that the chemistry of the materials as well as the methods of manufacture are rigidly controlled, from the melting phase through the forging processes, through manufacturing (including shear forming, if this is one of the methods), through the welding stage, through the heat treatment and through the final pressurization tests. To produce cases of these outstanding properties, we can depend not only on the steel selected but on the continuous control from melt shop to pressure test. The exercising of these controls, of course, adds greatly to the cost but, at the same time, increases the reliability and therefore tends to lower the total overall cost of the system.   Some of the factors of interest in selection are the alloy composition, the heat treatment, and the carbon content.   By selecting heats of steel at higher carbon contents, higher strength levels can be reached.   However, these higher carbon limits affect ductility and, particularly, weldability so an optimum range or level must be established.   The precipitation-hardening steels offer promise of extremely high levels but also yield lower ductilities and add to the processing problems.

Steel quality is one of the most important requirements for ultrahigh-strength steels; it includes freedom from inclusion, segregation, and composition variations.   All these factors affect fabrication, particularly shear forming; inclusions can cause some of these steels to exhibit brittle fracture.   Vacuum melting will alleviate this problem but adds considerably to the cost—as much as 50 cents per pound.   This type of material in the future will be mandatory for steels of extremely high stress level. Also, because of the requirements for large domes and ring forgings which necessitate very large billets, consumable electrode vacuum melting, with its freedom from segregation and inclusions, looks quite attractive. Fine grain size is also desirable for ductility and formability, particularly when shear forming is utilized.   Freedom from notch sensitivity is another criterion for high-strength steels.   This is one of the reasons that the carbon content is limited; carbon has a major effect on the weldability of a number of the steels.   The weld zone is one of the most critical areas in high-strength steel cases; therefore, weldability is an important factor, particularly if pressure vessels with yields of over 240,000 psi are to be produced.   Similar factors such as cleanliness, freedom from segregation, and uniform chemical composition affect weldability.   Sulfur and phosphorus contents have to be low also.   Mismatch and out-of-round conditions in welding produce stress raisers which lower the useful strength level of any pressure vessel.   Methods of grinding also can impose residual stresses and accentuate cracking and may cause inclusions to be trapped. Welding techniques must be rigidly controlled.   Another important factor in selection of rocket-case materials is ease of heat treatment.   This aids in maintaining dimensions during the heat-treatment cycle.   Decarburization has a definite beneficial effect on ductility and notch sensitivity, yet the degree and the steepness of the carbon gradient to the surface are open to question and argument at the present time.   As is expected, surface decarburization will also reduce notch sensitivity.

The methods of fabrication will exert a major influence on the cost of producing a rocket case not only in terms of the cost of each fabrication step but primarily in terms of the reliability of the pressure vessel being fabricated.   For example, certain fabrication techniques can remove the need for longitudinal welds and, although they may have a higher initial cost, they may in the long run be more economically sound. Thus, the trend to "flow turning" or "shear forming" the cylindrical sections and thereby alleviating the need for longitudinal welds goes far in terms of producing a larger number of acceptable pressure vessels. If flaws exist in the steel because of nonhomogeneity or inclusions, these flaws tend to cause tearing during the shear-forming operation and thus become evident. The material can then be rejected before all the expensive fabrication work is finished. Stock melted twice by the vacuum-arc process should be used for closures that contain ports and bosses for nozzles, ignition ports, and thrust reversal ports. Forged and machined heads with these bosses integral, although more expensive in their production and machining, may, in the final analysis, be cheaper. A large number of failures have occurred because of weld defects around thrust reversal ports, ignition bosses, etc., because of the complex stress condition existing under pressurization in these portions of the pressure vessel, in both the dome and aft end. By using either forged or 3D machined closures to obviate defects due to the welding, a much more reliable and, therefore, more economical pressure vessel can be obtained. At the present time, one of the ideal methods that has been developed is the use of (1) double consumable vacuum-arc-melted stock; (2) integrally forged closures that are machined to final shape; (3) ring forgings that are then flow-turned or shear-formed for the cylindrical sections; and (4) if the pressure vessel has a large L/D ratio, the girth welding of these forged and turned cylindrical sections to each other and finally to the closures. Typical sections are shown in Fig. 14.20.

Although the procedure just described is quite expensive in terms of material cost, fabrication techniques, and equipment, in the final analysis it yields a very high percentage of acceptable pressure vessels at much higher strength ratios than have been previously obtained; its use therefore can be considered to be economically sound.

It has only been recently that the B120 VCA titanium alloy has been seriously considered as a rocket casing material capable of developing a yield strength–density ratio of over 1 million. The 13% vanadium–11% chrome–3% aluminum alloy sheet possesses a yield strength after cold-rolling and aging of 180,000 psi or better, with elongation in the range of 5 to 10 per cent.

With a density value of 0.175 lb/in.³, it is evident that this alloy has a potentiality of a strength-density ratio of 1 million. Again, the use of rolled forged rings which are flow-turned, together with forged and machined ends joined by girth welding, seems to be the optimum fabrication method for the preparation of a pressure vessel of this material. To develop these optimum properties, controlled cold reduction and proper aging treatments are quite critical. A number of problems exist in terms of weldability for optimum properties after welding. The notch sensitivity of these beta-phase alloys still is not well enough known so that this material can be used with impunity for the design of high-strength pressure vessels. Again, this high strength-density ratio obtainable with titanium alloys must be considered in competition with other cheaper materials. There is an inference that a titanium vessel may cost up to four times as much as a steel vessel and almost ten times as much

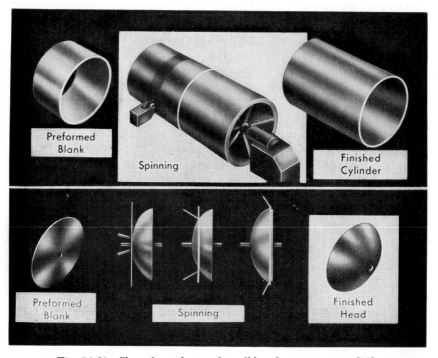

Fig. 14.20   Shear-formed parts for solid rocket-motor cases [23].

as a filament-wound composite structure made of E glass. In the homogeneous motor cases using materials of either steel or titanium, a number of fabrication techniques exist. All large thin-wall motor cases made from these high-strength materials demand the utmost in manufacturing performance for the satisfactory construction of these vessels. In the past, the predominant method has been roll forming and welding of sheet material, with cylinders and end sections formed separately and assembled with circumferential joints. The nozzle reinforcements and bosses are welded to end closures and domes. The presence of many joints in these parts is detrimental to the strength of the case, and welding may cause distortion. Special welding and heat-treating techniques become necessary. The production of reliable high-quality motors depends on large-scale fabrication methods employing automatic work procedures to the fullest extent. Forging and machining processes, using forged rings and caps made by machining the part to correct sizes, are also utilized for fabrication. Since the thickness of the vessels is small, elaborate tooling is necessary to produce the close tolerances required. A few girth welds, plus the welding of the nozzles, are the only joints, and these have no detrimental effect on the strength of the case. Three-dimensional machining operations for the integral bosses and the end domes is indicated. The technique has shown a high degree of reliability for achieving high strength. The power shear-forming process for the manufacture of cylindrical portions is a fabrication method that is moving rapidly into prominence in the pressure-vessel field. Parts with diameters up to 75 in. and lengths up to 100 in. can be produced by this process. The method is also useful for shear-forming heads and cylinders, or combinations of these. With a forged and preformed ring, and by complicated fabrication procedures, it is possible to form half the motor case with cylinder and heads carrying integral bosses. This method is very satisfactory with most of the high-strength alloys.

Deep drawing methods have also been used to produce heads and closures as well as some of the cylindrical portions of motor cases. Small- and medium-sized pressure vessels have been produced but, as yet, a large-scale drawing of large L/D ratio pressure vessels has not been obtained.

Composite Structures—Filament-winding Process. The high-tensile-strength fibers such as glass can be employed for this method. These materials are wound as filaments over mandrels in the shape of the motor and bonded with a resin. The complete structure is then cured under controlled conditions. This process permits a continuous winding so that many shapes can be produced without any joints or interruptions. Only the fibers are assumed to carry the main internal loads. The filaments must follow a prescribed direction of winding on the surfaces of the particular shape being produced. For cylindrical bodies, the circumferential and axial stresses are in the ratio of 2:1. Fibers are wound at an angle of 35° to the circumferential direction. End caps or closures have a concentration of fibers in their center regions because the radii become smaller, resulting in a thickening in the shell. In order to utilize the strength in the material, the domes must be shaped in new optimized forms. The winding of cylindrical and end sections as a unit requires special winding combinations as shown in Fig. 14.21. Hoop stresses of up to 80,000 psi can be sustained, with strength-weight ratios of well over a million. The processing is fast and economical and does not require heavy and elaborate tooling. The vessels are not notch-sensitive, but they cannot withstand high-impact loads. However, the temperature limit for present resins is about 500°F. The attachment of skirts and attainment of close tolerances on thicknesses and diameter require special attention. However, very rapid progress is expected in the field of filament-wound structures, and it would not be surprising if in the near future a large portion of the solid-propellant motor cases were manufactured by

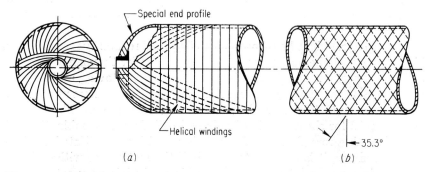

Fig. 14.21 Winding patterns for filament-winding methods. (a) Cylinder plus dome; (b) cylinder only [22].

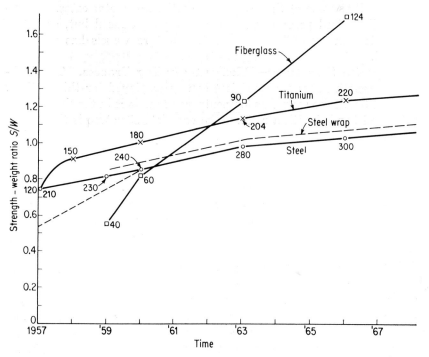

Fig. 14.22 S/W ratio as a function of time for motor-case materials selection. Numbers indicate σ_w = working stress, ksi.

this technique. Some idea of the strength-density ratios for the three types of materials discussed with a projection against time is shown in Fig. 14.22. Indicated in the figure are applicable burst pressures for filamentary structures and uniaxial yield strengths for homogeneous cases made out of steels and titanium. It is evident from these curves that the growth potential at the present looks the greatest for the filamentary glass structures, provided that some of the problems discussed can be

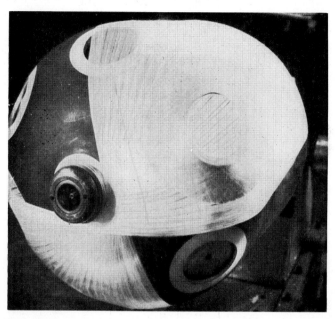

Fig. 14.23 Full-scale filament-wound motor case being wound; reverse port openings are shown [25].

overcome. However, before becoming overly optimistic in projecting the future of filamentary-wound structures, it is necessary to consider that it is very difficult to achieve the S/W ratio indicated in Fig. 14.22, which is for simple cylinders only; the performance of a whole pressure vessel may be quite different.

Winding inefficiencies due to the shape of the forward and aft closures, the need for off-center openings in these ends for nozzle inserts, and the need for thrust reversal ports on the forward end all require more windings than would be indicated from the material strength-weight values and thus tend to increase the total structure weight. The necessity for cutting of the fibers to provide for inserts requires that extra weight be used for safety. This is illustrated in Fig. 14.23.

However, it seems certain that better techniques for the preparation of

Table 14.9 Material Selection for Motor Cases [26]

Material	Reliability	Cost	Fabricability	Inspection	Geometric stability	Serviceability	Experience	Potential
Glass-reinforced plastic......	Poor	Medium	Fair	Poor	Poor	Fair?	Low	Good
Titanium..................	Fair	High	Fair	Fair	Good	Good	Low	Fair to good
Steel......................	Good	Low	Good	Good	Good	Fair	High	Fair
Steel strip................	Poor	Medium	Fair	Poor	Fair	Fair	Low	Fair

filamentary-wound structures will be forthcoming within the next year, so that the high strength-weight ratio for this very light material can be fully realized. Also, improvements in both glass strength and resin binders can be expected in the next few years. A comparative analysis of these major material potentials for selection for motor cases is given in Table 14.9.

Problems of Nozzle Selection; Economic Considerations for Nozzles and Vector-control Methods. In the case of the advances over the state of the art for solid-propellant rocketry, the area of nozzles and vector control presents critical material problems. Combustion products from the rocket motor must be exhausted through a properly contoured nozzle for control of thrust. This nozzle must be highly resistant to significant enlargement to prevent modification of the burning characteristics of the propellant. Temperature resistance and light weight with adequate structural strength is required. Since cooling systems are not as yet feasible in the solid motors, both the nozzle and nozzle throat are subjected to high thermal flux from the exhaust flames. In addition, the divergent section of the nozzle is a structural component to which vector-control devices may be attached, and it must have adequate modulus and strength at the elevated temperatures. The development of nozzles and vector-control devices has not kept pace with the increase in combustion temperature that has arisen as a result of advances in propulsion technology. Properties required are (1) light weight, (2) ultrahigh temperature resistance, (3) erosion and thermal-shock resistance, and (4) reliable performance.

Refractory metals and their alloys are at present the only refractory materials having sufficient thermal shock and erosion resistance. However, these materials have very high densities and thus impose a severe weight penalty unless used in very thin sections (backed up by lightweight insulation). They are also reactive with gases, and this compounds the problem. In many cases the complex shapes required are difficult to obtain because of the poor formability of the refractory metals. Vector-control methods have also been limited to either jetavators or gimbaled nozzles, where both of these vectoring methods have control surfaces exposed to extremely steep thermal gradients and highly oxidizing conditions. Such conditions cause troubles with mechanical linkages, seals, and so forth. A further complicating factor for both nozzle and control devices is the metallic additives to the propellants which accelerate deterioration and decrease nozzle reliability by increasing the erosive characteristics of the gas during firing. With solid-propellant rockets, the current and the immediate-future generations will utilize nozzle designs on the principle of insulated hot structures, as illustrated schematically in Fig. 14.24. High-strength steels and titanium alloys are used for nozzle housings to provide structural support and stability.   Reinforced plastics are used as ablative flame barriers in the nozzle entrance and exit sections. The severe conditions in the throat and portions of the exit cone require refractory materials such as molybdenum or tungsten.   These are often backed up by graphite heat sinks to reduce size and weight.   Refractory metals are also used for retaining rings and fasteners required for the assembly of components into a gastight structure.   Each motor design presents its own particular problem in respect to nozzle design.   The most important material criteria governing selection in design of the

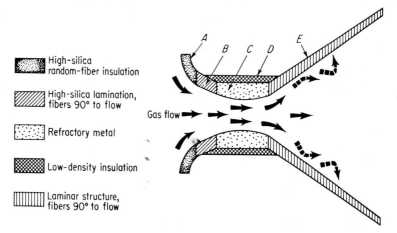

Fig. 14.24   Schematic of a solid-propellant nozzle showing the composite materials in make-up.

nozzle components are the time-stress-temperature relations developed during firing and the chemical and erosive environment resulting from combustion in the propellant.   Minor changes in these may affect significantly the performance of materials.   With increase of propellant flame temperatures from 4800 to well over 6000°F, radical departures in terms of materials selected for the nozzle and vector-control mechanisms are necessary.   In addition, the changes in temperatures will also mean increases in weight and, as discussed previously, the weight fraction must increase to yield greater performance [26].

Insulation.   Internal motor insulation is required to prevent overheating in the structural case and to prevent direct impingement of exhaust gases on any structural parts.   Insulation thus serves two purposes: heat insulation and flame-barrier insulation.   If the major problem were heat insulation, the total weight of insulation would be minor. This is illustrated by the fact that in most solid-propellant cases there is almost a complete lack of insulation in the central portion of the chamber.

It is a requirement of "resistance to char" by proximity to flame that imposes heavy weight penalties.   Highly erosion-resistant materials are required in the aft closure near the nozzle entrance port where gas velocities become high.   In present designs a number of insulation schemes are used.   Laminated glass cloth or graphite cloth phenolic resins are used in the massive sections of the aft ends and in parts of the forward end where resistance to char and erosion are required.   Asbestos epoxy resin lay-ups are also used.   For regions of lower erosion rate, particularly in fiber-glass chambers where plasticity is required, reinforced rubber-base materials are employed.   Reduction in the weight of insulation can be achieved in two ways: by the development of greatly improved materials or by design to minimum thickness for reliable operation.   In spite of the nearly three years of concentrated research, development, and testing of a wide variety of materials, discovery of greatly improved erosion- and char-resistant insulation materials is yet to be realized.   Although improvements in insulation performance and capabilities have been achieved, no significant breakthroughs promising a major weight reduction in insulation have occurred.   The present families of graphite cloth, phenolics, and reinforced rubbers will probably be the basic insulation materials for the next five years or more.   This material problem should be a major challenge to all materials engineers working in this field.   Major economies can be realized if better insulating materials having greater char resistance are found.

Material Selection for Reentry Vehicles.   Other chapters have dealt with thermal-protection systems and materials for applications at extremely high temperature.   The following discussion will be partially a review of information covered earlier.   The same holds true for the subject of thermal-protection systems for reentry, which is the third phase of material economics to be covered with reference to materials for ballistic missiles.

Reentry-vehicle structures must either withstand or be protected from severe thermodynamic heating.   Configuration research must integrate thermal-protection systems with the structural design and trajectory-control methods to determine the optimum vehicle configurations.   The heating loads of interest for various types of reentry are given in Fig. 14.25.   Such studies determine the total weights of various approaches and are carried to the point where trade-offs are indicated.   For example, manned reentry vehicles which use ablation for thermal protection will employ a different configuration and reentry trajectory from those which use radiative cooling.   Another class of vehicle uses very lightly loaded structures of the erectable variety to minimize its dynamic heating problem.   Possible devices of this nature include high-temperature parachutes, inflated drag brakes, and inflatable lifting surfaces.   Emphasis and design of reentry vehicles is now centered around the dissimilar problems of improving the accuracy of nose cones for ballistic reentry weapons and the development of highly efficient heat shields for satellite reentry capsules and boost glide vehicles.   Recently it has been adequately developed and demonstrated that both heat-sink and ablation nose cones work for both types of vehicles, but at present models have a substantial margin of safety that could be used to increase their performance.   Two types

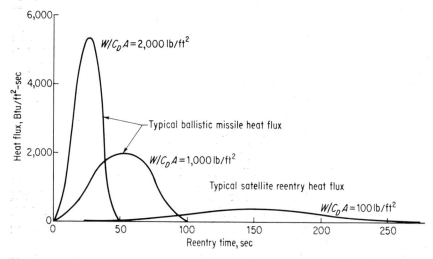

Fig. 14.25   Heat rate in Btu/(ft²)(sec) versus time for various types of reentry. Different design problems for warheads and manned satellites are shown.   New ablation-type warheads will tend toward short-period very-high-heat pulses [27].

of reentry materials concepts have been available, the heat-sink and the ablative design concepts; recently, a third has come to the fore: the radiative structure.   In the second type, the ablative, four general classes of material are of interest [28]:

1. Plastics that change composition chemically as they are heated.   As they change composition they also sublime and pass directly from the solid to the gaseous state without actually liquefying.

2. Materials that sublime but do not change their chemical composition and react with the constituents of dissociated air surrounding the nose cone during reentry.

3. Materials that first melt and then vaporize.

4. Composite materials such as the reinforced plastics that pyrolyze or char.

Nylon is an ablative material of type 1 that will melt and vaporize without reacting with the boundary layer.   Silicone, melamine, and 91LD resins all are types of the second variety that ablate and leave a char.

Glass is typical of the third class of material, which melts before it vaporizes and releases gases into the boundary layer.   Most practical materials do not sublime, and only those with very high viscosity, such as glass or silica, can be used as ablating materials for high-speed flight.   In general, glasses are substances with high silica content and are not good radiation materials unless they contain certain additives.   Graphite also is a member of the second class of materials.   Combustion takes place at the surface, and the substance does not enter a liquid phase as there is no char layer.   However, in satellite design, graphite acts essentially as a heat sink.   Teflon is a member of a class of ablating materials whose ablating process consists of a chemical change in which the Teflon depolymerizes into a monomer with a high vapor pressure and flashes directly into the vapor phase; about 750 Btu/lb is absorbed during this process.   At higher temperatures, incompletely depolymerized polymers diffuse to the surface, and a number of different chemical reactions can occur [28].

One of the major considerations concerning the selection of ablation materials for thermal shields is the rate at which they conduct heat. Many of them, including nylon and phenolic nylon, are good insulators. A light shield of these materials will not allow the substructure of a vehicle to heat significantly during ballistic and satellite reentries.   During the longer heating periods being discussed for hypersonic gliders, the insulation requirements are more severe, and the lightest design may be a combination of an ablation shield backed by a layer of more efficient insulation substance rather than by a thicker layer of ablative material. Also in these regimes, radiation-heat-shielding techniques may save weight and improve reentry velocities and accuracies.   There is promise of considerable economy, of greater weapon payload capability, of lighter reentry structure, of greater accuracy by reentering at high ballistic parameters, or greater $W/C_D A$, where W = weight, C_D = drag coefficient, and A = area.   The higher the ballistic parameter, the faster the warhead will pass through the atmosphere and the more accurate it can be.

In this area of reentry design and materials development, extensive development work is now underway on new graphite materials and structures.   These work principally through radiation rather than ablation or heat storage.   The new radiation-heat-shielding technique will lead to significant savings in weights and accuracy.   Structures with graphite may weigh only one-tenth as much as some of the newer ablation materials discussed.   These developments are based on pyrolytic graphite and pyrolitic graphite–base materials.

Oriented Graphite [29].   Pyrolytic graphite is essentially a highly oriented graphite.   Compared with commercial graphite, which may reach an orientation ratio of 3:1, pyrolytic graphite may have orientation ratios from 100:1 to 1,000:1.   The attraction of pyrolytic graphite is principally due to its high thermal anisotropy, that is, its ability to conduct heat readily in one direction and block it in another.   Thermal conductivity of pyrolytic graphite will run fifty to one thousand times higher in a direction parallel to the surface than in a direction perpendicular to

Fig. 14.26   Typical photomicrograph of pyrolytic graphite showing layering of structure and growth cones (100X).

the surface.   At the same time, the material retains the high sublimation temperature of regular graphite, i.e., approximately 6600°F.   Electrical anisotropy of pyrolytic graphite is even higher than the thermal.   A typical photomicrograph of pyrolytic graphite is shown in Fig. 14.26.

In addition to improved density and high-temperature tensile strength, pyrolytic graphite has overcome some of the drawbacks of ordinary graphite, such as the poor oxidation and erosion resistances that have caused missile engineers to turn from the use of graphite as a reentry material

in the past.   But more, perhaps, than any other single factor, it is pyrolytic graphite's unusual combination of high sublimation temperature and
high thermal anisotropy that accounts for the favorable consideration
currently being given to the material.

Until now, radiation heat transfer generally has been considered a comparatively unimportant factor in reentry heating.   The important phenomenon has been aerodynamic heat transfer.   But both types of heat

Fig. 14.27   Slab of 0.25-in. commercial graphite (top) and 0.25-in. slab of pyrolytic
graphite heated by oxygen-acetylene torches showing heat distributed in the pyrolytic
graphite.   (*Courtesy High Temperature Materials Company, Inc.*)

transfer vary with altitude (air density), velocity, and dimensions of the
reentry vehicle; and at high enough densities and velocities, radiation
becomes the dominant form of heat transfer from the hot compressed
gases ahead of the vehicle.   Moreover, under certain conditions, equilibrium is reached in which a body will radiate heat away as fast as it is
received.

An important drawback here has been the fact that equilibrium temperatures for today's reentry vehicles are well above the destruction temperatures of most materials.   Ceramic materials similar to those used on
the other ICBM reentry vehicles, for example, start to melt around
3200°F.   At this temperature, radiation heat transfer is not too significant.   However, radiation increases with the fourth power of the absolute
temperature.   Thus, at 6600°F, the sublimation temperature of graphite,
radiation heat transfer is roughly sixteen times greater.   A heat shield

made of pyrolytic graphite would reach an equilibrium temperature well before it reached the sublimation temperature of the graphite. In this temperature differential lies the potential for increasing the reentry velocity by further streamlining of the vehicle [28]. Local heat input per unit area is generally highest at the tip of the reentry-vehicle nose cone. Most materials would decompose quickly in highly streamlined nose cones. In the case of pyrolytic graphite, however, the material's thermal anisotropy would serve to spread this heat over the surface, therein turning the entire reentry vehicle into a radiating body. A comparison of normal graphite with pyrolytic graphite is shown in Fig. 14.27. At the same time, the anisotropic thermal conductivity characteristic serves to block the heat going through the pyrolytic graphite heat shield.

It is possible to obtain a temperature drop of approximately 4000°F across a piece of pyrolytic graphite only 0.125 in. thick, which means that the metal backup structures can be made from lightweight metals such as titanium, aluminum, or magnesium.

Joining or bonding pyrolytic graphite to other materials is one of a number of problems to be solved. Another is design. When a pyrolytic graphite structure cools, it tends to shrink more in one direction than another, inducing stresses in the material.

Conclusion

In conclusion, our progress in the aerospace field and in space flight is dependent on the solution of crucial materials problems. These have been discussed in great detail. A new concept of materials application has been presented. The tremendous increase in the number of materials, coupled with the rise of new and more severe service requirements, is bringing many changes in ways of applying materials.

Traditionally, the point of view of the user of materials was to fit the design or product to the properties of a material. This attitude has changed, as has been aptly demonstrated in the chapters in this book.

The major concern now is finding and applying a material or materials with the right combination of properties to meet the design and service conditions. This attitude is end-service-oriented. The next task in this process, as has been indicated with pyrolytic graphite as an example, is to tailor-make materials.

Many forces are interacting to bring a unity and discipline to the field of materials. Along with advances in science is coming a unified technology for materials. Traditional boundaries between classes of materials and between materials specialists are being swept away, and a new materials science is emerging [29]. Nowhere is this proceeding more rapidly than in the applications of materials to missiles and spacecraft.

REFERENCES

1. Anonymous: Materials Problems Associated with the Thermal Control of Space Vehicles, *National Academy of Sciences, National Research Council, Materials Advisory Board, Rept.* MAB-155-M, Oct. 20, 1959.
2. Stans, M. H.: Funding the Space Program, *Astronautics*, vol. 5, no. 11, p. 23, November, 1960.
3. Loebelson, Robert M.: Advanced AF Development Work Swings to Spacecraft, *Space/Aeronautics*, vol. 34, p. 42, December, 1960.
4. Koelle, H. H.: Economy and Techniques of Large Missile Booster Recovery, *Western Aviation*, December, 1960, p. 46.
5. Means, Paul: NASA Gives Congress 10-year Plan, *Missiles Rockets*, Feb. 8, 1960, p. 20.
6. Lyman, S. W.: The Metallurgical Challenge of Missilery, *Battelle Mem. Inst. Tech. Rev.*, vol. 9, no. 1, p. 3, January, 1960.
7. Rhode, R. V., and J. C. Houbold: The Impact of Space Technology on Research and Development, National Aeronautics and Space Administration (presented at the Advisory Group for Aeronautical Research and Development General Assembly held in Copenhagen, Denmark, Oct. 20–29, 1958).
8. Steinberg, M., J. Fox, and B. Augenstein: A Proposed Ground and Flight Program to Develop Space Age Materials, *Lockheed Missiles and Space Company*, LMSD/288244, Palo Alto, Calif., Apr. 6, 1960.
9. Yonts, O., C. Normand, and D. Harrison: High Energy Sputtering, *J. Appl. Physics*, vol. 31, no. 3, March, 1960.
10. Reiffil, L.: Structural Damage and Other Effects of Solar Plasmas, *ARS J.*, vol. 30, no. 3, p. 258, March, 1960.
11. Thostesen, T. O., A. R. Hibbs, and E. P. Berwalda: Temperature Control of the Explorers and Pioneers, in Clauss, F. J. (ed.): "Surface Effects on Spacecraft Materials," pp. 55–91, John Wiley & Sons, Inc., New York, 1960.
12. Dow, N. F.: Important Research Problems in Advanced Flight Structures Design, *NASA Tech. Note* TN D-518, June, 1960.
13. Camack, W. G., and D. K. Edwards: Effect of Surface Thermal Radiation Characteristics on the Temperature Control Problem in Satellites, in Clauss, F. J. (ed.): "Surface Effects on Spacecraft Materials," pp. 3–54, John Wiley & Sons, Inc., New York, 1960.
14. Spencer, H.: Noise and Signal Response in Lead Sulfide Photoconductive Films, *J. Appl. Physics*, vol. 31, no. 3, March, 1960.
15. Gaumer, R. E., F. J. Clauss, M. E. Sibert, and C. C. Shaw: Materials Effects in Spacecraft Thermal Control, *Lockheed Aircraft Corporation*, LMSD/704019, Sunnyvale, Calif., November, 1960.
16. Clauss, F. J.: Surface Effects on Materials in Near Space, reprinted from *Aerospace Eng.*, vol. 19, no. 10, p. 16, October, 1960.
17. Hess, R. E., and R. F. Badertscher: Space Radiation as an Environmental Constituent, REIC Memorandum, Battelle Memorial Institute, Columbus, Ohio, Jan. 19, 1960.
18. Clauss, F. J.: Lubrication, chap. 10 of this book.

19. Jahsman, W. E., G. G. Cline, Jr., H. V. Heline, and W. Nachbar: Mechanics Problems of Space Flight, *Lockheed Missiles and Space Division*, LMSD No. 288073, Sunnyvale, Calif., Nov. 16, 1959.

20. Special Report: Aerospace Electronic Components, *Space Aeronautics*, vol. 34, no. 6, December, 1960; Holahan, J., and B. Kovit: Electronic Components Lag behind Systems Demands, p. 93; McNaul, J. P., and S. F. Dauko: Microminiature Components, p. 107; Kovit, B.: Environments Guide for Aerospace Electronics, p. 127.

21. Cooley, W. C.: A Comparison of Nuclear and Solar Power Systems for Manned Space Stations, *Proc. Symp. Manned Space Sta.*, Institute of the Aeronautical Sciences, Los Angeles, Calif., Apr. 20–22, 1960, pp. 207–213.

22. Boccius, W. C.: Development and Structural Aspects of Large Solid-propellant Rocket Motor Cases, *Lockheed Missiles and Space Division*, LMSD No. 288196, Sunnyvale, Calif., p. 46, Feb. 1, 1960.

23. Zwissler, L. E.: Spinning Makes Stronger Rocket Cases, *Metal Progress*, vol. 78, no. 6, p. 71, December, 1960.

24. Moran, M. J.: Material Selection for Motor Cases, private communication, Lockheed Missiles and Space Division, Sunnyvale, Calif., Oct. 26, 1959.

25. Anonymous: Goodrich Filament Winding Saves Money and Time, *Missiles Rockets*, vol. 7, no. 22, p. 28, Nov. 28, 1960.

26. Perkins, R.: State-of-the-Art-Inerts for Solid Propellant Rockets, private communication, Lockheed Missiles and Space Division, Sunnyvale, Calif., December, 1960.

27. Mace, W. C.: Pick the Right Plastic—in the Rocket Nozzle Environment, *Aircraft and Missiles*, October, 1960, p. 44.

28. Butz, J. S., Jr.: Growth Potential Defined for Heat Sink, Ablative Shields, *Aviation Week*, Sept. 7, 1959, p. 68.

29. Yaffee, M.: Pyrolytic Graphite Studied for Re-entry, *Aviation Week*, vol. 73, no. 4, p. 26, July 25, 1960.

Index

Index